ULTIMATE
FUN CROSSWORD BOOK
IT'S A BLAST!

284
CROSSWORD PUZZLES

Puzzles edited by Timothy E. Parker

creative EDGE

by Casey Rumblach
Edited by Timothy E. Parker
Answers in back

ACROSS

1 Distinctive doctrines
5 Pinochle combos
10 Word with "side" or "satellite"
14 It comes on 10-Across
15 Numskull
16 Letter from Greece
17 Trujillo locale
18 Bowed instrument
19 Chaotic happenings
20 Some relatives
23 Omega's opposite
24 Trader's word
25 Tierra ___ Fuego
26 MGM lion
27 No spring chicken
30 What we have here
32 Settle (into)
34 Expungement
38 Exotic destinations
42 Bait fish
43 It might be skinned in the fall
45 Offered one's seat
48 Computer key
50 Sieging weapon
51 Fun-house cries
52 Target of fawning
56 Parts of molecules
58 Gizmos for couch potatoes
62 "Who Framed Roger Rabbit" character
63 Scent source
64 Like some singing
66 Gaelic tongue
67 Even the score again
68 Moose, for one
69 Hair salon stock
70 Took second, in a way
71 Withered

DOWN

1 Gremlin
2 Cotyledon
3 Lily plant
4 Not-so-pretty snow
5 Thin-leaved mineral
6 Setting in Haydn's "The Creation"
7 Lively songs
8 Gabbana's partner
9 Seat without a back
10 "Buenos ___!"
11 Salt of element 53
12 Paving pieces
13 Pester
21 Certain religious ideal
22 Radical
23 Draft choice?
28 Lecherous
29 Wind resistance
31 Undeleted expletive
33 Word in a Descartes conclusion
35 Nautical affirmative
36 TV commercial
37 An arm bone
39 Taxpayer's nightmare
40 Register signer
41 Tailor
44 They're worth three points in Scrabble
45 Performed a database operation
46 Hypothesis
47 Be absorbed slowly
49 Cordial surroundings?
53 Darling people
54 Double quartet
55 Drawing interesting to many?
57 Grown-up polliwogs
59 Low-value wad
60 Accomplish flawlessly
61 It leaves in springtime
65 Vein glory

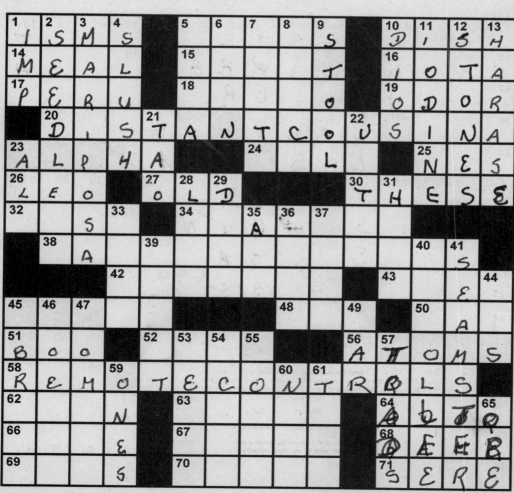

by Leana Bloom
Edited by Timothy E. Parker
Answers in back

ACROSS

1 Plant deeply (Var.)
6 Self-help level
10 Hare tail, e.g.
14 Mother-in-law of Ruth
15 Lot measurement
16 Backside
17 Online activities
18 Start of a quote for mature solvers
20 "___ gratia artis"
21 Guitar legend Atkins
23 Snoopy sorts (Var.)
24 Provokes
26 X, in old Rome
27 Cyclotron particle
28 Flier Corrigan's nickname
33 Transit map markings
36 Tender legbone
37 Verdi opera
38 Middle of the quote
41 Ending with "buck" or "stink"
42 Sea in Antarctica
43 Reagan Cabinet member Ed
44 Narcotic drug
46 Signature piece?
47 First lady
48 Patient's problem
52 Containing neither flesh nor its juices
56 Popular belief
57 Networked computers, for short
58 End of the quote
60 ___ fro
62 Caffeine source, often
63 Cabinetmaker's tool
64 Jay Silverheels role
65 Was acquainted with
66 Spinning toy
67 Bend into an arch

DOWN

1 Machu Picchu resident, once
2 Olympic skiing medalist Phil
3 Do some chest-thumping
4 911 responder, briefly
5 Reveal
6 Hotel conveniences
7 Horseback ride
8 Poetically always
9 Caller's instrument, perhaps
10 Dog show command
11 Medical breakthrough
12 Cold War participant
13 The item here
19 Moran of "Happy Days"
22 Mother ptarmigan, e.g.
25 Highest point
26 New parents' purchases
28 "___ Life Is It Anyway?"
29 Soft blue-gray mineral
30 Expansive
31 Sweetened fruit beverages
32 Easily maneuverable, as a vessel
33 Used the pool
34 Poi source
35 ___ about (approximately)
36 Fourteen pounds, in Britain
39 One place to park the car
40 Brunch fare
45 White-hat wearer, stereotypically
46 For each
48 Juliet's love
49 Try this if things don't work out
50 ___ Domingo
51 Provide income for
52 Kind of truck
53 Shakespearean "soon"
54 Not up to much
55 Emulate a beaver
56 Shiftless
59 Words before a kiss
61 ___-pah-pah (tuba tune)

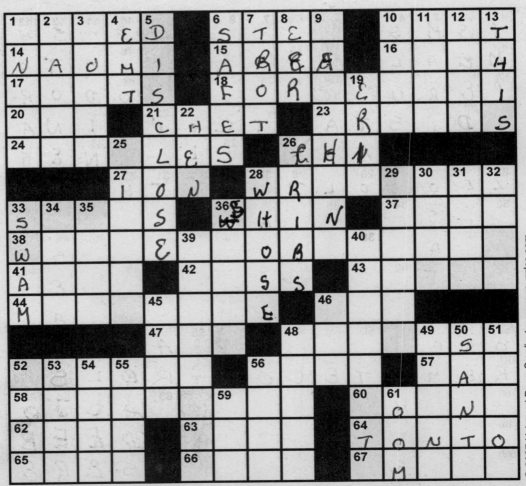

3 All in All

by Lewis Graham
Edited by Timothy E. Parker
Answers in back

ACROSS

1 Mambo relative
6 Part of a profit calculation
10 Talk casually
14 Newton of gravity fame
15 Cambodia's continent
16 Add punch to punch?
17 Horse blanket
18 Large quantity
19 On the sheltered side
20 Oppose
23 Keep under control
25 Deli bread
26 Tossed cube
27 Get a lode of this
28 Cardiology concern
31 Cake portion
33 Drying chamber
35 Snooker stick
36 Commandment violation
37 Wall Street fixture
42 Pit stop commodity
43 Rue Morgue culprit
44 Needing liniment, e.g.
46 Earth bound?
49 King David output
51 It's next to nothing?
52 Lifting device
53 It's after sigma
55 Structure for climbing
57 With a large trunk?
61 Continental currency
62 Satisfactory
63 Allowances for waste
66 Web filter target
67 "Present" alternative
68 Internet message
69 Suckers
70 Instruments of war
71 Peppy gathering

DOWN

1 Wheel part
2 "Born in the ___"
3 Most macho
4 Conductor's stick
5 Source of gum arabic
6 Simplest form of payment
7 Norwegian seaport
8 Rugged mountain range
9 Yellow-brown
10 Lobster's pride
11 Compound with a halogen atom
12 Acid found in vinegar
13 Giggle
21 Disparages
22 Art photo shade
23 Eeyore's bookmate
24 Notable times
29 Wish things otherwise
30 28th state
32 Cozy country lodges
34 Roman robe
36 Conchs, e.g.
38 Hindu social group
39 Apr. workhorse
40 What a poker player may seek
41 Long-winged sea eagle
45 Poetically "always"
46 Sisters' superior
47 Severe emotional shock
48 Thrash
49 React to a lemon
50 Substance
54 Hawaiian "hello"
56 Inner layer of the skin (Var.)
58 Deteriorates
59 Damage
60 Peepers
64 "___ death do us ..."
65 Like a fox

4 Place Your Bets

by James E. Buell
Edited by Timothy E. Parker
Answers in back

ACROSS

1 "Wine" partner
5 Hard work
9 Toots one's own horn
14 Dumb ___ ox
15 Outstanding
16 Provide with another point?
17 Speaks the unvarnished truth
20 Schoolyard taunts
21 Blows one's top
22 "Roll Over Beethoven" grp.
23 Singer Bonnie
24 Puts it on the line (with 47-Across)
28 Word with "curtain" or "fist"
32 "Now ___ seen everything!"
33 Conditional words
34 Like winter in Buffalo
36 Syringe contents, perhaps
38 Fore opposite
40 You could get hit there
41 Stomach divisions, in some animals
43 Unhurried gait
45 Ma Bell
46 Goblet feature
47 See 24-Across
50 One way to set a clock
52 TV dinner morsel, perhaps
53 Enjoying continuing success
56 Delinquent
60 Bets the farm
62 Swift
63 Zeno's home
64 Early Icelandic prose
65 Remarkable deeds
66 Drinks politely
67 Belmonts frontman

DOWN

1 "The Persistence of Memory" painter
2 "No man ___ island"
3 Negative votes
4 Comes as a result
5 Bicep decorations
6 What's needed to go from millionaire to billionaire
7 Room offerer
8 Deadly
9 Top point of a mountain
10 Kinsman
11 Ear-related
12 Drunkard
13 Gush out
18 Infamy
19 Catches a cabbie's eye
23 Sold chances
24 Central points
25 In plain view
26 Uncanny, and a bit spooky
27 Narrow inlet
29 Fit for a king
30 Address an audience
31 They're out on a limb
35 Highest mountain
37 Not easily affordable
39 Dick and Harry's partner
42 Engraved marker
44 Juicy fruits
48 Even splits
49 Took to the tub
51 Masters of ceremonies
53 "Carmina Burana" composer Carl
54 Cairo Opera House location
55 Between ports
56 Kind of school
57 "___ do that?" (Steve Urkel's question)
58 Edit menu option
59 "Magnet and Steel" singer Walter
61 Wallach or Whitney

by Lucky Barrett
Edited by Timothy E. Parker
Answers in back

ACROSS

1 Ballet move with bended knees
5 Expensive car trips?
9 Where it all begins
14 "Five Women" author Jaffe
15 Smell ___ (suspect something)
16 In the beaver state?
17 Redundant partner of "done with"
18 It's better than never?
19 Strong adhesive
20 Grammarian's concern, perhaps
23 Displayed sudden interest, in a way
24 Capital near Lillehammer
25 Special gift
28 Mythomaniac
30 Better
33 Grp. that whistled "Dixie"?
36 Shearing sound
38 It may have a cross to bear
39 Constitutional guarantee
43 Imp's opposite
44 Verbal attack
45 Suffix with "computer"
46 Old British gold coins worth 21 shillings
49 Indochinese republic
51 Moscow-to-Baghdad dir.
52 Legendary first name in sitcoms
54 Small cuts
58 If you make this, there can be no possible change
61 Express verbally
64 Optimistic, as an outlook
65 Emotional request
66 Dough
67 Canal of song
68 Right-angle bends
69 Art of verse
70 D'Urbervilles miss
71 "Portnoy's Complaint" author

DOWN

1 Actors handle them
2 "I ___ Parade"
3 Quiescent
4 A load of gossip
5 It's softer than gypsum
6 "Messiah," for one
7 Charlie of the Rolling Stones
8 Addison's writing partner
9 Visualizes
10 Runner's destination
11 "... and seven years ___"
12 T. follower
13 Determine judicially
21 New Testament letter
22 Palindromic prefix
25 ___ nous (confidentially)
26 Confidence games
27 In and of itself
29 Member of a colony
31 Concord
32 ___ mode
33 Steep rocks
34 Skull cavity
35 Playing marble
37 TV network letters
40 Cooped-up female?
41 ...
42 Battery size
47 Nabokov heroine
48 Whispered item
50 Smile derisively
53 Salt away
55 Jacqueline Du Pre's instrument
56 Kowtowed, e.g.
57 Hidden supply
58 Serpentine swimmers
59 Doctored photo?
60 Motion-carrying votes
61 You could be safe with him
62 Overly
63 Darned spot?

by Alice Walker
Edited by Timothy E. Parker
Answers in back

ACROSS

1 Croatian, e.g.
5 Ghostly in appearance
10 Perplexing path
14 Street corner call
15 Unwavering look
16 Vehicle for hitting high notes, perhaps
17 "Be it ___ so humble …"
18 Goatlike antelope
19 Some reading areas
20 Underdog's motivation (Part 1)
23 Extremist's prefix
24 Collect
25 Mixtures of metals
28 Baskin-Robbins purchase
30 Some forest animals
31 Enthusiastic approval
33 It may be a victim of blight
36 Underdog's motivation (Part 2)
40 Mary's Knight
41 Car protector
42 Type of pricing
43 Propagated
44 Not quite a sentence
46 Africa's largest city
49 Sound of an undignified landing
51 Underdog's motivation (Part 3)
57 Kin of hot pants
58 Art photo shade
59 It may form underground connections
60 Loving god of myth
61 Deal prerequisites, sometimes
62 Mark's replacement
63 Network of veins, e.g.
64 "Cabaret" director
65 Slumgullion

DOWN

1 Move a foot
2 Magma on the surface
3 They may go to blazes
4 Whiz
5 Owned properties, e.g.
6 Brenda the reporter
7 Port city north of Tel Aviv
8 Conclusion starter
9 Approach
10 Tussaud's title
11 Sports locale
12 Magnesium relatives
13 Assuages
21 Tissue layer
22 Ray of the tropics
25 Entrance for extraction
26 Misplace
27 Front the money
28 Bisque morsel, perhaps
29 Boathouse item
31 "My word!"
32 Junkyard canine
33 Vesuvius relative
34 Floral circles
35 Parcel (with "out")
37 Predictable cards?
38 Pilsner alternative
39 Fosters
43 Wound
44 The magic word
45 Is laid up with
46 Promising new arrival
47 Belching flames
48 "Otherwise …"
49 Clan divisions
50 Uses a crowbar on
52 Mil. branch
53 It's full of slots
54 Vulgarian
55 Came apart at the seams, e.g.
56 Stick overhead, e.g.

7 Body Snatcher

by Lester Mapple
Edited by Timothy E. Parker
Answers in back

ACROSS

1 Move on ahead
5 Box score data
10 "I'll ____ brief as possible"
14 Epithet of Athena
15 Contents of some booths
16 Angle between a branch and stem
17 Hard, sweet treat
19 Not lethargic
20 By the year
21 Kind of wool
23 1002, to Nero
24 Neuters, as a horse
26 "Leave It to Beaver" character
28 Likely ____ (with equal probability)
30 Oft-used article
32 Pig ____ poke
33 One was civil in America
35 Mermaid's home
36 "Don't delete this"
37 It's hard to say
41 Men-children
42 Type of league
43 Grazing land
44 Org. overseeing summer and winter competitions
45 It's for the money
46 Crustaceans with stalked eyes
50 "The Republic" writer
52 Less likely to be found
56 Tell's home canton
57 Theatrical hit
59 Bengal tiger, for one
61 "____ a Lady" (Tom Jones)
62 Thing that's hard to miss
64 Lively and jaunty
65 Fiddle of yore
66 Statistics calculation
67 "An apple ____ …"
68 Get the ball rolling
69 Gaelic tongue

DOWN

1 Kind of top or party
2 "Jagged Little Pill" singer Morissette
3 Like many coat linings
4 "Jungle Book" star
5 Upright stone slab
6 "… and ____ a good-night"
7 Resin in adhesives and paints
8 Rat tail?
9 Some Eur. Union members, once
10 Headquartered
11 Speed the progress of
12 Large passenger plane
13 Underhanded
18 Disorderly
22 Kind of square
25 Dwell on anger
27 Break bread
29 Has possession of
31 Icy precipitation
34 "Wrack" partner
35 Place of much wallowing
36 Luminary
37 Digs for a pick and shovel?
38 Being shot
39 "For," "how" or "what" ending
40 Skeleton in the closet, e.g.
41 Enjoy a quaff
45 Agents like Bond
47 Anonymous one, sometimes
48 Livestock lineages
49 Slangy ending for "yes" or "no"
51 Savory
53 Biology 101 subject (Var.)
54 Indy 500 competitor
55 Make into law
58 The lady's
60 Summit
61 Where some losers hang out?
63 "Are we there ____?"

8 Shake Sound

by Sefton Boyars
Edited by Timothy E. Parker
Answers in back

ACROSS
1 Speak in Spanish
6 Sherry bar appetizer, perhaps
10 Corkboard item
14 Dim
15 Surfer's diary
16 Wind in the pit?
17 Box office draw who doesn't act
20 Aucklander, casually
21 Roman goddess of plenty
22 Puppies' cries
23 Bobbsey twin
25 Some ostentatious outerwear
27 Shirt stainer, often
34 Need medical attention
35 Golden Rule word
36 Nearly extinct
38 Ditsy
40 Turn state's evidence
41 Wild and menacing
42 Type of salad
43 Niblick and brassie relative
45 Kind of meeting
46 Place to get some air
49 Chaucer offering
50 Drop the ball, e.g.
51 "Frutti" intro
54 With mouth shut
56 Seagirt land
60 Lawn staple in the Southwest
64 Elemental particle
65 Wee bit
66 First-string group
67 Used cars?
68 Point-of-honor settler
69 Energetic

DOWN
1 Corn residue
2 Proposal opposer
3 Botched
4 It can have a high cost
5 Had egg in one's face?
6 Recipe amt., perhaps
7 Italian high spots
8 Island dish
9 Delicate subject, to some
10 Without doubt
11 First victim
12 CEO's domain
13 They keep your powder dry
18 Trio of trios
19 Vega's constellation
24 Call from the crow's nest
25 Long, narrow estuaries
26 Letters on some ships
27 Pretzel add-on
28 Devoutly religious
29 Single-handedly
30 Ancient land east of Macedonia
31 Kid
32 Groups of wrist bones
33 Keats' muse
37 Distinctive flair
39 Kind of worker
41 Phobia
43 1/1000 inch
44 Checkout units
47 Conceited
48 Mournful in Marseilles
51 Ivan or Peter, e.g.
52 "I've had it ____ here!"
53 Trampled
54 Parcel (with "out")
55 Kazakhstan river
57 How-to part
58 Kind of year
59 Small-screen trophy
61 "The Karate ____" (1984)
62 Bud's funny buddy
63 Big, fat mouth

9 Great Ex-speck-tations

by Mark Milhet
Edited by Timothy E. Parker
Answers in back

ACROSS

1 Ritzy health resorts
5 One may have only one big part
10 Suck wind
14 It may have fallen on a foot
15 "The Rural Muse" poet
16 One of 50 in a united group
17 Nick's spouse, in film
18 Jack-in-the-pulpit cousin
19 Indian helmet
20 What 5-Across may sometimes wear
23 Playable serves
24 Ship deck
25 Turkish Angora, for one
28 Inscribe
31 State-of-the-art
35 Oil well fire fighter of note
37 First-rate
39 A big fan of
40 Pilot's boundary
43 Joule fractions
44 Lowly laborer
45 "I don't know" gesture
46 Speak sharply to
48 Cones partners
50 Tommy has a couple
51 Chop copy
53 Japanese delicacy
55 Potential start-up
62 Notice of demise, briefly
63 Column style
64 To ___ (precisely)
66 "Father" prefix
67 Supercilious
68 Did in the dragon
69 Chicken dinner?
70 Olympic measure
71 Legendary entertainer

DOWN

1 ___ Francisco 49ers
2 Theatrical object
3 Part of a large plot?
4 The voice of Lamb Chop
5 Greet obtrusively
6 Not bare
7 Baby-powder ingredient
8 Ship deck
9 Syllogist
10 Tolerate
11 Mite
12 Neck feature
13 That alternative
21 Like neon
22 Ballerina's perch
25 Some lighthouse sites
26 Bedeck
27 North American and Eurasian forest
29 Tearoom relative
30 Kind of "system" or "society"
32 Habituate (Var.)
33 Play, as a mandolin
34 Hinged kitchen utensils
36 Scrutinized
38 Taboo
41 The search for the silver lining
42 German steel city
47 Brouhaha
49 Rear window feature in some cars
52 Delmonico alternative
54 Pet checker
55 Tip, as a topper
56 Clarinet cousin
57 Kind of iron
58 "One Adam Twelve," e.g.
59 Rectangle part
60 French town of WWII fame
61 Slowly permeate
65 Bighorn's mom

10 Brief Statements

by Alice Walker
Edited by Timothy E. Parker
Answers in back

ACROSS

1 It may be compact
5 Whole ball of wax (with "from")
9 Inquires
13 Cookie jar denizen, perhaps
14 Show validity
15 Word with "gift" or "thrift"
16 Pond swimming duck
17 Parcels of earth
18 Have feelings
19 Short-lived success
22 New hire
24 Upturned
25 Like a has-been (with 41-Across)
29 Islamic princes
30 Hamlet, for one
31 "Mystery!" channel
34 ___ serif
35 Rock opera by The Who
37 Something to raise
38 Celebrated twin
39 Burt's wife, once
40 Body trunk
41 See 25-Across
44 It's bound to show the way
47 Ozzie and Harriet, e.g.
48 Terse
52 Feudal serf, e.g.
53 Pauline's problem
54 Citrus fruit
57 Sea eagle
58 Ranks contestants
59 Organic compound
60 Swallow flat
61 Leg up
62 Exclamation of the work-weary

DOWN

1 Small circle
2 Blood-pressure raiser
3 Oceangoing
4 Coal miners
5 Like a frightened cat's back
6 Spelling or Amos
7 Baker's pride
8 Gusto
9 Go to a higher level
10 Mold or fashion
11 Islamic text (Var.)
12 Pass bills
14 Former Toyota model
20 Wee workers
21 Fine-tune
22 Nearby objects
23 Put on a new crew
26 Word on a ticket
27 Orange food
28 "___ takers?"
31 Mindlessly repeating
32 Buffalo kin
33 Bamboozles
35 Cargo measure
36 Small cardinal
37 Breastplate
39 In need of a map
40 Metalware
41 January birthstone
42 Type of kick, in football
43 Whimpers
44 Vail rival
45 Yonder
46 Batty-sounding birds
49 Cathedral area
50 It can be pressing
51 Small amount
55 Miss Piggy's pronoun
56 Mischievous little creature

11 Back It Up a Little

by Leana Bloom
Edited by Timothy E. Parker
Answers in back

ACROSS

1 Stereotypical hobo fare
5 There's no accounting for it
10 Turkish topper
13 ___ Major
14 Greek alphabet starters
16 George's musical brother
17 Nature personified
19 Music genre
20 Breakfast of centurions?
21 Courage
22 Cheer for the matador
24 Incriminate falsely
26 Owing payments
30 Negligent
32 Clinging part of a climbing plant
33 Start to dominate?
34 Cartridge holder
35 Mortar rounds, e.g.
36 Form of English
39 Valuable weasels
42 Create a dart, e.g.
43 ___ mater (brain membrane)
45 Mighty long time
46 Type of reaction
48 Pizza sauce enhancer
50 Properly clothed
53 Put into a new order
55 Has down pat
57 Butting bighorn
58 Molded, frozen dessert
60 By way of
61 Slugging stat
63 A bit too serious
66 Standard product, once
67 40th U.S. president
68 Pot additive
69 Exclamation of wonder
70 Improve, as a text
71 Angler's prize, sometimes

DOWN

1 Large Japanese guys
2 Common-law action to recover damages
3 Mansion and grounds
4 Half a trumpet's sound
5 Poi source
6 Joan's "Dynasty" role
7 New World colonizer
8 Imperil
9 Gormandize, e.g.
10 Combat supplies
11 Historic time
12 Laser gun sound effect
15 Like many a cold sheep
18 Darth Vader's dominion
23 "___ and the Swan" (Yeats)
25 Guy who cries foul
27 Fail to keep a promise
28 Icy cover
29 Give me a brake?
31 Star close to Venus?
34 Word with "ten" or "hair"
36 Olfactory perception
37 Tackle box item
38 Without much cheer
40 Night light
41 Chump
44 Indian tourist site
47 Pin number?
49 Museum suit
50 Abase
51 Series of repeated Catholic prayers
52 Ironic turns
54 Eat more than one's fill
56 Eats more than one's fill
59 Boston or Chicago, e.g.
61 Scottish hero Roy
62 Short life story?
64 Rock singer Bobby
65 Capture a crook

by Mark Milhet
Edited by Timothy E. Parker
Answers in back

ACROSS
1 Member of the common class
6 Withhold wages from
10 Heron cousin
14 Less experienced
15 First name in scat
16 "Bringing Up Father" girl
17 Lend ___ (pay close attention)
18 Not having much fat
19 Loretta's "M*A*S*H" co-star
20 Behave, letter-perfectly
23 Fury
24 "___ to you, buddy!"
25 End of a dry spell
28 Victorian, for one
31 Buffet selections, often
35 Barley fibers, e.g.
36 Finished
38 Part of the Fertile Crescent
39 Slap the cuffs on
40 Tic-tac-toe plays, letter-perfectly
42 Treat leather
43 Bleak, in verse
45 They're cut by dancers
46 Locate
47 Sketch over
49 Ring around the collar?
50 Swing a scythe
51 Tournament freebies
53 "Before" of yore
55 Complete a contract, letter-perfectly
63 Brief notice in passing
64 Popular summer destination
65 Place for a Chicago touchdown?
66 Glittering vein
67 Popular cookie brand
68 Fracas
69 Satyric stare
70 Spider's home
71 Scrooge's expression

DOWN
1 Soho stroller
2 One-time Delhi queen
3 "A Prayer for ___ Meany"
4 Introductions
5 Kind of message
6 Take-out order?
7 Picadors' praise
8 Puts palms together
9 Dorothy's home
10 In a silly manner
11 Font property, sometimes
12 Modern Mesopotamia
13 Word with "souci" or "serif"
21 Requisites
22 Accrue
25 Abbreviated vacation goal, letter-perfectly
26 Hardly oblivious
27 Under cover
29 Sound in the jungle
30 Make void
32 Shaw of swing
33 Paul Anka's first hit
34 Wall St. "500," letter-perfectly
37 Defeat by a hair
40 They give the inside picture
41 Willow for wicker
44 Dispute settler
46 Add ice, as to an old drink
48 It can be concealed
52 Midnight rumble
54 Suite things
55 Kewpie, e.g.
56 Clarinet cousin
57 Almanac topic
58 The Johns we don't know
59 Congeal
60 Retail lure
61 Bat's beginning
62 Soothsayer

© 2007 Universal Press Syndicate www.upuzzles.com

13 Ride Along

by Lucky Barrett
Edited by Timothy E. Parker
Answers in back

ACROSS

1 Word introducing Johnny
6 Greasy spoon fare
10 Sidney Poitier, e.g.
14 Counting everything
15 Little pat on your buns?
16 Basilica center
17 Certain carriage
19 "Rag Mop" brothers
20 One on a golf scorecard
21 Shoulder protection
22 Proposals
24 West End attraction
26 Run at the mouth
27 Pink lady ingredient
28 Checkers, across the Atlantic
31 Wimps' opposites
34 Buck or Bailey
35 Alleged paranormalist Geller
36 Outback creatures
37 Sentimental one
38 Industrial-strength air?
39 Need nursing
40 Church parts, perhaps
41 Perception factor
42 One with the shivers, e.g.
44 Bonnet invader
45 Mah-jongg equipment
46 Some sugar containers
50 Head of a pen
52 He hit 66 homers in 1998
53 Miss Piggy's pronoun
54 "Good heavens!"
55 Nintendo hit
58 Billiard cushion
59 Clarinet cousin
60 Digested
61 Seabird
62 Some are prime
63 Color changers

DOWN

1 Part of a drum kit, informally
2 Father of Methuselah
3 Public performance (with "show")
4 Two-time U.S. Open winner Ernie
5 Rose late
6 Nomadic group
7 Old-style "Bummer!"
8 Put in stitches
9 Like some degrees
10 Bewildered
11 Mound in the Sahara?
12 Done
13 "Good" or "bad" ending
18 Sock-mender's oath?
23 Ball for the fans
25 Awfully long time
26 Old-fashioned exclamations
28 Postpone an action
29 Run without rushing
30 Audible breath
31 What mobsters pack?
32 Arab potentate
33 Frankie Laine hit of 1949
34 Does modeling work
37 Magnificence
38 "___ and ye shall find"
40 Having the means
41 Less radioactive
43 Waistline
44 Statue part
46 Nudges
47 Be a drama queen
48 Photocopying need
49 Speaks without speaking
50 Existed
51 Lab media
52 One looking down on you?
56 ___-Wan Kenobi
57 Diane in "The Godfather"

by James E. Buell
Edited by Timothy E. Parker
Answers in back

ACROSS

1 Cookbook instruction
5 Irritation
9 Souvenir of the past
14 ___ of operation
15 100 centavos
16 Drama at La Scala
17 Have a blast!
19 Web destinations
20 High, rocky hill
21 It's found among needles
23 From head to foot
27 Room service decanters, e.g.
28 Italian liqueur
30 Dirty money
31 Word in a Hitchcock film title
32 Stored away
34 One-time stratospheric streaker
37 Carpenter and harvester
38 Actor Leary
39 Snorkel's pooch
40 Myrna of "The Thin Man"
41 Some night sounds
42 Golf great Sam
43 Kind of trigger
45 Broken off, musically
47 First Mets skipper Casey
50 Buildings with steeply pitched roofs
51 Pressured
53 Type of computer memory
54 Ahead of time
55 Have a blast!
60 First name in mascara
61 Bird of Old Rome
62 Licentious man
63 Tense (with "up")
64 Son of Eve
65 Provide with a hideout, perhaps

DOWN

1 It's headquartered in Munich
2 "That's awesome!"
3 Terse vow
4 Dancers' wear, sometimes
5 Apparition
6 Invoice word
7 "The jig ___!"
8 Debaters' need
9 Like cheeks, at times
10 Long and impressive
11 Have a blast!
12 Cara or Ryan
13 Detective's assignments
18 Vatican honchos
22 Locks may hide them
23 Junta
24 Organic acid form
25 Have a blast!
26 Anesthetic liquid
29 Sow sounds
33 Western scene
35 Union member
36 Hoo-has
38 Tested one's courage
39 Being shot
41 Filled with awe
42 "Beat it!"
44 Founder of the Shakers, in America
46 From the beginning
47 Streamlined
48 Display poor sportsmanship, in a way
49 ___ de Zamora, Argentina
52 Basilica center
56 "Caboodle" partner
57 Take the wrong way?
58 Lament
59 Thus far

by Pepper Castling
Edited by Timothy E. Parker
Answers in back

ACROSS
1 Taxi or taxi driver
5 45 and 78, e.g.
9 Empty-headed
14 Symptom of malaria
15 "Brian's Song" star
16 Inflexible
17 Three grand things
20 Exordium, informally
21 "... ____ forgive our debtors"
22 King Kong's co-star
23 Passionate pair
25 ____ Lanka
27 It's grand
34 Plane's place
35 Spot for the masses?
36 Big D.C. lobbyist
37 Could be fine, could be graphic
38 No. cruncher
39 Service entrance location, sometimes
40 "Infant" ending
41 Feast with a roast pig
43 Excessively
45 Two grand things
48 Loop for 41-Across
49 Roman emperor
50 Animal advocate (Abbr.)
53 Unlikely to bite
56 Creator of a count
60 Three grand things
63 Correct a tire pull
64 Where to find most of us
65 Unpleasant thing to eat
66 On edge
67 Center of Miami
68 Sweethearts, once

DOWN
1 Traveler to Mecca (Var.)
2 "Son of ____!"
3 Rudely brief
4 They hold jingly things
5 Magnavox rival
6 Noted canal
7 Baseball legend Willie
8 April or November surprise
9 Kind of agent
10 Birdbrain
11 Lab gel
12 Columbian ship
13 Whirlpool
18 Terra ____
19 Hatchling homes
24 Commit a faux pas
26 "Diff'rent Strokes" actress
27 Waitress with Sam and Coach
28 Stage direction
29 Emulate a cat with milk
30 Restorative resort
31 Sluggish by nature
32 Doctorate exam hurdles
33 ____ a one (zilch)
34 Rare weather forecast
38 Reef in the Florida Keys, e.g.
39 Swear off
41 Director Spike
42 Military groups
43 Miner's quest
44 "Falstaff" composer
46 Loud metallic sounds
47 Result of iron deficiency, perhaps
50 Young oyster
51 Carpet thickness
52 Genesis slayer
54 Woeful word
55 Trapper John's post
57 Noted critic of capitalism
58 Lotion addition
59 Applies patches, e.g.
61 Undivided
62 Common requests for info

by Lynn Lempel
Edited by Timothy E. Parker
Answers in back

ACROSS

1 Elephantine
5 Shoe part
11 Two in a billion?
14 Onerous concern
15 Eyetooth
16 "Norma ___"
17 Beginning of a solver's thought
19 Certain road runner
20 Cube with spots
21 Pick a card, say
22 Jackrabbit, actually
23 Most definite
26 Moon feature
28 Solver's thought (Part 2)
32 Slithery Egyptian
33 Run
34 Sail supports
37 First name in pharmaceutical giants
38 Many Eastern Europeans
42 Air current heading skyward
45 Start for "colonial"
46 Solver's thought (Part 3)
51 Renaissance rulers of Florence
52 Grasslands
53 Hippies' quarters
54 Halloween persona
57 Populous city area, slangily
58 Jack Horner's last words
59 End of a solver's thought
64 Serve that doesn't count
65 Scold
66 ___ fixe
67 Whichever
68 Jackson or Johnson
69 Workout spots

DOWN

1 Ad ___
2 Family card game
3 "Goody, goody" candy
4 Observes
5 It has a chilling effect
6 Alliance est. in 1949
7 Make little cuts
8 Window shade?
9 Chang's brother
10 Word with "shooter" or "soup"
11 Margarine, vis-a-vis butter
12 Hardy companion?
13 Like some winter weather
18 Of reduced degree
22 Shirley Booth role
23 Dupe's undoing
24 Star bear
25 Number for the show?
26 IRS calculator?
27 Tiresome routines
29 "Lulu" or "Norma"
30 Switching device
31 Windblown snow pile
35 Capital of Tunisia
36 Done on ___ (without contract)
39 Disease-fighting protein
40 Shrimp discard
41 Part of Buck's trilogy
43 Motorist's crime, briefly
44 Highest part
46 High-jumping antelope
47 Mariners
48 Three-legged calf, e.g.
49 Oversupply
50 Insect with pincers
54 It can be rounded up
55 Winged
56 Yard portal
59 Letters of indecision, on a schedule
60 She lays around the farm
61 Use needle and thread
62 Sleep stage
63 ___ Plaines, Illinois

17 Questions, Questions

by Turner Givens
Edited by Timothy E. Parker
Answers in back

ACROSS

1 That alternative?
5 Pursue wild geese?
10 Slimy sci-fi menace
14 Ridge of sand
15 Type of ship
16 Like the cream of the crop
17 Apply, in a way (with "on")
18 Like some nail polish
19 "Follow me!" slangily
20 Tasty zoo
23 Parabolic trajectory
24 Much-used pencil
25 "Spring forward" letters
28 Realtor's sign of success
31 Footless
35 At the summit
37 Start of an explanation, perhaps
39 Singer/judge Abdul
40 Carrot patch, e.g.
43 Cockamamy
44 French town of WWII fame
45 It has two black suits
46 Medicating
48 Reach across
50 It's often blue
51 Amos or Spelling
53 Poetic pasture
55 What a geologist makes at the bank?
62 Setting in Haydn's "The Creation"
63 Mover's challenge
64 Osmatic stimulant
66 College book
67 Some continental currency
68 Time for a break, often
69 Studio structures
70 Relative of the salmon
71 Big game?

DOWN

1 QB successes
2 Fad hoop
3 Words before "instant"
4 Art photo shade
5 Classic drink
6 Faith in country?
7 One of the acting Baldwins
8 Blackens
9 Novel flubs
10 Rim holder
11 Capital of Togo
12 ___ about (circa)
13 Cartwright and Franklin
21 Wifey (with "the")
22 Tea serving, in Britain
25 King of psalmists
26 Dictation taker, once
27 Roman wraps
29 Some tennis shots
30 Not exactly Einsteins
32 Ranch visitors
33 Smart guy
34 Gangling
36 Some fasters
38 Edible seaweed
41 Highest natural adult male voice
42 Crossbar holder
47 Raisins' predecessors
49 New beginning?
52 Latin name for Troy
54 In harmony
55 N.Y. team
56 ___ fixe (obsession)
57 On deck
58 Truth alternative
59 Chemical compound
60 Object of devotion
61 Commandeered
65 They may administer IVs

by Lester Mapple
Edited by Timothy E. Parker
Answers in back

ACROSS

1 Blacken, as barbecue fare
5 On the ball
10 Boat launch
14 Actor Alan of "Gilligan's Island"
15 It needs a good paddling
16 Pennsylvania lake port
17 "Ghostbusters" director Reitman
18 Composer Bruckner
19 Cinco de Mayo snack, perhaps
20 Card game for textile workers?
22 Word with "blight" or "guerrilla"
23 Crossing medium
24 Verb form for Virgil
26 Kind of club or column
33 Artistic touches
36 Potential progeny
37 Severe trial
38 Strange sighting
39 Figures in Hinduism
41 Willfully go downhill
42 Reach one's destination
44 Browning's "before"
45 Kind of son or daughter
46 It's falling down, in song
49 Venetian farewell
50 Outmoded
54 It's usually dressed before eaten
57 Conflict won by a horse
61 Olfactory nerve stimulator
62 Unwavering look
63 Dove shelter
64 Long-lasting hostilities
65 Tiny amounts
66 Julia's brother
67 Industrious six-footers
68 Silvery food fish
69 Telegraphed

DOWN

1 Marx born Leonard
2 Bad thing to cause
3 Having winglike extensions
4 Blockbuster's business
5 Use a certain office machine
6 Be suspended
7 Disapproving
8 "Boys Town" star
9 Part of it may be felt
10 Secondhand tire
11 Cairo league
12 Sparkly rock substance
13 Lowly laborer
21 Name in the Beatles' inner circle
22 Patrons
25 Buttressed (with "up")
27 Nine-day series of Catholic prayers
28 Zsa Zsa's sister
29 Word to a gator?
30 Relaxation partner
31 Third-base coach's sign, sometimes
32 Piece of paper
33 Twofold in nature
34 Crew cut's opposite
35 Brought forth
39 Bypass
40 Jackie O's spouse
43 Airport check-in essentials
45 Deadly meetings?
47 Baby part
48 Univ. admission criterion
51 Used inelegant language
52 Ellington's "___ Doll"
53 Upright, as posture
54 Chesterfield, for one
55 Oil port
56 Ill-mannered boor
58 Bank posting
59 Like gentlemen's agreements
60 Bit of banter
62 Venus, to Serena

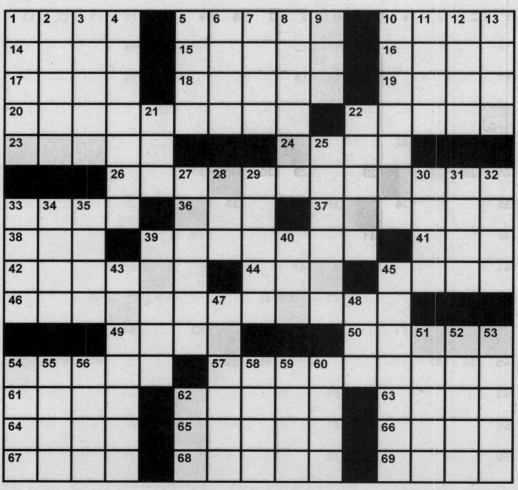

ACROSS

1 Spread outward
6 "… your goodness ____ a morning cloud" (Hosea)
10 Sackcloth material, perhaps
14 Large ocean vessel
15 Juicer refuse
16 Good opponent
17 Western
18 Captain Hook's assistant
19 Ballistics, dynamic or lite starter
20 Three eye openers?
23 Hot time in Paris
24 Lined up (with "in")
25 "Dallas" character
28 Surmounting
31 Make a mistake
35 Detroit River's destination
37 "Your turn," in radiospeak
39 Margin of victory at the track, perhaps
40 Three cold fronts?
43 Any of various willows
44 Father figures
45 Blind piece
46 Covert
48 "Uh-uh"
50 Kind of dog
51 "An Inconvenient Truth" star
53 New Haven collegian
55 Three kick starts?
63 Forsaken
64 It's usually screwed up
65 Skip a syllable, e.g.
66 DeMille specialty
67 Peak of perfection
68 Begin, as winter
69 Refuse to admit
70 "____ we forget"
71 Way the wind blows

DOWN

1 Complete failure
2 One with no capacity for veracity
3 Oppositionist
4 Parish official
5 Published mistakes
6 Dixit lead-in
7 Type of wrestler
8 "The Downeaster ____" (Billy Joel song)
9 Weapons, long ago
10 Concerns for sailors and pilots
11 Unceasingly
12 Tract of wet ground
13 Walk heavily
21 Wyoming mountain range
22 First name in strikeouts
25 River to the Rio Grande
26 Cropped up
27 Imitate
29 Poet of Rome's Golden Age
30 Praline ingredient, often
32 Certain water containers
33 Commonplace
34 Trivial
36 Hospital sign
38 Change the decor of
41 Three-part cookies
42 Colorado ski resort
47 Kind of ceremony
49 Most senior
52 Draw out
54 Good-for-nothing
55 Ran in fear
56 Piece of rodeo gear
57 Role for Julia
58 Trees in an O'Neill title
59 Aid in crime
60 Ceremonial act
61 Thor's dad
62 Hang in the balance

20 Time Check

by Casey Rumblach
Edited by Timothy E. Parker
Answers in back

ACROSS

1 Certain tunics
5 Pound of flesh
9 Mental picture, e.g.
14 Lead-in for "graph"
15 Manipulative one
16 Nail-___ (tense situation)
17 Oft-used Latin abbreviation
18 Org. with eligibility rules
19 Course intro?
20 Of lesser importance
22 Some basketball game highlights
23 Coward of England
24 Leave it, editorially
26 Prohibit
29 River duck
31 Breakfast order, perhaps
35 It's larger than Lincoln
37 Old Soviet news agency
39 63,360 inches
40 Puerto ____
41 Concession stand offerings
42 Lily Pons specialty
43 Stocking shade, sometimes
44 Nonkosher
45 Small flying insects
46 Lead-in for Madre or Leone
48 Jules Verne character
50 "Dick and Jane" verb
51 Actress Lollobrigida
53 Swarm
55 Chew out
58 Does some woolgathering
63 Vatican-related
64 Certain Japanese people
65 "Dagnabbit"
66 Be the life of the party
67 March fifteenth, to Caesar
68 Crowning point
69 In disarray
70 Pro ___ (proportionate)
71 Rich soil

DOWN

1 Natural mimics
2 Type of shift
3 Bric-a-___
4 Where to make waves?
5 Hogan movie role
6 It'll give you a lift
7 One of a storied threesome
8 Airline seat parts
9 Word in footnotes
10 Revolutionary War figure
11 Abbr. on a business envelope, perhaps
12 Carnival oddball
13 Plays a wrong note, e.g.
21 "___ creature was stirring …"
25 Fail to fall asleep, in a way
26 Tiresome ones
27 Latin friends
28 Mother-of-pearl
30 Heavily burdened
32 Turkish money units
33 Social creme de la creme
34 Badger
36 Primitive timepiece
38 Trapeze artist's security
41 Spider-Man creator Lee
45 "Movie" or "party" attachment
47 Director Scott
49 Snake-haired woman of myth
52 Noted fighter of oil fires
54 Olympian's quest
55 Some junk mail
56 "And it ___ to pass …"
57 Major musical composition
59 Noted opera
60 With the bow, in music
61 Nursery word
62 Cherry part

ACROSS

1 She followed Eleanor
5 Conserve
9 Emcee with White
14 Way out
15 Throw in the towel
16 Decorate
17 Dey's revolving tray?
19 Sheet of print
20 Aviator Earhart
21 It was given to you
23 Give permission
24 Screwed up
26 Antiknock fluids
28 Noted horn blower
31 Flexible ___ sled
32 Feeling poorly
33 Conventions
35 Propels a wherry
38 Swindles
40 Just a bit
41 Like the color purple
42 Author Uris
43 Defunct Chrysler marque
45 Epoch
46 They were used for many calls
48 Military force, once
50 Orville Wright's city of birth
52 Seat weaver, of a sort
53 Cola mixer
54 Jazz plays there
56 Candied
60 Yikes!
62 Pesci's sandwich?
64 High spot for eggs
65 Mallet game
66 Molten spew
67 Salon fixture
68 There's one under 67-Across
69 They were once together

DOWN

1 Lugosi of film
2 Student stressor
3 Junior or jumbo, e.g.
4 Salon fixture or employee
5 Certain shapes
6 Salzburg's nation, briefly
7 Delicious dish
8 Volcano near Messina
9 It's supposed to come first
10 Commotion
11 Ebert in a merry mood?
12 Mischievous spirit in "The Tempest"
13 Pine feature
18 Dog Star
22 Gibson and Torme
25 Lifts, as spirits
27 This place
28 Kind of scout
29 Hand cream enhancer
30 What Moore may put on her bar tab?
31 Felt hat
34 Laughing matter?
36 Lovesome
37 Assassin's order
39 Purl partner
41 Arrived on horseback
43 It might be created by accident
44 Slangy Andrew Jackson
47 Skilled housecat
49 Patterned sock
50 Great fear
51 When you use it, it's boring
52 Daphnis' lover
55 Dangerous Middle Easterners
57 Comet competitor
58 Wander about
59 Votes in favor
61 It may be cast
63 Pay stub?

22 Not Grade AA Meals

by Lester Mapple
Edited by Timothy E. Parker
Answers in back

ACROSS

1 Resigner of October 10, 1973
6 Famous fabler
11 "It's freezing!"
14 Dill swill
15 Sri ___
16 Tolstoy's first
17 Fruity loaf
19 Actress Gardner
20 Asner's cheese choice?
21 Chicago political name
22 Desert Storm missile
23 Vein pursuit?
25 Second-chance exams
27 Ribbed cover
32 Drab partner
33 Cigarette stat
34 Turns sharply
36 Keep ___ to the ground
39 Worship
41 Command to a horse
42 European nation
43 Axman, e.g.
44 "Don't ___ the small stuff!"
46 Born as
47 Untouchable lawman
49 Backs a candidate
51 Paper pads
54 Anger
55 Stouts, e.g.
56 Uplift
59 No-see-um
63 Mass. school
64 Meaty wrap
66 Guinea pig, often
67 Paris landmark (with "L")
68 Not on deck
69 Random choice
70 Financier John Jacob
71 Wish list entries

DOWN

1 Ex of Cugie
2 Commencement honoree, briefly
3 A historic ship
4 Win the heart of
5 Harmless cyst
6 ___ Longa (birthplace of Romulus and Remus)
7 British peer
8 Scornful smile
9 Authorized
10 Toad's stool?
11 Feijoada ingredients
12 Vaudeville production
13 Many have shoulders
18 Fred Astaire's sister
22 Louisiana athlete
24 Kind of discrimination
26 Turncoat
27 State of the union address
28 Crafted
29 Baked dessert
30 Calf locales
31 "___ having fun yet?"
35 "No man hath ___ God at any time" (John 1:18)
37 Away from the wind
38 Bread choices
40 Emulates a toper
45 "Cheerio!"
48 Prepares in a teapot
50 Feel sorry about
51 Florida bay
52 It's out of this world
53 Winter driving hazard
57 Spheroid hairdo
58 Lifting device
60 Khartoum river
61 Tiny particle
62 Expensive car trips
64 It'll put the squeeze on you
65 Box score stat

23 Higher and Higher

by Leana Bloom
Edited by Timothy E. Parker
Answers in back

ACROSS
1 Feel sore
5 Carp relative
9 In the boondocks, e.g.
14 Seafood item
15 Many a Norwegian king
16 Standing-foot link
17 Introduce opposition
20 "To the max" indicator
21 Maui shindig
22 Classic TV series set in Calverton
23 He is holy, to many
25 "Keen!"
27 Polo competitor
29 Going on and on and …
33 Make an effort
37 As well
38 Canal of renown
39 Blip on a polygraph
40 School established in 1440
41 2 oz., e.g.
42 Come to ruin
46 Classic U-boat film
48 "The Little Red Hen" denial
49 Lucy's best friend
51 Family reunion activity
55 Number five iron
58 Landers and others
60 Contend
61 Rise to preeminence
64 Leavening agent
65 Culinary directive
66 They need refinement
67 ___ Domingo
68 Like a busy mechanic's rags
69 Literary governess Jane

DOWN
1 "Green ___" (classic sitcom)
2 Necklace fastener
3 Dominican Republic's neighbor
4 Maximum limits?
5 Swindle
6 Goya's "The Duchess of ___"
7 Like some Louisianan cuisine
8 Woman in a garden
9 Pitcher's cuff
10 Homophony
11 Outback leapers, briefly
12 MMVII and others
13 ___-majeste
18 Flower girl Doolittle
19 ___ Boothe Luce
24 Ceremonial act
26 Squeeze beside
28 Thin, as a solvent
30 "Leave ___ Beaver"
31 Sheltered and secluded place
32 Neither here nor there
33 Cause of painter's colic
34 "The Madwoman of Chaillot" role
35 Looks great on
36 Tiny bite
40 Send off, as broadcast waves
42 Became involved with
43 Expressed wonderment, in a way
44 What "Keep out!" means
45 Put away for a rainy day
47 Urgent prompting
50 Christine of "Chicago Hope"
52 Coast or tower
53 Frisco gridder
54 Gaggle members
55 Aaron contemporary
56 Between ports
57 Observatories do it
59 Lunar Armstrong
62 General one can take out?
63 Caviar

by Emery Glasso
Edited by Timothy E. Parker
Answers in back

ACROSS

1 Disney elephant
6 Caribbean Eden
11 Insult, slangily
14 Newton of gravity fame
15 Kingdom
16 Picnic scurrier
17 Nature personified
19 Attachment to ox or roads
20 Heavy metal
21 Barbara's role on "Dallas"
23 Snore
27 "The Human Comedy" novelist
29 Takes into one's family
30 Arises unexpectedly
31 Arctic floaters
32 Blow one's top
33 It was dropped in the '60s
36 "Deck the Halls" syllables
37 Dizzying painting movement
38 Between the lines, in baseball
39 Ancient times, in ancient times
40 Narrow openings
41 New York's ____ Island
42 Jukebox verb
44 Record jacket, e.g.
45 Sound systems
47 Kitchen appliance
48 Welsh canine
49 Monopoly token
50 William Tell's canton
51 Movie award since 1944
58 Common Father's Day gift
59 Shoe-repair shop stock
60 Ghastly strange
61 Bro counterpart
62 Gives an effort
63 Interior designer's doing

DOWN

1 Lacking brightness
2 Wartime entertainers
3 Floor covering
4 Kin of phooey
5 Spotted wildcats
6 Localities
7 Crack a book
8 Short-lived Middle Eastern federation (Abbr.)
9 Sandwich initials
10 Emily Dickinson's Massachusetts birthplace
11 Lois Lane's employer (with "The")
12 "Gunga Din" setting
13 Dutch painter Jan
18 Rules' partners, briefly
22 Baseball legend Gehrig
23 Weasel cousin
24 "Let's Make ____"
25 October sports event
26 Org. for Annika Sorenstam
27 Worsens, as relations
28 Meeting with an M.D.
30 Engine maker ____ & Whitney
32 Extended narratives
34 Colander kin
35 Laundry machine
37 Ersatz butter
38 Contenders
40 Adroitness in using the hands
41 Sounded like a trolley?
43 Small bit of work
44 Any time now
45 Rabbits' tails, e.g.
46 Shinto temple gateway
47 Plait of hair
49 Not up to much
52 "____ the ramparts ..."
53 Hawaiian welcome token
54 "Enter the Dragon" star Bruce
55 "The Lord of the Rings" monster
56 Life story, for short
57 Occupational suffix

by Turner Givens
Edited by Timothy E. Parker
Answers in back

ACROSS

1 Puts suddenly, as a question
5 Sixth-day creation
9 Martin or Lawrence
14 It could provide a pat on the buns
15 Solemn observance, e.g.
16 Anecdotes
17 Air
18 Grand poetry
19 It's valuable
20 North and south, e.g.
23 Agitate
24 Comically off-the-wall
25 Expected to arrive
28 Assorted
30 Zebra kin
33 Da Gama destination
35 Took the bait
36 One in an old empire
37 Hardly a warm welcome
41 Bloodsucking arachnid
42 "So, there you are!"
43 Disputed matter
44 Bright, as a pupil
45 Unseen troublemaker
48 Make a wrong choice, e.g.
49 Cool off like a boxer
50 Rainfall measurement
52 Take a break
58 "___ Attraction" (1987)
59 Lead, for one
60 Computer image
61 Fanny of the Ziegfeld Follies
62 "___ Rhythm"
63 "Buzz off!"
64 Like some triggerfingers
65 Frightens
66 Grant's landmark

DOWN

1 Ceremonial elegance
2 Salmagundi, e.g.
3 Sunburn aftermath
4 Submarine tracker
5 Nipple ring
6 Big or Little in the sky
7 Resting on
8 One era
9 Sloppy eaters' problems
10 Scrumptious
11 Word in a conditional statement, perhaps
12 Vivid twosome
13 Md. setting
21 Be in competition with
22 Recipe direction, sometimes
25 Forma pronouncements
26 Not very cool
27 ___ of Nantes, 1598
29 Type of iron girder
30 Absinthe flavoring
31 Scrub strenuously
32 More sound
34 Variety
36 Part of FWIW
38 Adventurer's inventory
39 Pretentious speech
40 Small amount
45 Ship's kitchen
46 Stay off the radar
47 Some blowups
49 Hunt illegally
51 Yegg's job
52 Option for golfers
53 Involving the ear
54 NASA scratch
55 Kind of cardiogram
56 Appear imminent
57 Highbrow
58 Department of Justice div.

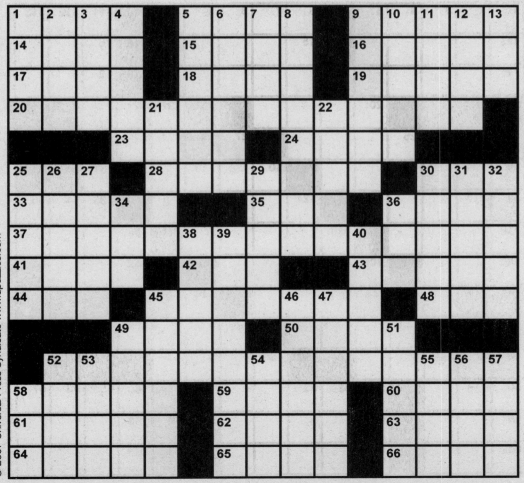

by Henry Quarters
Edited by Timothy E. Parker
Answers in back

ACROSS

1 Civil rights activist Parks
5 Nursery rhyme Jack
10 What to do "in the name of love"
14 Cartel since 1960
15 Island in the Netherlands Antilles
16 "One More Night" singer Collins
17 Ethiopian slave of opera
18 Cuban VIP
19 Slippery and slithery
20 Huddle outcomes?
23 Feebleness
24 Secret supply
27 Pewter containing about 80 percent tin
28 Rail transport, perhaps
31 Island instrument, for short
32 Brit's raincoat
34 Tex-Mex dish
35 Projecting edge
36 Like a bad photographer's subject?
40 "Human Concretion" artist
41 Well-informed
42 Fish story suffix?
43 Smoker's amassment
44 Buddhist shrine
45 Curative place
47 Turns sharply
49 Flowering shrubs
53 What the marksman took at midnight? (with "a")
57 It has a cream center
59 Revere
60 Major or minor constellation
61 They're made only at home
62 Red Cross volunteer
63 Stop the bleeding
64 Network of nerves, e.g.
65 Aspen area
66 Daly of the stage

DOWN

1 Meat cut
2 State as an opinion
3 Enclosed automobile
4 Mexican cruise port
5 Kind of zone
6 Quite expensive (Var.)
7 Fashion designer Gernreich
8 Vigoda and Lincoln
9 Anklebones
10 Exhausted
11 Book of synonyms
12 It eases friction
13 Tissue layer, e.g.
21 Six-sided game piece
22 Containing element number 76
25 Evade
26 Complex, red organic pigment
28 Pointed-out direction
29 At fruition
30 The Greatest
32 Subway artwork, e.g.
33 Currently
34 Bloke
36 Cereal ingredients
37 String bean's opposite
38 Tango requirement
39 Weeping conduit
45 Heavenly body shape
46 Thanksgiving dessert
48 A question of possession
49 Sharpening strap
50 With time to spare
51 Insurance-scamming crime
52 It has wheels on its heel
54 Small amounts
55 False god
56 Forbidden action
57 Canadian hockey legend
58 Have regrets

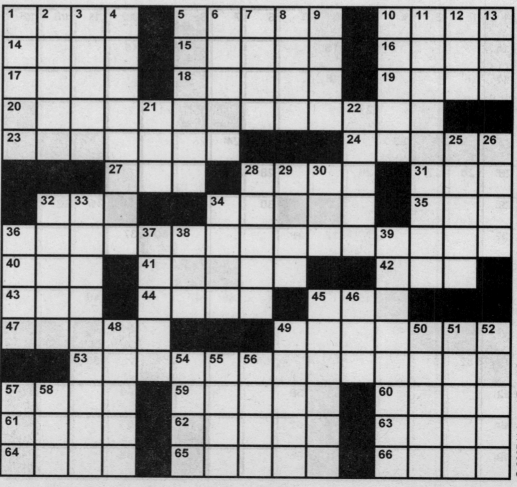

27 It's Your Choice

by Alice Walker
Edited by Timothy E. Parker
Answers in back

ACROSS

1 Rounded end of a church
5 Sportscast tidbit
9 Wrapped up
13 Shaving aid
14 Steno's goof
15 Spanish flick
16 Choice many face
19 Looks perfect on
20 Greek letter
21 Give great pleasure to
22 Otherwise called (Abbr.)
23 Sweet-smelling necklace
24 Crayola user
26 Choice many face
29 Places bets
30 Big commotions
31 Short smoke?
34 Exercise judgment
35 On the wagon
37 Pueblo Indian
38 Trip or slip, e.g.
39 Broad, thick piece
40 Backs, anatomically
41 Choice many face
44 Surgical implements
47 "How soothing!"
48 Newt wannabe
49 It may be heard coming and going
50 Feel malaise
51 Significant times
52 Choice many face
56 Islamic prayer leader
57 Sound made by a swinger?
58 Speak angrily
59 Thumb condition?
60 Tennyson's title
61 "Let ___!" (advice to the obsessed)

DOWN

1 Boer
2 Inferior rhymer
3 Gives under a load
4 Bird raised for its red meat
5 Kind of electricity
6 Banks, formerly of the runway
7 Mil. address
8 Rocky peak
9 Yellow and black cat
10 Bishop's assistant
11 Maternally related
12 Give someone the business?
17 Masher's look
18 Sub stations
19 Pretense
23 Part of LAX
24 Relinquish
25 Permeating quality
27 Fashion's bottom line?
28 Temple official
31 Gaining control over, in a way
32 By the fact itself
33 Some fairy tale characters
35 Coin destination, sometimes
36 Wilkes' plantation Twelve ___
37 Biblical mount where Aaron was buried
39 Stain or smudge
40 Homer Simpson expletive
41 Crook's plan, e.g.
42 Got just right
43 Lavish celebration
44 ___ lazuli
45 Mission in San Antonio
46 Without face value, as stock
50 One who sincerely flatters?
51 French state
53 Screech producer
54 Letter after pi
55 Mr. in Bombay

Page 29

28 Box Office Poison

by Thomas Lucas
Edited by Timothy E. Parker
Answers in back

ACROSS

1 Opposite of c.o.d.
4 Viking reading
8 Deli counter order, perhaps
14 Thole filler
15 Created a sketch
16 Having wings
17 One of every two hurricanes
18 Abyss
19 Posts on the stairs
20 Deli counter order, perhaps
23 Settle (into)
24 Festive occasion
25 Joie de vivre
29 Lithesome
31 Corporate routine
34 Emphatic ending (Var.)
35 "It's ___ the other!"
37 Ante matter?
38 It creates a big splash
41 Burier of Pompeii
44 Hoity-___
45 Multicolored pattern
49 "Uncle Vanya" playwright
51 Puddinglike dessert
52 Popular lunch salad
53 Lake, city or canal
56 "Dial ___ Murder"
57 It was first tested in 1952
61 Churchill's successor and predecessor
64 Recipe direction
65 Portuguese king
66 Repairman's reading
67 For, how or what ending
68 Soldier's fare, for short
69 Instruments with teakwood necks
70 Feudal peasant
71 Man of Steel monogram

DOWN

1 Call one's own
2 Shah's surname
3 "An American Tragedy" writer
4 Borderline
5 Hard worker at boring tasks
6 Geological formation
7 Not just bad
8 Went down like a cement block
9 Toward one side of a ship
10 Someone on the defense, perhaps
11 "Thanks, I already ___"
12 Cartoon voice Blanc
13 Proofs of age
21 Paparazzi's quarry, briefly
22 Make more subtle
26 Part of some college courses
27 Powerful heart
28 Angler's entangler
30 Gum attachments
32 Cyberspace initials
33 Prefix with sphere
35 Musical based on Dickens
36 Gotham paper (Abbr.)
39 London restaurant feature
40 Weight that sounds like a fruit
41 Step into character
42 Moo ___ pork
43 She may feel cooped up
46 Words preceding a personal preference
47 Chemically related compounds
48 Bowlers
50 Black Russian ingredient
51 More self-effacing
54 Judicial gowns
55 "___ at the office!"
58 Time for a revolution?
59 Shannon and Monte
60 Type of ball
61 Pre-noon hrs.
62 Mai ___ cocktail
63 You'll have a blast with it

29 Guys' Names

by Eugene Newman
Edited by Timothy E. Parker
Answers in back

ACROSS

1 Lover's keepsake, perhaps
6 Babushka, e.g.
11 Zodiac symbol
14 Therefore
15 International court site (with "The")
16 Bravo kin
17 Good name for an electrician?
19 Salon preparation, perhaps
20 Debatable
21 Highland dance
22 Sluggish
24 Cargo deck
26 Magazine fallout?
28 Plied a needle
31 One way or another
33 Colorful perennials
35 CEO, e.g.
36 Teeny bites
39 Zilch
40 "The Public Enemy" sound effect
43 Summer zodiac sign
44 Moolah
46 Pied Piper devotee
47 Indian sailor
49 Matterhorn vocalist
52 Elected
53 Circular saw part
55 It's useful in October
57 Sharp and bitter
58 Endings for pay and plug
60 Otherwise
64 Baseball's Ripken
65 Good name for a healthcare specialist?
68 Fashion monogram
69 Painkiller made by Bayer
70 Vaudeville production
71 Pig's home
72 1960 Everly Brothers tune
73 Utopias

DOWN

1 The other team
2 Renovate
3 Prefix with morph
4 They cut quite a swath
5 Wine adjective
6 Destroys files, in a way
7 Upkeep
8 Bars have one
9 Seek office
10 Charm believed to embody magical powers
11 Good name for a flier?
12 Wide-eyed
13 Dissolves
18 You may bookmark it
23 Gas that's hard to ignore
25 Czech river
27 Himalayan country
28 Try out for "American Idol"
29 Clinton's canal
30 Good name for an inefficient efficiency expert?
32 Skunk cabbage shape
34 Asian garment (Var.)
37 Porridge legumes
38 Vexed
41 Beer hall orders
42 Small fastener
45 Lincoln's wife
48 Swerved
50 Fuel additive, perhaps
51 Like "The Godfather"
53 Noted parade sponsor
54 "With ___ of thousands!"
56 Type of tray
59 Units of money in Bulgaria
61 Wash
62 Told, as a tale
63 Watches
66 "Evil Woman" band
67 Before, poetically

by Timothy Winton
Edited by Timothy E. Parker
Answers in back

ACROSS

1 Wedding symbol
5 Louts
10 Show signs of life
14 Wavy lines, in comics
15 Be in competition with
16 Purplish brown
17 Armed Forces option
18 It's larger than Lincoln
19 Dorsal bones
20 Vestige
21 Knowledgeable
23 Certifiable, so to speak
25 Munchhausen and Ananias, for two
26 Tear maker
28 "Big deal!"
32 Tied the knot
34 Farmer's necessity
35 Ebenezer's expletive
38 Chronological brinks
39 Blank tapes?
41 Physics force measure
42 Its floor is wet
43 Work at a diner, e.g.
44 Part of a baseball's seam
46 Reference point
48 Phoenix origin
49 Hollywood treasure
52 Draw out
54 Like a simple task
58 "SOS" singers
61 Yule follower
62 Capital of Tibet
63 It's over your head
64 Without advantage or disadvantage
65 Pointed a bow, e.g.
66 One word of advice
67 Like a Granny Smith apple
68 Subdivision maps
69 "The ___ the limit!"

DOWN

1 Interest-bearing certificate
2 Month before Nisan
3 Original thought
4 Fabrics for sale
5 Jack broke it
6 English gobs
7 Geometric shape
8 "James and the Giant Peach" author
9 Eastern European
10 Medium contact?
11 City on the Arkansas River
12 More gelid
13 Is a bibliophile
22 Spirited self-assurance
24 Its root is itself
26 Has to return a favor, e.g.
27 Alpine snow field
29 Emulate Demosthenes
30 Is no longer?
31 Scurries
33 Precious
35 How officials do things?
36 Suffix for allow or annoy
37 Derisive laughs
40 Big truck
41 Scraps
43 Hospital unit
45 Sigma follower
46 Kind of scout
47 Afternoon trayful, perhaps
49 Merger of two quartets
50 The Hindu destroyer
51 Juice from a press
53 Groups of two
55 Delivery after a delivery?
56 Marlo's man
57 Tibetan holy man
59 Without much meat
60 Some times of the day, briefly

31 Timespan

by Emery Glasso
Edited by Timothy E. Parker
Answers in back

ACROSS

1 Electronics brand
5 Oahu adieu
10 Sharp pain
14 Melancholy instrument
15 Tend to final details
16 Kind of steak
17 Happy time for landlords
20 Convenience store convenience, perhaps
21 Primitive shelters
22 Minipicture, maybe
23 Stunted
24 He can't bear anyone
26 Support
29 The color of honey
30 Comb maker
33 Bit of evidence
34 DVD player button
35 Pool table success
36 Hinterland, e.g.
40 Half-picas
41 Hovering in the sky
42 Nuclear energy source
43 Firmament
44 Brown alternative
45 Type of bow
47 Top-of-the-line
48 Opposite of flushed
49 Boat on a lake, perhaps
52 Type of cotton
53 It's placed in a setting
56 It comes about every 100 years
60 Caramel-and-chocolate candy brand
61 Testimonial dinner, e.g.
62 Judicial document
63 Jump on the ice
64 Gossipy gal
65 Sound of pain

DOWN

1 Daybed of sorts
2 News item for a scrapbook, briefly
3 100, I.Q.-wise
4 One of two definitive responses
5 Check entry
6 Like some ideas
7 Puts an end to wavering
8 "Say what?"
9 Wild way to go
10 Carry out Old Testament justice, in a way
11 Vintners' vessels
12 Deserve a hand?
13 Thailand money
18 Consequently
19 Fungi caused by moisture
23 Two-colored
24 Organize, as an exhibit
25 Among other things
26 Pinnacles
27 Move stealthily, in a way
28 Producing foamy lather
29 Social blunder
30 Quarterback Favre
31 Transnational money units
32 Kind of aircraft
34 British city on the English Channel
37 Unemploy temporarily
38 Distinctive flair
39 Fabled underachiever
45 Word with ready or shy
46 ___ Bator, Mongolia
47 "___ and his money ..."
48 Embroidered loop
49 Title word in a Doris Day song
50 Fort with a fortune
51 Like some rumors
52 Teller's partner
53 Maven
54 Norwegian navigator
55 Legend
57 "___ will be done"
58 Farmer's tool
59 Binary base

by Casey Rumblach
Edited by Timothy E. Parker
Answers in back

ACROSS

1 With the stroke of ___
5 Vasco da ___, Portuguese explorer
9 Texas landmark
14 Withering
15 They're found in pockets
16 Palindromic tales
17 They may hang around delis?
20 Swahili honorific
21 Israeli dances
22 Niger end?
23 Minister, slangily
25 It's all over the streets
26 Word with monkey or serpent
29 Clears, on a pay stub
31 Locale of a small stirrup
33 Enjoyment in cruelty
35 Member of the crow family
38 Chivalrous chaps
39 Card fit for royalty?
41 Aristide's former home
43 Advertise for new tenants
44 Chronic respiratory disease
46 Campaigned
47 Keeps company with
51 Opposite direction of a Hitchcock classic?
52 Sharp-penned Coulter
54 Steeped beverage
56 Historic Swiss canton
57 Take the wrong way?
59 Fistfight result, perhaps
61 Top10 tune of 1966
65 Broadcasting warning
66 Buffo performance, perhaps
67 Representative symbol
68 Witches' brew creatures
69 Revolutionary Trotsky
70 Hems but doesn't haw

DOWN

1 Furnace waste container
2 Olive-gray flycatcher
3 Off-course
4 Fluorine neighbor in the periodic table
5 Score of zero
6 Flight board abbreviation
7 Dovetail
8 "It's worth ___!"
9 Young vegetable shoot
10 Passes on the track
11 Eligibility factor
12 Render imperfect
13 1940s spy grp.
18 Kind of dance or bride
19 Things that can be rolled over, for short
24 Cloudy, diffused matter
26 Results from bad acting?
27 Ultimate ending
28 Wake-up times, typically
30 Pseudonym surname, often
32 More plentiful
34 Outstanding issues?
36 Cel creators
37 Conspicuous success
39 It operates on wind power
40 Grid official
41 Is down with
42 Cousin of a zebra
45 From a fresh angle
48 Carol Burnett character
49 Poetic "until this time"
50 Alluring women
53 Type of spray
55 "So, there you are!"
57 Narrow aperture
58 Fly on a hook, to bass
60 Flower of one's eye?
61 Hither partner
62 Ending for ethyl
63 Partner of order
64 Brief outline of life and work

33 Go Forth and Multiply

by Lester Mapple
Edited by Timothy E. Parker
Answers in back

ACROSS

1 Cops' decoy
5 Metric measure
9 One way to be wanted
14 Spread out on a table?
15 Freedom from hardship
16 Stage platform
17 Contents of some tablets
20 Line providers
21 1/60 of a trillionth of a min.
22 Squirt
23 Stars have them, briefly
25 Contented murmurs
27 Science degree
30 Anatomical pouches
32 Chorus syllables, perhaps
36 Caesar's wings
38 Reveille opposite
40 Ancient Greek colony
41 Conflict beginning in 1337
44 Line of work
45 Cleansing bar
46 Suspend
47 Send water flying
49 Relaxed rejection
51 Word of support
52 Bedding item
54 It's lost at the gym
56 Travel over powder
59 Mishmash
61 Citizens can make it
65 Part of an epic film, perhaps
68 Dispense
69 Mexican family circle members
70 Hypnosis ender
71 Sounds from the hood?
72 Worst kind of loser
73 Tony Fifth Avenue store

DOWN

1 "___ creature was stirring ..."
2 Sir Guinness
3 How to have a flat?
4 Winter treat
5 Idaho's nickname
6 Southdown male
7 In a New York minute
8 Bright group
9 "All in the Family" prop
10 Bad thing to be caught in
11 That special leader?
12 Presidential power
13 Formerly, formerly
18 Assns.
19 Result of an agreement
24 A bunch
26 Wade through mud
27 Money of Thailand
28 Drink undaintily
29 Artificial waterway
31 Secretly watch
33 Menachem's peace partner
34 Vine
35 Exasperation exclamation
37 Icelandic works
39 "___ Love" (Pacino film)
42 Does a director's job
43 It can be canned
48 First of two parts
50 They may hold pencils
53 Little League equipment
55 Kind of band
56 Union defier
57 Cabbagelike plant
58 "Robinson Crusoe" locale
60 Place for Reds and Browns
62 Sicilian province or its capital
63 Pierre's place (Abbr.)
64 Recipe amounts, briefly
66 It may be blown
67 Flat-ended instrument

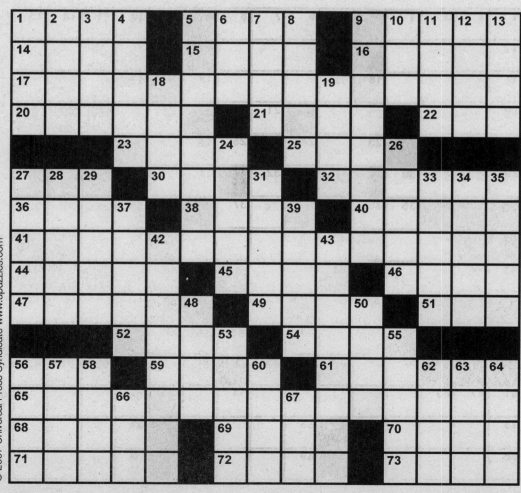

ACROSS
1 Clock radio switch
5 Firm parts, briefly
10 Soldiers for old Dixie
14 Casa component
15 Uncovers
16 Floor measure
17 Commiserator's word
18 Have a life
19 Parental admonition
20 Fires
22 Hindu social group
23 Exploit
24 Ingrain
26 Adagio, allegro, etc.
30 "Ghost Story" novelist Peter
32 WWII maritime hazard
34 Garment edge
35 Hands-on classes
39 Cartoon Betty
40 Biblical peak
42 Cannes brainstorm
43 Cost to be dealt in
44 Direct extender
45 Seem
47 Hindu queens
50 Bone of contention
51 Baseball position
54 They might give you a jump-start
56 Some precious stones
57 Some acrobatic maneuvers
63 Prefix with freeze
64 Words with may or might
65 American prefix
66 Bissextile year
67 Hogs' homes
68 "___ ain't broke …"
69 Disrespect, in a way
70 Mae and Adam
71 Isn't a natural

DOWN
1 Posthaste, briefly
2 French Sudan, now
3 Bakery offering
4 Camouflage
5 Adam's son and others
6 Prepares to take off
7 Misstep
8 Emphatic agreement
9 Craft that once landed at Heathrow
10 They're seen in air traffic control towers
11 Notched and jagged
12 Dispositions
13 Surfeits
21 Birthday attire?
22 PC's brain
25 Cobra relative
26 Hefty instrument
27 Deep black, in poesy
28 Subject to debate
29 Office items
31 Storied bear contingent
33 Shoe finish
36 Orange and lime, for two
37 Bringer of wine and flowers
38 Withering
41 Job for an orthodontist
46 Edith, the "little sparrow"
48 Sounds of delight
49 Soft bag containing perfumed powder
51 Embers
52 Breathing irregularity
53 Bye-byes
55 Words sung after "You must remember this"
58 How some cars are sold
59 Installed, as carpet
60 Not a done deal
61 ___-dieu (kneeling bench)
62 Elbow benders
64 Milan-Turin direction

by Carl Cranby
Edited by Timothy E. Parker
Answers in back

ACROSS

1 Booted, e.g.
5 Old-fashioned tie
10 Lux. neighbor
14 Homeroom response
15 Picked out
16 State forcefully
17 Lot measurement
18 What trains travel on
19 Home video format, once
20 Lowlifes
23 Foundation for something
24 Ancient fable spinner
25 Light measures
28 Ave. relative
30 Opera solo
31 Site for some rites
33 Chapter in history
36 Inventor's goal
40 Remained unused
41 "The Rose" penner
42 Opening bet, in poker
43 Symphonic silence symbol
44 Disturbing sounds
46 Prefix meaning "bone"
49 Changdeok Palace site
51 Lucille Ball musical of '43
57 ____-TASS (Russian news agency)
58 Holiday numbers
59 "That makes sense"
60 Edible tuber of Polynesia
61 Bones once called cubiti
62 A tide
63 Flat sound
64 Personal histories
65 Like some basements

DOWN

1 Carpet type
2 "My ____!"
3 Snack since 1912
4 Freeloader
5 Unlike this clue
6 The voice of Lamb Chop
7 They have heads and tails
8 Artist Edvard Munch's home
9 Kind of pattern
10 Mollycoddled
11 Becomes equal (with "out")
12 Can
13 Perceive
21 Athletic supporter
22 Le ____, France
25 Castle basements, in some films
26 Fertilizer chemical
27 Burn protection
28 Heating measures
29 Start of some Spanish place names
31 Bit of Latin conjugation
32 Place to pick lemons?
33 Fish-eating shore birds
34 Ad sales rep's quote
35 Anthropoids
37 ____ newt (witch's ingredient)
38 Legal matter
39 It may help move aircraft
43 Backup rockets?
44 Cattle snares
45 Possession indication
46 Last writes?
47 Words with "an example" or "a goal"
48 1917 marked their end
49 Antique guns
50 Black key
52 "Movin' ____" ("The Jeffersons" theme)
53 "Return of the Jedi" character
54 Under sail
55 Stationery order, perhaps
56 Gilbert Grape portrayer Johnny

by Leana Bloom
Edited by Timothy E. Parker
Answers in back

ACROSS
1 Mantra chanter of note
5 Kind of shot
10 Many have little ones
14 Superior to
15 Helpful sort
16 What you might be as busy as
17 Contract part, often
19 Sullivan had a really big one
20 ____-neck (horse defect)
21 Nickname for Rocky's portrayer
22 Place for landlubbers
24 Piggery
25 Like most homes
27 Gossipmonger
30 Revved, as the engine
31 About intro
32 Job for the board?

33 "Witness" actor Lukas
37 Wrinkled fruit
38 They may roll off the production line
39 Christiania today
40 Reduction
41 Hands over
42 Kind of bog or moss
43 Natural in Vegas
45 They may be engaged
46 Like some checks
49 What may be bro kin?
50 Legally responsible
51 Comedian DeLuise
52 The hot saison
55 Film lioness
56 It may come in pads
60 Some pub servings
61 One-celled protozoan (Var.)
62 Abbreviated version

63 Shannon and Monte
64 They may be before your eyes
65 Current letters

DOWN
1 Deposit of valuable ore
2 State
3 Distribute
4 Type of studio
5 With a heavy heart
6 Easter flower
7 "The Last King of Scotland" subject Amin
8 One-time closer Robb
9 Enormousness
10 They bring on disappointment
11 Regard with loathing
12 Inventor of the steel plow

13 Darned it
18 Spanish 101 word
23 Joan of Arc title, for short
24 Fish with lines
25 Kind of optimism
26 Invisible
27 "____ better believe it!"
28 Civil or elec. expert
29 "____ contendere" (no contest plea)
30 Feel mournful
32 List extenders
34 Not on solid ground?
35 Having wings
36 Chronic imbibers
44 Former Indian P.M. Shastri
45 Ribbonlike, braided fabric
46 Appeal earnestly
47 Valley on the moon (Var.)
48 Flip-chart support

49 Some are kept behind bars
51 Liability
52 Impressive in scope
53 Serve up the drinks, e.g.
54 "Layla" singer Clapton
57 One whose chest is protected, briefly
58 Bloom in "The Producers"
59 "I ____ lineman for the county"

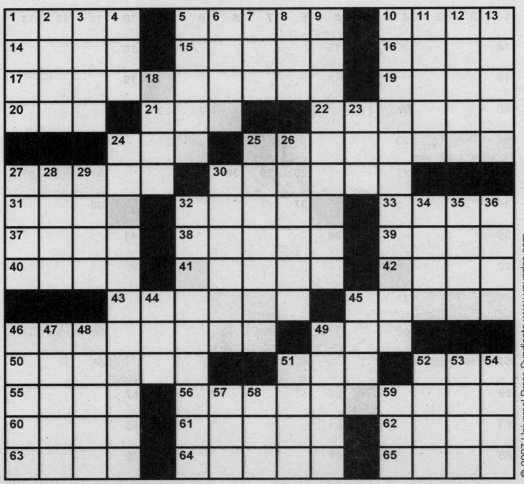

37 Cut and Dried

by Fred Jackson III
Edited by Timothy E. Parker
Answers in back

ACROSS
1 Round number
5 Syringe contents, perhaps
10 ___ Helens, Wash.
14 Hosp. room
15 Metal in Montana's motto
16 Tibetan oxen
17 Ricky Ricardo was one
19 Berth place
20 Narrow inlet
21 They give a hoot
22 Lusters
24 Bring charges, perhaps
26 Shakespearean prince
27 Wastebasket, in jest
34 Spill the beans
37 Listing
38 Sauce type
39 Persia, today
40 Long journeys
41 Popular succulent
42 ___ Lingus
43 Big name in farm equipment
44 Lends a hood a hand
45 Legendary sleeper
48 Earnings on a bank acct.
49 Words sometimes said with a nod
53 Geological formations
56 Opera that opens in Memphis
58 It may provide a snug feeling
59 Wimbledon score
60 Type of clothing
63 One pushing a mouse around?
64 "Coffee ___?" (host's question)
65 Monkey wrench
66 Clothing category
67 Wrinkle with age
68 See-through item

DOWN
1 Striped quadruped
2 Web letters
3 Kidney-related
4 Former fort near Monterey
5 Erupting volcano, e.g.
6 Carrier to the Holy Land
7 X-ray units
8 Colorado native
9 Some law enforcement officers
10 Reflexive pronoun
11 Chaucer offering
12 Largest organ
13 Letters on measuring spoons
18 Enter one's password
23 Certain deer
25 The "dismal science," for short
28 Seven-time A.L. batting champ Rod
29 Where humans evolve?
30 Make a comparison
31 Seagirt land
32 Something to split
33 Some are behind glasses
34 One not to be believed
35 "... ___ saw Elba"
36 Ground cover
40 Circus or carnival attraction
41 Busy as ___
43 Hans Christian Andersen, by birth
44 Aquatic organisms
46 Some hollow-fanged snakes
47 "Bewitched" star
50 Steakhouse order
51 Davenport denizen
52 Zippy tastes
53 Live beneath one's station
54 Take it on the chin
55 Kind of thermometer
56 Animated film of 1998
57 Cannes brainstorm
61 Uris protagonist
62 Broadband choice

© 2007 Universal Press Syndicate www.upuzzles.com

Page 39

by Timothy Winton
Edited by Timothy E. Parker
Answers in back

38 Double Dose

ACROSS
1 Throaty utterance
5 Take, as a nonrequired course
10 Weather-beaten
14 Double-curved molding
15 Hawaiian veranda or island
16 Customary function
17 Consoling words
19 Sunset-tinged, perhaps
20 Dealer's employer
21 Partition
23 Hoisting device
26 Sailor's employer
27 Sap-sucking insect
30 Kanga's tyke
32 Aboveboard
35 Regulated item
36 Pester
38 Lennon's wife
39 Type of scene

40 Knocking noise
41 Legendary Mel of the Giants
42 Flood stage
43 No longer shrink-wrapped
44 Polish literature
45 Converges on
47 Cell letters
48 ___ Canyon National Park
49 Wickfield's clerk
51 Site for some rites
53 First satellite
56 Takes the floor
60 Duchess of ___ (Goya model)
61 Start of a joke
64 Far Eastern desert
65 Causing goose bumps
66 Flat-bottomed vessel
67 Nine inches
68 Published again
69 Pivot on point

DOWN
1 Campus military org.
2 Title with Khan (Var.)
3 Matches, as a poker bet
4 Dandy's topper
5 "Your Song" singer John
6 Di-dah lead-in
7 Vane direction
8 Pack member
9 Make a logical connection
10 Reach one's destination
11 Squeal of delight
12 Alternative word
13 Cervine creature
18 British author Blyton
22 Clothes holder
24 Evidence of a major impact
25 Palm Sunday salute

27 They intentionally make spots
28 Deep-space mission
29 "What a babe!"
31 Bone-related
33 Clownish act
34 Singer Lenya
36 Chance occurrence
37 Young fellow
40 1953 AL MVP Al
44 Things to run
46 Keep possession of
48 Initials may be carved in it
50 Tight-fisted one, in slang
52 Kind of resistance
53 Gives under load
54 Tumultuous sit-down
55 Word with skinned or bended
57 Word with kit or around
58 Raw silk color

59 ___ terrier
62 Canadian hockey legend
63 Kind of operation

ACROSS

1 Vaulted church section
5 Hog filler
9 Redundant partner of "done with"
13 Shaver's purchase, perhaps
14 Pitchfork piece
15 Motion picture
16 Choice at breakfast, perhaps
19 "If the shoe ___ ..."
20 When a plane is expected in, briefly
21 Opposite of deject
22 Alias, initially
23 Orchid necklace, sometimes
24 One trying to stay between the lines?
26 Choice at the register, perhaps
29 Gets the pot going
30 Chaotic happenings
31 One of 20 pack items, informally
34 Make judgments
35 Like a judge, proverbially
37 Peaceful Indian
38 Be on the side of caution?
39 Rib order
40 Backs, anatomically
41 Choice at the hotel, perhaps
44 Surgeon's tools
47 Physical sound?
48 Small newt
49 See ya in Hawaii?
50 Need medical attention
51 Times of note
52 Choice at the grocer's, perhaps
56 Scholar of Islamic law
57 Playground cry
58 Quitter's word
59 Thumb condition?
60 Creator of heaven and Earth
61 "Let ___!" (advice to the obsessed)

DOWN

1 Boer
2 Inferior rhymer of verses
3 Loses rigidity
4 Australian ratite
5 Radio interference
6 Italian coin no longer minted
7 Bride of a famous musician
8 For each
9 It's spotted in South America
10 Church official
11 Related via one's mother
12 Direct elsewhere
17 Facial expression of contempt
18 Meat markets
19 Pretense
23 Part of UCLA
24 Turn over
25 Fish market feature
27 Haw partner
28 Synagogue leader
31 Treeing
32 By its very nature
33 Baseball or football team
35 Hole in a Vegas machine
36 Mighty trees
37 Biblical mountain
39 Stain or smudge
40 Homer Simpson expletive
41 Crook's plan, e.g.
42 Tackled hard
43 Lavish celebration
44 ___ lazuli
45 Memorable mission
46 Without face value, as stock
50 Creator of impressions
51 Pennsylvania, to a Parisian
53 Pussycat's partner
54 Letter after Pi
55 ___-fi (film type)

40 Born Free

by Alice Walker
Edited by Timothy E. Parker
Answers in back

ACROSS

1 Barbecue offering
5 Lawn game (Var.)
10 Exceedingly
14 Caron film of '53
15 Big name in petroleum, once
16 Get an ___ effort
17 Bone anagram
18 Site of 1988 Olympics
19 Rural mail delivery services, once
20 Meaningful silence
23 Mortarboard danglers
24 Mollusk shell material
27 Poker winnings
28 Big Apple river
31 AAA specialty
32 Resort with a mineral spring
34 Cause of yawning
35 "___ Got You Under My Skin"
36 Lou Diamond Phillips film of '88
40 Musical "Joey"
41 Some woodwinds
42 Light color?
43 Get ready to fire
44 A way to conjoin
45 Make imperfect
47 Hirsute lock
49 Outcasts
53 Disney film featuring twins
57 Female singing voice
59 "___ we all?"
60 Mythical ship of literature
61 It ultimately loses its head
62 Egyptian peninsula
63 Ballyhoo
64 There may be a fracture inside
65 Chinese weight units
66 They'll give you a bleating

DOWN

1 Got some shut-eye
2 Sign of the zodiac
3 Plants with healing properties
4 Airplane measure
5 Common volcanic rock
6 Forebodings
7 Eccentric oldster
8 Bra size
9 "___ Leroy" (Frances E. W. Harper novel)
10 Vice ___
11 Able to accomplish a purpose
12 Lightning attractor
13 Jr. and sr., for two
21 Classic prefix
22 To that time
25 Wandered about
26 Pitcher by the sink
28 Put a stop to
29 "No ifs, ___ or buts!"
30 Ambulance chaser's advice
32 Word with way or well
33 Leaf shapes used decoratively
34 An organic compound
36 Petty quarrel
37 Use a divining rod
38 "Honest" president
39 Nettle
45 Devout insect?
46 Type of studio
48 Strapped for cash
49 Type of code or colony
50 Hood's weapon
51 The ___ (Netherlands city)
52 An ocelot has lots
54 Historian's concern
55 Opera highlight
56 First Cartesian
57 Start of a kindergarten song
58 Meadow

41 Start to Finish

by Kelly Wilmark
Edited by Timothy E. Parker
Answers in back

ACROSS

1 Rock concert necessities
5 Head dog
10 Print with acid
14 Like a blue moon
15 Sorrow
16 Pervasive quality
17 Desertlike
18 Arboreal ape, briefly
19 Alluring skirt feature
20 Earliest period
23 Like fresh cake
24 Biblical outcast
25 Worry compulsively
28 Habitat of many wild animals
30 Means of restraint
31 Walkway material, sometimes
33 Make upset
36 Panamanian, e.g.
40 Indiana Jones found it
41 Slip by
42 Terrible market share
43 Skull and crossbones holder
44 Steep, rapid fall
46 An Italian dish
49 Her face "launched a thousand ships"
51 Wonderful wrap-up
57 Piece for a diva
58 Remove, as a brooch
59 Hebrew month
60 Flower associated with 10-Down
61 Food quality
62 Morrison or Tennille
63 Physics calculation
64 Overrun with marsh plants, e.g.
65 Verve

DOWN

1 Fine equine
2 Dark part of the moon
3 Snob
4 It may be found in a riverbed
5 Handsome lad of myth
6 Large-eyed, nocturnal lemur
7 Assembly-line setting
8 ___ Kong
9 Ship in search of the Golden Fleece
10 Holiday also known as Resurrection Day
11 Sign of spring
12 It may be abetted
13 One full of odium
21 What many park signs start with
22 Small handbill
25 Whale type
26 Cold one
27 Drop to the bottom
28 Fabric with metallic threads
29 Went to Wendy's, e.g.
31 Slight verbally
32 Young fellow
33 Bob Hope, for one
34 Tried to get a hold of, in a way
35 Elbow counterpart
37 Clear, as a debt
38 In the manner of
39 Flood
43 Moves away from the flock
44 More than enough
45 Cariou of Broadway
46 "The Lord is my shepherd" begins one
47 Central courtyards
48 Renders unclean
49 Crossed one's fingers
50 Getting with great strain (with "out")
52 Lay one on the kisser
53 "For ___ in My Life" (Stevie Wonder)
54 Teen magazine profilee
55 "Peter Pan" dog
56 It shows a lot of teeth

42 All Aboard

by George Keller
Edited by Timothy E. Parker
Answers in back

ACROSS

1 Jackson Five hairstyle
5 Attacked on all sides
10 Straw man's target
14 Dropping-into-water sound
15 Plant with spinachlike leaves
16 Freight car hopper, stereotypically
17 Copycat's request
18 ___ voce (almost in a whisper)
19 European auto
20 Speak from the heart, e.g.
23 Islamic prince (Var.)
24 Room with a view
25 Desert flora sight, perhaps
28 Mass. neighbor
30 What little things mean?
31 Newton knighted in 1705
33 Supplement (with "to")
36 It may be used in minor surgery
40 Albanian monetary unit
41 Head roaster
42 Mountain pass in India
43 Window frame
44 Having a diamond-shaped pattern
46 December mail recipient
49 Mechanical helper
51 Bibliophile's treasures
57 Retrocedes
58 Wandered about
59 Space race goal
60 Motion-carrying votes
61 Rudimentary seed
62 Book before Nehemiah
63 Steak specification
64 Blinds a falcon
65 Realize, as profits

DOWN

1 Church feature
2 Pale grayish yellow
3 An easy win
4 Bernstein's "Trouble in Tahiti," e.g.
5 Givers of orders
6 Irregularly edged
7 Mythical goatlike creature
8 Prefix meaning "outer"
9 Commandment starter
10 Appointed
11 "Three's Company" landlord
12 Manuscript marks
13 Stout detective Nero
21 Three-toed Australian
22 French alternative
25 Work a square dance
26 Shower gel ingredient, often
27 Tilt, as the head
28 Grammatical category
29 Kind of bran
31 Rainfall measure
32 Finger-pointer's word
33 Pallid
34 It's on the watch
35 Social outing
37 The absolute minimum
38 12-hr. stretches
39 It's flipped in the kitchen
43 Landlocked federal republic in central Europe, to the French
44 Puts up with
45 Decompose
46 Plain as the nose on your face
47 Nation with a solid green flag
48 Waves of grain color
49 Show full of skits
50 "The Life of Riley" character
52 Cupid counterpart
53 Bird of peace
54 Sludge
55 Asta's mistress
56 Lose it

ACROSS
1 Tropical food staple
5 Little star?
10 Nuclear energy source
14 Spicy stew
15 You can get steamed here
16 Excellent review
17 Old-timer, perhaps
20 Where you can get down
21 Spiritedness
22 It's sometimes bitter
23 Hinny's kin
24 Subsidy, e.g.
27 "This ____ good as it gets!"
29 First among siblings
32 Strike while the iron ____
35 Paradise lost
38 Take a shine to
39 Type of oarlock
40 They typically occur July through August
43 Black beef cattle
44 This could become late if mixed up
45 Geological time
46 Distributes (with "out")
47 Promotional phrase
49 Goddess of fertility
51 Persona-grata link
52 Meteorological phenomenon
55 Skeptic or cynic follower
57 "Major Barbara" author
60 It's fit for a queen
62 1968 Hepburn film
66 Apple section
67 Sit through again, as a film
68 When doubled, it means quickly
69 It may go to blazes
70 Sound from the birdcage
71 Amoco rival

DOWN
1 South Pacific nation
2 Therapeutic plants
3 What the sun does every day
4 Sound before the crash of dishes, perhaps
5 CBS forensic drama
6 Caesar following
7 Winter Olympics event
8 Abbr. on a business letter, perhaps
9 Believer in spiritual unity
10 Joan of ____
11 Makes, as pay
12 Pizza producer
13 Convalesce
18 Not a figment of your imagination
19 Not having been moved
25 How some people chatter
26 Certain believers
28 Trash collector
29 Gives qualities or abilities to
30 Toast word
31 Discovery of 1938
33 Toast-topper
34 Graceful seabird
35 Imported cheese
36 Completed
37 Kitchen gadgets
41 Home of St. Francis
42 Lily of Utah
48 "Nay!" sayer
50 Pint-sized
52 Machine for shaping wood
53 Popular cookies
54 Bends out of shape
55 Reason to scratch one's head?
56 Skedaddle!
58 One way to start
59 Healthy, wealthy partner
61 Move at a snail's pace
63 "Do the Right Thing" director
64 Maiden name intro
65 Allowing alcohol

by Tucker Mathis
Edited by Timothy E. Parker
Answers in back

ACROSS
1 Los Angeles area
6 Big game, briefly
11 Percussive dance
14 Frontiersman of knife fame
15 "Jack Sprat could ___ fat"
16 Moronic beginning
17 Anacin alternative
18 Gambler's game, perhaps
20 Agreed, in a way
22 Hairdresser's forte
23 Does a thespian's job
25 Beauticians, sometimes
28 One with at least one below?
29 Kind of trader
30 Goes up and down
32 Martin's "That's ___"
34 Wanders idly
39 A Catholic sacrament
42 Oriental appetizer
43 Wrestlers' maneuvers
45 Prefix meaning sun
46 Entertains with fine food and drink, e.g.
49 Words exchanged with love
50 Toga party venue, sometimes
54 Wild and menacing
55 Escalator part
56 Half of a TV transmission
58 "Evangeline" setting
60 Gambler's game, perhaps
63 Get together
66 Chicken order, sometimes
67 Sidewalk amusement (with "show")
68 Fairy tale monsters
69 Before, to an odist
70 Change a bill
71 Blinds, as a bird of prey

DOWN
1 Pugilism org.
2 Gateway to a logon, for some
3 Age many can hardly wait for
4 Modern recording devices
5 It could lead to something big
6 Photo mishap
7 At the top of the Mohs scale
8 "Make ___ double"
9 Grenoble-to-Dijon dir.
10 Butterfingers' word
11 Its name means "Eastern capital"
12 Some skating moves
13 Funeral conflagrations
19 Type of betting, briefly
21 H.S.T. successor
23 Make books into movies, e.g.
24 An Alfred Hitchcock film appearance, e.g.
26 Atypical
27 Plunderer's take
30 Spanish title of respect
31 They may be heaved
33 Word often heard in triplicate
35 Beginning for tend or text
36 Gem set by itself
37 Omit in pronunciation
38 One-masted sailboat
40 Staff symbol
41 A bit of superiority
44 Desert nomad
47 Was in need of
48 Highest musical note of yesteryear
50 Aesop's output
51 Pencil-box accessory
52 Traditional saying
53 First X
55 Burn slightly
57 Gumbo vegetable
59 Twosomes
61 Toast topping
62 Ear anagram
64 Prefix meaning distant
65 Count conclusion?

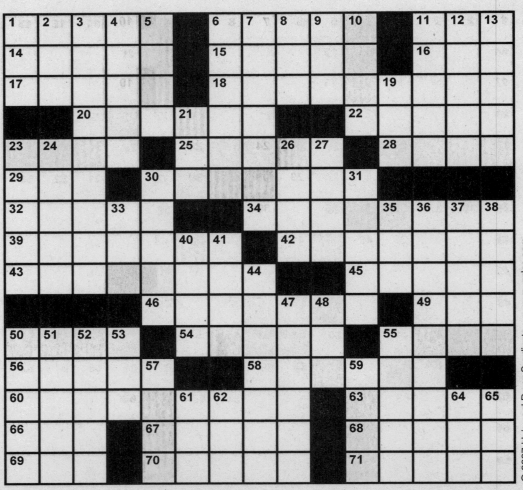

45 The Sty's the Limit

by Thomas Lucas
Edited by Timothy E. Parker
Answers in back

ACROSS
1 Whimper
5 Smart-mouthed
10 Upright framing piece
14 Charley horse, e.g.
15 Rounded like an egg
16 Component used as fertilizer
17 Bill in a restaurant
18 Jackknife and others
19 ___ vase (precious porcelain)
20 State of utter bliss
22 Fair grade
23 Climber's challenge
24 Up to now
26 Onion variety
30 Waftures
34 School dance
35 Sight-unseen purchase
38 Lower in public estimation
41 Go astray
42 Popular aquarium fish
43 Source of patronage jobs
46 The piper's son
47 Regard with respect
48 Gets gas, in a bad way
51 Wilder co-star
54 Prefix with political or logical
55 Key's middle name
58 Bumbling
63 Pueblo Indian
64 Something to kick
65 Fizzy quaff
66 Obi-Wan player
67 Crop up
68 Start of many exclamations from Robin
69 Real layers
70 Dovetail part
71 Cream-filled cookie

DOWN
1 Ratio of fast flight
2 It's said once but heard twice
3 Supporter of the American Revolution
4 Deadly
5 Nehi, e.g.
6 Tel ___
7 Backs up, on a computer
8 Shorthand whiz
9 Doorbell-answerer's word
10 Double Dutch equipment
11 Seed sheath
12 Carte before the course?
13 They may be checked
21 Architectural wing, perhaps
22 Diamond weight
25 Geisha's accessory
26 Physical condition
27 Rail riders, in stereotypes
28 Like pieces requiring assembly
29 Shea section
31 "In God We Trust" is one
32 Rubber hub
33 Tailor's specialties
36 Sound from a boxer?
37 Cholers
39 "Show me" types
40 Critic Roger
44 "Little Women" woman
45 Decrease, as a load
49 It rattles in a whistle
50 Boss (with "head")
52 Illinois arrival site
53 Former Israeli political leader
55 Former Iranian ruler
56 Nat or Natalie
57 Frank
59 Soy-based soup
60 Slammer?
61 Vogue rival
62 Belafonte refrain
64 This may be over your head

by Leana Bloom
Edited by Timothy E. Parker
Answers in back

46 Bird Feed

ACROSS

1 Raines of old films
5 "Presto!"
10 Drops below the horizon
14 Nectar harvesters
15 Reptile that's really sumthing?
16 City map
17 Grocers stock them
18 With no weaning
20 Hydrotherapy facility
21 Have the moxie
22 Maroon
23 Isn't straight?
25 Herring young
26 Type of union
28 One lingering aimlessly
32 Utilizes a library, in a way
33 They sometimes accompany ejections
34 Ringside cheer, perhaps
35 Bit of ocean life
36 It's good to meet them
37 Catamount
38 Intimate friend
39 Informal attire
40 Made a grand grander?
41 They help you acquire contacts
43 Use a clothesline, e.g.
44 Sciences partner
45 WJM's Mr. Grant
46 Set a lofty goal
49 Tap-on-the-shoulder alternative
50 Stumblebum
53 Foolish one
55 Band from Stockholm
56 It may get a good licking
57 Prodigious
58 Pajama material, perhaps
59 Adrenaline releaser
60 They pull their load
61 Deliver a low blow, in a way

DOWN

1 Is retrocessive
2 Sudden transition
3 Top-notch lawyer
4 Cousin of a zebra
5 Unoccupied
6 They can be offensive
7 Not up to much
8 Spearheaded
9 Highway system components
10 Soft drink since 1961
11 Brotherhood since 1868
12 1.3-ounce Asian weight
13 Lid infection
19 Apartments
21 Speaker's stand
24 Icelandic writing
25 Connery and Moore, e.g.
26 Black band of mourning (Var.)
27 Four-legged race
28 Title clouds
29 Type of tournament
30 Wabbit hunter
31 Starter's alert
33 Notable achievements
36 Seniors may use them
37 Unsullied
39 Tom's prey, in cartoons
40 Sunglasses feature
42 Adapt, as for a specific purpose
43 Company possessions, e.g.
45 Very, to the maestro
46 Starting from
47 Mudder's father
48 Emotional request
49 It has been compared to a tree
51 Having sufficient skill
52 Charlatan
54 Zincite, e.g.
55 Request permission, e.g.

ACROSS

1 Gomer of classic TV
5 Scimitar, e.g.
10 Place in a race
14 What a salesperson may follow
15 Where eggs may be very high?
16 Screen symbol
17 Opposing voice
18 Unpolished
19 It may be due, get the point?
20 Stodgy one
23 Type of ray
24 Central religious principle
25 Type of maniac
28 Burdened beast
29 "Hasta luego!"
33 Boarding house occupant
35 Like Arbuckle's films
37 It comes with strings attached
38 Treacherous one
43 Subject to a draft
44 An earth color
45 Medical staff member
48 It's home to Castro?
49 Something to hang your hat on
52 Hawaiian garland
53 Oft-contracted word
55 Flat replacement
57 Forty-niner's dream?
62 Piece for one voice
64 Engaging individual?
65 Word with goods, history or study
66 Prepare for an overseas vacation
67 Growing outward
68 ___ and terminer
69 Archaic pronoun
70 Not too astute
71 "Two Mules for Sister ___"

DOWN

1 TV type
2 Busybodies
3 Some Americans
4 ___ of Nantes, 1598
5 Bombay wraparound dress
6 Longest division of geological time
7 Very dry, as champagne
8 Skater's figure
9 Try again
10 In ___ of (replacing)
11 The educational community
12 It may be tapped out at sea
13 Demolitionist's charge
21 Bar-the-door gal
22 Cattle call?
26 Fathoms
27 They're found in pockets and seams
30 "When We Were Kings" profilee
31 Accountant's column
32 Shenanigan
34 Stew vegetable
35 Terrier breed
36 "Take ___ Train" (Duke Ellington performance)
38 Harness the wind
39 Comfy cloud
40 Deceptive maneuver
41 Some dash lengths
42 Grind, as teeth
46 Letters with messenger or transfer
47 Had a snack
49 Juice source
50 Student's accessory
51 Taxonomic groups
54 "To ___ own self be true"
56 Bill of legend
58 Superior, for one
59 Farsi-speaking nation
60 Court partitions
61 It leaves in springtime
62 Suitable to the occasion
63 Word of support

48 Traffic Problems

ACROSS

1 Caddie's bagful
5 One more than sieben
9 Fruit desserts
14 TV statuette
15 Name akin to Wm. or Robt.
16 Hundred-eyed giant
17 Horse with a gray-sprinkled coat
18 Plantation of literature
19 Shopping memos
20 Problem for some car buyers
23 Smoked delicacy
24 Cleverly skilled
25 Perturbed state
29 Buck follower
30 Genealogy word
32 Compass heading
33 Holiday driver, in a phrase
36 Scout gathering, e.g.
38 "Shaft" singer Hayes
39 Laughing matter?
40 Constructed of interlaced strips
41 Commuting time for many, obviously
43 Turns documents into confetti
44 Morse code sound
45 Your financial advisor advises it
46 Legal action
47 Chunk of marble, e.g.
49 Impassioned
51 Rose-rose connector
54 Late braking result?
57 First name in Spanish art
60 The Beatles' "Let ___"
61 Kind of belt
62 Apply for ___ (seek assistance)
63 Fleshy seed covering
64 Consumes
65 They may come from using plastic
66 Shipshape
67 Oversatisfy

DOWN

1 Short and to the point
2 Ham it up
3 Electronic communication
4 Lip-___ (mouth the words)
5 More than accepted, as advice
6 1969 Elvis oater
7 Silent screen star
8 Russian empresses
9 It's lowest on the Mohs scale
10 April 7 sign
11 Certain NFL linemen
12 Boy king
13 Steam iron sound
21 Pakistan's largest city
22 Two stars dating, e.g.
26 Word with gas or cell
27 "You're All ___ to Get By"
28 They're coming of age
29 Asian nanny
31 "Charlotte's Web" author
33 Word in a Hitchcock film title
34 Commonplace
35 A 33-Down in "Peter and the Wolf"
36 It holds the mayo?
37 ___ cloud (solar-system region)
39 Protector
42 Mediterranean port
43 The South and the Southwest
46 Side in a 1999 war
48 It's a bit higher than A
50 Raison ___
51 Standard of excellence
52 "From ___," shining …"
53 Showy and pretentious
55 Untold centuries
56 One sixty-billionth of a min.
57 Gym mat
58 Ginger follower
59 Rock's Dylan

49 Furniture Shopping

by Wesley Holman
Edited by Timothy E. Parker
Answers in back

ACROSS

1 Uncle Miltie's sidekick, Arnold
6 Bryn ____ College
10 Ship's post
14 Bar-the-door gal
15 ____ fixe
16 Audio effect
17 Nerve-cell conduits
18 It has two heels
19 Have the gumption
20 Some arithmetic to memorize
22 ____ about (approximately)
23 Fill with freight
24 Whitewater enthusiast
26 Go along with
30 Child of fortune?
31 Unsocial sort
32 Some rural festivities
36 Some donations
37 Slowly trickles
39 George Bernard ____
40 Quintet on a calendar
42 "I ____ Symphony" (Supremes hit)
43 Jazz lingo
44 Gliding ballroom dance
46 "Cheers" proprietor
49 Coffeehouse reader, perhaps
50 "Lawrence of Arabia," e.g.
51 Orchestra position
57 Put on the line
58 Warts and all
59 Blood line
60 Maroon's locale
61 Inviting word
62 What rookies need to learn
63 Group's pronoun
64 Genesis grandchild
65 Philatelist's purchase

DOWN

1 Bridgelike game
2 Cry on a rainy night, perhaps
3 Molecule component
4 Midmorning
5 William Tell adversary
6 Address for a countess
7 Western building material
8 Well-being
9 Instant replay viewers
10 Luxurious ease
11 First words of "Satisfaction"
12 Violent spasm
13 Start of a saying on forgiveness
21 Keyboard word
25 Lend a hand
26 "There ought to be ____!"
27 Trunk of a tree
28 "She Believes ____" (Kenny Rogers song)
29 Typical office worker
30 Bygone school event
32 The Chiffons' "____ So Fine"
33 "Come again?"
34 Nostril
35 Cashless deal
37 Avoid embarrassment
38 Needle part
41 Huge racket
42 Chop shop inventory
44 Discards
45 Not toweled off
46 Basis for some raises
47 Given to imitation
48 Knit goods thread
49 First-class
52 "Time — My Side" (Stones song)
53 Knee-slapper
54 Florentine angel's instrument
55 Checklist bit
56 Carpenter's tool

by Kyle Gray
Edited by Timothy E. Parker
Answers in back

50 Road Hogs

ACROSS

1 A's in communications
6 Provide with an overhead surface
10 Applies ointment
14 Cookout food, for short
15 Breathe with a rattling sound
16 Oscar winner Jannings
17 Goodbye, in Grenoble
18 Song for Callas
19 Wine partner
20 Hands-on communication?
23 CD-___
26 Any French king
27 Entrance requirement, often
28 Hot-weather treat
32 Team stat
33 Spring addressee, for short
34 Secured
37 Net receipt?
38 Firmament
39 Underneath
41 "May I help you?"
42 "The Purloined Letter" writer
43 Cheap, vulgar tastelessness
44 Snub
47 Antithesis of surfeit
50 Taiwan or Peking addition
51 Sixth sense, briefly
52 Measure of the wealth of groups of families
56 They can embrace you
57 Miner's entrance
58 Go one better than
62 Go bananas
63 Las Vegas alternative
64 Spacious window
65 Brooding sorts
66 Wine connoisseur's concern
67 "… with ___ in sight"

DOWN

1 Legal org.
2 Young fellow
3 Calendar abbr.
4 Vigoda and Lincoln
5 Arboreal rodent
6 They have brains
7 British blue blood
8 Skater Kulik
9 Simple shacks
10 Truncate, e.g.
11 Boat used in Alaska
12 Brief indulgence
13 Winter-weather word
21 "What ___ up, must come down"
22 Card game or drink
23 The life of ___ (luxurious existence)
24 "___ All Ye Faithful"
25 Plateaus' kin
29 CBS forensic drama
30 Some stage props
31 Have a bawl
34 Forest clearing
35 Exudes, as confidence
36 Twit
38 Landscaper's need
39 Relatively long period of time
40 Japanese delicacy
42 All-inclusive, as a meeting
43 Leaving something to be desired
44 Potato chips, to a Brit
45 Reproductive cells
46 Boss around
47 Destroy, as a pumpkin
48 Tin-lead alloy
49 Billboard designer
53 ___ fixe
54 One of Columbus' ships
55 Prefix with bond or dollar
59 Railroad beam
60 Place for a nap, maybe
61 ___ Hickory

51 Everywhere

by Tucker Mathis
Edited by Timothy E. Parker
Answers in back

ACROSS

1 Impersonate
6 Once, once upon a time
10 Anthroponym
14 Dictatee
15 Wacko
16 Stylish elegance
17 Bridge maven
18 ___ de force
19 What an anemometer measures
20 Make excessive corrections
23 "Fudge!"
24 ___ Lanka
25 Heavy-hearted
26 A major broadcaster
29 ___ vu
31 I, for Claudius
33 Damaging precipitation
35 Princes, but not princesses
37 Shot the breeze
41 Not up to par
44 They travel in formation
45 Foreign refusal
46 Go it alone
47 Enjoy a quaff
49 Grades K-12, for short
51 Dangerous reptile
52 Embargo
55 It fills in between E and F
57 Color quality
59 Ceaselessly
64 Sounds of unhappiness
65 Sugar substitute?
66 Make ___ of (write down)
68 "Robinson Crusoe" locale
69 Like an inveterate procrastinator
70 Ruses
71 Pippin
72 Barely made (with "out")
73 Performer's minimum wage

DOWN

1 Chinese restaurant additive, perhaps
2 Langston Huges title
3 "Wheel of Fortune" creator Griffin
4 "___ Your Love Tonight" (Presley song)
5 "Lord Jim" novelist
6 "Rocket Man" performer
7 Part of a Clue accusation
8 Coastal water fishes
9 El Toro's adversary
10 It's breaking, at times
11 Identity disguiser
12 Ocean ray
13 Put a stop to
21 Cockatoo's pride
22 Japanese mercenary
26 Gulp down
27 Source of misery
28 Them or us
30 Words before and after for
32 Beanery offering
34 With a discount of
36 Suffered in the heat
38 Word shouted to the team?
39 Elongated wonders
40 Word with anchor or off
42 Exercise of sovereign power
43 Work ___ (code of the dedicated)
48 Swim like a dog
50 Wedding acquisitions
52 Rationale
53 Sprung up
54 Highborn
56 Chateaubriand, e.g.
58 Bubbly mixer
60 Exploited
61 Powerful emotion
62 Vending-machine offering
63 Record label in some TV ads
67 Paris-to-Troyes dir.

by George Keller
Edited by Timothy E. Parker
Answers in back

ACROSS

1 Early recording systems, familiarly
6 Entranced
10 Source of illegitimate income
14 To one side
15 Salty salute?
16 Fruit juice alternative
17 One over you, perhaps
19 Preindication
20 Tomboys' counterparts
21 Curricula vitae
23 Professional charges
25 "Harper Valley ___"
26 Tote with effort
30 Last name in spydom
33 Wizards perform here
36 Two-dimensional measurement
37 Middle Eastern currency
38 Spanish company?
39 One in front
43 Explain further
44 John's label, sometimes
45 Some years back
46 Homer Simpson's shout
47 Gift for a diva, perhaps
48 Made typo-free
50 "To what do I ___ ... ?"
52 Take out of context?
54 Roman Forum regular
58 Soup cracker, perhaps
63 Treaty between nations
64 Imposer of hard work
66 Muscle malady
67 "Cast Away" setting
68 Type of spray or passages
69 Norse god of thunder
70 Blacken by burning
71 Wax eloquent

DOWN

1 Fisherman's lure?
2 Decorative toiletry case
3 Rewards for waiting
4 Pub potables
5 Disharmony
6 Corporate kudo
7 Expressions of pain relief
8 Impecunious
9 Ancient capital of Phoenicia
10 Reconnoiterer
11 Title for a senior officer, perhaps
12 Not aweather
13 Takes, as battle stations
18 Second in command, informally
22 Skyline feature
24 Utilized a clutch
26 Type of plate, bar or fork
27 One's own ism
28 Boss of bosses
29 Eton attendee, perhaps
31 Pangolin's diet
32 Word of support
34 Italian bowling game
35 Wanted to know
37 Gets decked out in
40 Plumed avian
41 Vintage auto
42 Tasty paste
48 Jack of "Big Bad John"
49 Part of F.D.R.
51 Word with buffalo or chestnut
53 Glacial ridge
54 Little dustup
55 When purchased alone
56 Ear-related
57 Unthought-out
59 Russian ruler of yore
60 Words with shame or boy
61 Sans ice
62 Colleague of Agatha
65 Tania's "army"

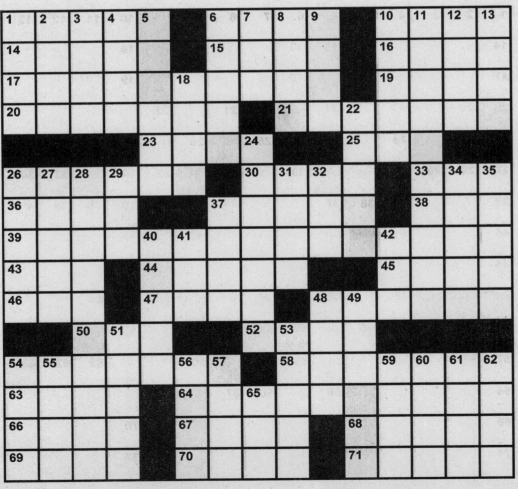

53 We Did It!

by Alex Henry
Edited by Timothy E. Parker
Answers in back

ACROSS

1 Guys' goals?
5 Celeb's hiree
10 Subtle "Over here!"
14 Leave unacknowledged
15 Marshy lake outlet
16 Lung opening?
17 Won unconvincingly
19 Has put words to music
20 Configurations
21 One who serves and receives
23 Old hat
26 Hard to come by
27 Handled clumsily
30 Pantry intruder, perhaps
32 Nissan rival
35 Japanese Prime Minister Hirobumi
36 Office chair feature
39 Chance upon
40 Gives no stars to
42 Flared dress
43 ___ fixe (obsession)
44 Napoleon's home, for a while
45 Doohickey
47 Sports car protector
48 With cunning
50 Wheel track
51 So far
53 Fervent
55 ___ voce (softly)
57 Bunched fruits
60 Emulated 5-Across
64 Tingling with excitement
65 Near miss
68 Bit of chicanery
69 Middy counterpart
70 It's on the agenda
71 Exploit
72 Helps in a bad way
73 Plane beginning

DOWN

1 Seamen, slangily
2 Nurse in the Orient
3 One-time Venetian coin
4 Extensive plain without trees
5 Deep gulf
6 Some people have it as a gift
7 Peacock tail feature
8 Father of Shem and Japheth
9 Help with homework, e.g.
10 Rye partner
11 Got off a packed subway train, in a way
12 Grabs some rays
13 Plates that move
18 Shows how
22 Frodo's friend
24 Hand on deck
25 Jealous
27 Vocal cords, in slang
28 In the least bit
29 Was barely victorious
31 Take care of
33 Big name on the farm
34 Corroded
37 Small mass of soft material
38 It's suitable for grazing
41 Snatched from the fire, e.g.
46 They're set for marriages
49 Yang counterpart
52 Tom Jones' love
54 Bangladesh's capital (Var.)
56 Waste allowances
57 Epithet for Shakespeare
58 Chills and fever
59 Hunk of marble
61 Fancy spread
62 "Be it ___ so humble ..."
63 It may be taken for a ride
66 Poetic form
67 Place for an acting president?

by Alice Walker
Edited by Timothy E. Parker
Answers in back

54 Asking for Directions

ACROSS

1 "Ivanhoe" writer
6 Wealthy one
11 Part of a famous soliloquy
14 Half of an '80s crime-fighting duo
15 Zinc ____
16 "Shogun" sash
17 Open, as a bottle
18 Poet's concern
19 Perch, at first
20 Point of the Earth's axis
22 Took out the king?
24 Feminine pronoun
25 Couple's pronoun
26 No-thing connector
27 Geometrical figure
28 Obliquely
31 Luster
34 Charge on an electron
35 Something borrowed
36 Country of Juan Carlos
38 Wallet stuffers
39 Teach
41 Short-tailed lemur
42 Groups of four
43 Type of deal
45 Noted Broadway debut, October 1982
46 Role for a star
47 "____ was saying ..."
50 String instrument
52 Yul Brynner film
54 Historical chapter
55 Famous Roman fountain
57 Bovine trademark
58 It may go up in smoke
59 More fit for the task
60 Hotelier Helmsley
61 Blasting sticks
62 Appellation
63 Has a strong craving

DOWN

1 One reason for boots
2 Birch bark craft
3 Transpire
4 Udder part
5 Tropical tempest
6 "Enough!"
7 Figure skaters' feats
8 Take the bait
9 English I reading
10 Famous triangle
11 Boreas
12 Reed instrument
13 Having no loose ends?
21 "I can't ride my bike. It's two tired," e.g.
23 Paint remover or solvent
26 Communicate silently
27 Like some air conditioning
28 Type of whale
29 State confidently
30 "____ Can" (Sammy Davis Jr. autobiography)
31 Narrow aperture
32 Perfect, as one's skills
33 Where to find New Yorkers
34 Turner in history
36 Spume
37 Many home computers
40 "The Public Enemy" sound effect
41 Live inside, as a spirit
43 Name of Tennessee's streetcar
44 Granola morsel
46 Carpenter's need
47 Firebug's crime
48 Broken arm support
49 Lightbulbs, in the comics
50 Three-piece suit part
51 Nutritive mineral
52 Whipping memento
53 Bread spread
56 Baseball stat

by Kelly Wilmark
Edited by Timothy E. Parker
Answers in back

ACROSS

1 Der ____ (Adenauer)
5 Attire for the Headless Horseman
9 Monk's hood
13 Reverse knit
14 "… more than one way to skin ____"
15 Fishing craft
16 Some punches
18 Breaks a computer code
19 It can be simple or compound
20 Sprinter's assignment
21 Emulate a bull
22 Plea a-sea
23 Thick-brick link
26 Groups within groups
30 Japanese capital
31 Farmland measure
35 Make angry
36 Like Inspector Clouseau
38 Frisky
41 Items on a to-do list
42 A good one is usually square
43 Ice holder
44 Low or high tail
45 Greek tycoon Aristotle
48 Matter to the jury
49 Fond du ____, Wisc.
50 Former capital of Nigeria
55 Mouse catcher
57 "Backdraft" criminal
60 More or less
62 Ground beef dish
63 Run out, as a subscription
64 "____ Leroy" (Frances E.W. Harper)
65 "Return of the Jedi" green-skinned dancer
66 Prefix for while
67 Little props for Augusta
68 Experience in a tactile way

DOWN

1 Sap-sucking insect genus
2 Greg Evans comic strip
3 Words before Remember and Forget, in song titles
4 Wabbit pursuer Fudd
5 Birthday party centerpiece
6 They might be found up sleeves
7 Actor's quest
8 Little green men?
9 "Brian's Song" star
10 Annually
11 Chinese cooking pan
12 "____ Miserables"
15 Major car part
17 ____ and sciences
20 Parking or odd follower
22 Recognized to be
24 Nasal partitions
25 Fidgety
27 "What's a Grecian ____?"
28 Food item introduced in 1968
29 Fruits of the blackthorn
31 End of a fairy tale
32 Knock off
33 They break up long trips
34 Forest ranger?
37 End of Ripley's statement
39 A way to single out
40 Hebrew priest
46 Pile on the rug
47 Hardly haute cuisine
51 "Don't give me ____ your lip!"
52 Army figure
53 "____ mio"
54 Inappropriately appropriate
56 Sign of age
57 Facial tissue additive, perhaps
58 Butler, to Gable
59 Health establishments
60 It may be pale
61 Lush surroundings?
62 Warm chairs

by Lucille Evanstone
Edited by Timothy E. Parker
Answers in back

56 Get Some Exercise

ACROSS
1 Condescending clucks
5 Saunter along
10 Librarian's admonitions
14 George Lucas creature
15 Dr. visits
16 Drinking spree
17 Infamous Colombian city
18 Half of catorce
19 Start of a hocus-pocus phrase
20 Demand formality
23 Visits Spago, e.g.
24 Basilica sections
25 Male seals' group of devotees
28 Hauteur
30 Ubiquitous lily relative
31 Incinerated
33 Guy's counterpart
36 React eagerly
40 Rambunctious child
41 ___ number on
42 Bombay garb
43 Property law topic
44 Personal preferences
46 Black tea from Sri Lanka
49 John who wrote "Butterfield 8"
51 Must finally come clean
57 Hieroglyphics bird
58 Man from Muscat
59 Land for the loony?
60 Building location
61 "I kid you not!"
62 Sussex streetcar
63 Shambles
64 They stay ahead of heels
65 All there

DOWN
1 Sleuths, slangily
2 Certain crisis team
3 Tree with caffeinated pods
4 Superficial
5 Stoneworkers
6 State as an opinion
7 Building plans, for short
8 Suffix with super
9 Flanders' river
10 Letter attachments
11 Rail riders, in stereotypes
12 Songstress Lena
13 What an obedient dog does, sometimes
21 Make less bright
22 Gore's "___ in the Balance"
25 Traveler to Mecca
26 Styptic substance
27 Play boisterously
28 Lot measurement
29 "Murder, ___"
31 One of a vitamin complex
32 Hesitation sounds
33 Buzzing annoyance
34 Farmland measurement
35 Organic necklaces
37 Bye, in France
38 Big or little digit
39 Offensives
43 Releases
44 Prepares for takeoff
45 ___ de Triomphe
46 Light reflector
47 Jazzy Blake
48 Makes mittens, in a way
49 Words with most or first
50 1928, 1932 and 1936 Olympic gold medalist
52 An awful lot
53 Melville sequel
54 ___ Lee
55 Panache
56 Unvaried

ACROSS

1 Salty sea of Asia
5 Ouida's "___ of Flanders"
9 Capital of Morocco
14 Port of southeast Italy
15 Drudgery
16 Love to extremes
17 Mideast gulf
18 Beanery handout
19 Plucky courage
20 Social services employees
23 Quirky
24 Type of patch
25 Inventory item's place
27 Narrow openings
30 Beautiful sight to behold
33 Santa's mo.
36 Breakfast fare
38 Italian wine
39 Pigment source (Var.)
41 Swellhead's trouble
42 Prickly plants
43 Sandwich cookie
44 Go over and over and over
46 Longest time
47 Yeltsin's bailiwick
49 Valentino title role (with "the")
51 Too much, musically
53 Cause of weakness
57 It may be connected to Christ
59 Move rapidly
62 "___ words were never spoken"
64 Facial expression
65 Morally reprehensible
66 English liquid measure
67 Slack-jawed
68 Today's Persia
69 Emitted coherent radiation
70 Well-known loch
71 Small salamander

DOWN

1 Old calculators
2 Classic TV's O'Reilly
3 "You ___ Beautiful" (Joe Cocker hit)
4 Sheets, tablecloths and such
5 Suffocating solution
6 Achiever
7 Sty sound
8 Affixes in a scrapbook, say
9 1990s news subject JonBenet
10 "Much ___ About Nothing"
11 Ticket seller
12 Saharan
13 Started the golf game
21 Author Tom or Thomas
22 Flightless bird
26 Units of money in Bulgaria
28 Apple or cherry
29 They may be heaved
31 "Lamp ___ My Feet"
32 Meat cut
33 Site for a bell
34 Shade of hosiery
35 Golden-brown or reddish-brown horses
37 Father of Shem
40 Historic Parks
42 Fancy dinnerware
44 Pro ___ (in proportion)
45 Bearings, of a sort
48 Like an inherent characteristic
50 Temperature unit
52 Piano relative
54 Wavelike pattern
55 Words with mother or brother
56 Ten percenter
57 "___ be a pleasure!"
58 Solo in the opera
60 Fury
61 Grand poetry
63 Before, once

by Fran & Lou Sabin
Edited by Timothy E. Parker
Answers in back

ACROSS

1 Milady's coronet, perhaps
6 Dillinger's pursuer
10 Rover's summons
14 Blacksmith's block
15 White House staffer
16 Seaweed product
17 Team that boasted 26-Across, 1947-1956
20 Darn it!
21 Member of many families
22 Teammate of 26-Across, Pee Wee
23 Sax section member
24 Landfill problem
26 Pioneering star of 17-Across
32 Sap-sucking insect
33 Remove a rind, e.g.
34 Court judge, briefly
36 Show delight, in a way
37 All in
39 MGM film lion
40 Jupiter, to Saturn
41 Take off
42 Artist's category
43 What 26-Across played in
47 "The Vampire Lestat" author Rice
48 Some require tags
49 ___ Gay
52 Etiquette authority
53 Check for accuracy
56 Honor won by 26-Across in 1947
60 Tool with a curved blade
61 Definitely the case
62 Fashionably old-fashioned
63 Supply with startup money
64 Begin to awaken
65 Kind of silence

DOWN

1 Barkeep records
2 Heading for a memo subject
3 Claim to be true
4 Former capital on Guanabara Bay, briefly
5 Crop-killing salts
6 Mitzi of "South Pacific"
7 Julep enhancer
8 Word on a dipstick
9 Prefix with colonial or conservative
10 Hoopsters
11 S-shaped molding
12 Pathfinder's path
13 Talk of the Gaels
18 Renaissance instrument
19 Stingless honeybee
23 Comparable
24 Scottish resort
25 Ground cover
26 Binges
27 Airport parking place
28 An Olympic team
29 Covent Garden presentation
30 Arboreal ape, informally
31 India's first prime minister
35 Unfettered
37 Any time now
38 Sheet of stamps
39 Meadows
41 Mount in Egypt
42 Fast-track types (with "go-")
44 Had a discussion
45 Pillager
46 AA candidate
49 Significant times in history
50 Lymph gland
51 Seep out
52 "That's awful!"
53 Presidential power
54 Make, as income
55 "The Iliad" setting
57 Sci-fi extras
58 Food morsel
59 "On the other hand …"

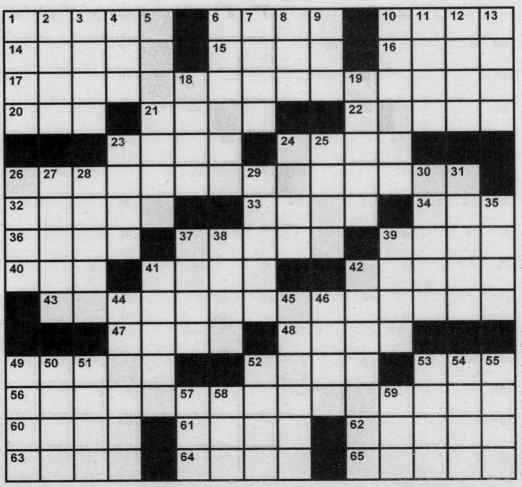

59 Laundry Day

by Cole Cooke
Edited by Timothy E. Parker
Answers in back

ACROSS

1 Weeps audibly
5 Suspect's defense
10 Polite word to a woman
14 Slender reed
15 Log home
16 Jamaican citrus fruit
17 Mean prank
19 Forest denizens
20 "Thanks, I already ___"
21 Questions
22 Window sills
24 Mardi ___
25 Mayor's bailiwick
26 Plaques and trophies
29 Out-of-control horse
32 Closet staples
33 Floating ice block
34 Pub potables
36 Bar Mitzvah dance
37 Agatha Christie and Judi Dench
38 How perfectionists do things?
39 CPR pros
40 It controls a pupil's size
41 King who had six wives
42 Creditor's demand
44 Peaceful
45 Talk disrespectfully to
46 ___ and feathers
47 Taiwan city
50 Type of part
51 "To Kill a Mockingbird" author
54 "Not only that …"
55 Stepping on them can lead to tetanus shots
58 Individual performance
59 "___ your instructions"
60 Look before you do this
61 Finely sharpened
62 Moderates
63 Undersized

DOWN

1 Word with water or fountain
2 News item for a scrapbook, briefly
3 Dullsville denizen
4 Math term
5 Assumes the role of
6 Carefree or spirited adventures
7 Heron's cousin
8 Pen brand
9 Vague notions
10 Legendary blues performer
11 Eager
12 On the sheltered side
13 It's as good as a mile
18 Measurements of fabric
23 Greek letter
24 Beanery, in slang
25 Smokes meat
26 Legendary tennis star
27 Defeat decisively
28 It comes from the heart
29 Send a payment
30 In isolation
31 Pine
33 Rural sights
35 Eyelid flare-up
37 Hymn about the Day of Judgment
41 Marsh wader
43 West, of films
44 Goatlike creatures
46 Student
47 Mission
48 Shower gel ingredient
49 Seagirt land
50 Egyptian cobras
51 In ___ of (replacing)
52 Distinctive flair
53 See at a distance
56 It's a free country
57 Monte Leone, for one

by Kyle Gray
Edited by Timothy E. Parker
Answers in back

ACROSS

1 It tops some lists
5 Talks one's ear off
9 Natural dos
14 Foreign car make
15 Word with hygiene or exam
16 Unwary
17 Cry weakly
18 Famous portrait model name
19 Some juice from a press
20 Inn fare
22 "Goodnight, ____" (1950 hit)
23 Authority to decide
24 Archipelago feature
26 British corp. designation
29 Far from uninterested
33 Over the first floor
38 Condition of equilibrium
39 Clairvoyant
40 Proofreader's discoveries
42 Grist for some processors
43 Spread the gospel
45 Better than average
47 Dessert not for the diet-conscious
48 Blood-pressure raiser
49 Exam part, sometimes
52 Event in a ring
57 Ore corridor
60 Basketball tactic
63 Having melodic harmony
64 Fare-well link
65 Pro ____ (proportionately)
66 Movie Hall of fame?
67 Lengthy time units
68 "Now ____ me down to sleep ..."
69 Uncle Sam characteristic
70 Retinal cells
71 Tu-144 and Concorde, once

DOWN

1 Burial chambers
2 "Carmen," e.g.
3 Loser to Truman
4 Earthen water jars
5 It involves a lot of Sunday drivers
6 Highlight of 2-Down
7 Bad men of opera, often
8 Bed stiffeners
9 Antiquated
10 Equitable deal
11 Tease mercilessly
12 It's hot in here
13 Like desert growth
21 Coke nut?
25 Landlord, e.g.
27 Charitable fractions
28 Lacking moisture
30 Quickly, quickly
31 Pocket sandwich bread
32 Peter the Great, e.g.
33 Package delivery org.
34 Tacna's country
35 Witnessed
36 Exhibit for an industry
37 Place to be pampered
41 Shogun's sash
44 Protected the king, in a way
46 Run or hide, e.g.
50 End of a fairy tale
51 "Gulliver's Travels" savage
53 Rootstock used in perfumes
54 Does a casino job
55 Sandwich board words
56 Green-lights
57 Employ a dirk
58 Cutting edge creator
59 "The King and I" schoolteacher
61 Fax function
62 Lass in a Hardy tale

61 Pep Talk

by Alice Walker
Edited by Timothy E. Parker
Answers in back

ACROSS

1 "Brandenburg Concertos" composer
5 They have their roots
10 Williams and Turner
14 Shield border
15 Elementary school teaching
16 It can come to a head
17 "Come ___!" ("Welcome!")
18 Scorpion product
19 Lab course, briefly
20 What a good pep talk will do
23 Sea dogs
24 Seventh Greek letter
25 Evaluate
28 "No ifs, ___ or buts!"
30 Make a selection
33 They may be between you and earth
34 Stead
35 Windward's opposite
36 What a good pep talk will do
39 Asian housemaid
40 They fly by night
41 Sturdy fastener
42 Ltrs.' appendages
43 Ornamental gemstone
44 Parts of a stairway
45 "What a view!"
46 Conclude one's case
47 What a good pep talk does
55 Sitcom legend
56 Brick of clay and straw
57 Agrippa's apparel
58 It may be plain or sweet
59 Gain succulence
60 Appear imminent
61 On the ocean
62 Showed reverence
63 Word in a conditional statement

DOWN

1 Palindromic ninny
2 Florence is on it
3 The muse of history
4 Symbols of scarcity
5 Relishes, as flavor
6 Many fast-food workers
7 Ulm article
8 Sounds from the pasture
9 Totaled
10 Jeweled coronet
11 "Show Boat" author Ferber
12 Bargain hunter's delight
13 Glut
21 "Jerusalem Delivered" poet Torquato
22 4th-qtr. followers, sometimes
25 Give ___ on the wrist
26 Wedges
27 Some sleeping places
28 Nuptial lane
29 Bitter end?
30 Greek salad morsel
31 Pumpkin lover
32 They're held for questioning
34 Like a dirty old man
35 Alexander the Great's tutor
37 Place for two of a kind
38 Kind of jig
43 Average guy
44 Take offense at
45 Honshu port
46 James Dean persona
47 Pro ___
48 "Ah, me!"
49 Twiddling one's thumbs
50 Norse god
51 "I don't think so"
52 Combine
53 Teamwork obstacles
54 Equivalent

by Alex Henry
Edited by Timothy E. Parker
Answers in back

ACROSS

1 Cuba libre ingredient
5 Tie holder
10 Dishwater
14 Mass utterance
15 Start of a Schwarzenegger quote
16 Does the chasing in tag
17 Closing remark
19 State bird of Hawaii
20 Ego type
21 Admits one's error
23 Just out
24 Newt-born babe?
27 Head toward evening
28 Put away the groceries?
29 Lee in freezers
31 Angel of the first order
34 Heart chamber
36 City in the southwest United States
37 1950, in copyrights
40 Lesson taught at the end, sometimes
42 Minimalist's catchword
43 Reduced to ___ of rubble
45 Marbles you don't play with
47 Video game classic
49 Creep-y look?
50 Tell a better joke than
53 Green tea
55 Word with "the pant's off"
56 Need to be corrected
57 Type of key or crew
60 Sleeping problem
62 Part of A.D.
63 Closing remark
66 Chicken style
67 Fragrant organic compound
68 Skye writing
69 Raison d'___
70 They often make the grade
71 Person of equal standing

DOWN

1 A changing place
2 It may be folded in the morning
3 Famous words with "forget"
4 Poker buy-in
5 Greek letter
6 "Viva ___ Vegas"
7 "Days of Grace" author
8 Inappropriately appropriate
9 Bow ties and macaroni
10 Closing remark
11 Requirement for access, maybe
12 Rat Pack nickname
13 Hasenpfeffer, for one
18 Take away by force
22 Proof word
25 Sharecrop, e.g.
26 Some lounge groups
30 Involving one of the senses
32 Second notation at the bottom of a letter
33 The Crystals' "___ a Rebel"
34 Closing remark
35 Crowning glories
37 You may be lost without it
38 Filing asst.
39 "Space" man
41 In ___ of (replacing)
44 Repose
46 Part of a holiday phrase
48 Reply to the impatient
50 Academic achievement
51 Threatening option
52 Devout request
54 Necktie party item
57 Drink often served with sushi
58 Heal, as a radius
59 Bananas or crackers
61 Type of school
64 Emeritus, briefly
65 Certain high school students (Abbr.)

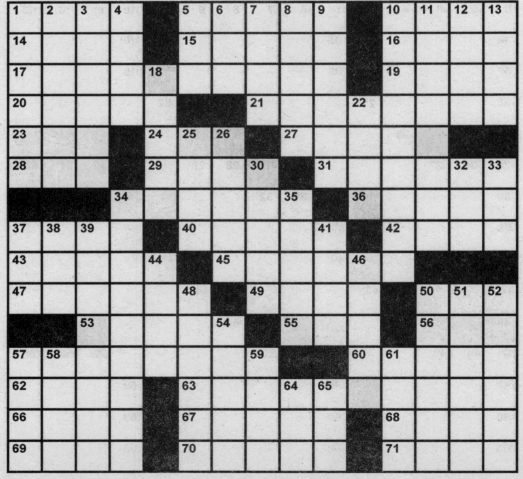

63 Battlefields

by Wesley Holman
Edited by Timothy E. Parker
Answers in back

ACROSS

1 Moby Dick, as a baby
5 Musical interludes
10 They're big in Australia
14 One destined to receive?
15 Bother terribly
16 Harangue
17 Eagle by the sea
18 Of superior grade
19 It's enough, in an expression
20 Patriots' battlefield
23 Target for middle management?
24 Lemon peels
25 Marzipan nut
28 You may find some lying around the house
30 Offensive expression
31 "___ Were the Days"
33 Clear plate after plate
36 Kings' battlefield
40 Words from the sponsors
41 They give inside information
42 Point in a network
43 "The Ghost and Mrs. ___"
44 Prepare the house for guests, perhaps
46 "Doe" followers, in song
49 Motorist's aid
51 Giants' battlefield
57 Ural River city
58 Synthetic fabric
59 Ubiquitous lily relative
60 Gas or elec., e.g.
61 Approached with stealth
62 Comfy cloud
63 People in general
64 Green pods
65 Companion of gloom

DOWN

1 Emeril, for one
2 Prefix with space
3 Start to type?
4 Ornamental three-dimensional pattern
5 Made good on, as a loan
6 Countess complements
7 Height enhancer
8 Caps on the Clyde
9 Manuscript marking, perhaps
10 Slowly washes away
11 "No ___ an island"
12 Not abridged
13 Quarter note parts
21 Prohibit
22 Empire conquered by Cortes
25 Duchess of ___ (Goya model)
26 Take charge on the dance floor
27 Total disorder
28 Smoke-filled room folk
29 Immigrant's study, for short
31 Ski-lift device
32 Manger contents
33 Boating area marker
34 Literary language of Pakistan
35 Dance bit
37 Outlying area
38 Start for "ode" or "pod"
39 How some movies are delivered
43 In a mousy way
44 Renders impure
45 Your financial advisor advises it
46 Give or take
47 Vader's title
48 "Ah, Wilderness!" mother
49 Radio ___ (popular wagon)
50 Drug used in treating parkinsonism
52 With the bow, in music
53 Something one may be as happy as
54 Incongruous mixture
55 Words to Nanette
56 Exercise judgment

by Anthony J. Salvia
Edited by Timothy E. Parker
Answers in back

ACROSS

1 Extent of loss
5 Surname for Joe?
10 Hood
14 Bread spread
15 Smooth with the beak, as feathers
16 Old Germanic character
17 They come in after many projections
20 Loses light
21 Nocturnal American wildcat
22 Gold or silver sources
23 Genesis name
24 Debate ender
29 Colorful stone
31 Trig function
32 Carnival city, briefly
33 Disorganized crowds
34 Indian money
36 Affleck and Vereen
37 In the past
38 He loved Lucy
39 Tall, thin and somewhat ungainly
40 Something or nothing
44 Zither's forerunner
45 Actor Guinness
46 Torah tongue
49 Surgically ties
53 Out-of-the-mainstream genre
56 Fastening material
57 Discharge gradually
58 Cultural leader?
59 Talk back
60 Restrain through intimidation
61 Drawn tight

DOWN

1 Word with pointy or pigeon
2 Spicy Spanish stew
3 Lust-filled look
4 Tactics employed in some labor disputes
5 Mineral containing magnesium
6 Stick in a field sport
7 Egg supplier
8 Debussy's "La ____"
9 Up close and personal
10 Most loyal
11 Ship's frame
12 Biblical preposition
13 Tale of adventure
18 Third monastic hour
19 Range
23 Lake, city or canal
24 Rich man
25 Jelly used as a glaze or garnish
26 Dunne of "I Remember Mama"
27 Sound from Old McDonald's farm
28 Overly curious
29 Asian housemaid
30 Type of dancer or boot
34 Celebrated
35 One-time superpower
36 Monte Carlo game
38 Pharmacist, at times
39 City of eastern Belgium
41 Garments worn in India and Pakistan (Var.)
42 Photo lab emulsion compound
43 Twist of literature
46 Witches
47 Singing Fitzgerald
48 Air-conditioning measures
50 Roman robe
51 Hose hue
52 "Saturday Night Live" segment
54 Hatchet relative
55 Notable boy king

65 Geography, Sort Of

by Lucille Evanstone
Edited by Timothy E. Parker
Answers in back

ACROSS

1 Emulate a high roller
6 Vacation excursion
10 School for martial arts
14 Site for some rites
15 Things one sings?
16 Abreast of
17 Overcharge excessively
18 Of majestic proportions
19 Certain column
20 Beef entree
22 Alberta native
23 Neither good nor bad
24 Struck by overwhelming shock
26 Wry expression
30 Ump parallel
31 One of many who are one
32 Work to get
33 Small apts.
35 Prima donna's repertoire
39 Painter Marc
41 Rhythm of speech
43 Shells
44 Tall story
46 Arabian Sea gulf
47 "___ be my pleasure!"
49 "The Confessions of ___ Turner"
50 "Sweeney ___" (Sondheim musical)
51 Shipwrecked Defoe character
54 Pinhead
56 IRA variety
57 Peck in Paris?
63 Gossip column squib
64 One-time Delhi queen
65 City northeast of Casablanca
66 What a hog wants
67 Problem that's hard to face?
68 Mixed drink garnish
69 Poetic name for Ireland
70 Orbital period
71 Attacked on all sides

DOWN

1 Doesn't hold up well
2 Farm implement
3 Bag for small articles
4 Old horses
5 Kind of code
6 African disease carrier
7 Enclose, in a way
8 Pelvic bones
9 Find fault with
10 It requires individual checks
11 Phantom's passion
12 Quincy of music
13 Dawning
21 City on the St. Lawrence
25 Provoke
26 Auto fixer, for short
27 Waikiki locale
28 Europe's third-longest river
29 Many Brits
34 More bony
36 Prefix for China
37 Got a perfect score on
38 "___ in the Clowns"
40 Regarding, in memos
42 Monkeyshine
45 Reception device
48 Bear the expenses of
51 Breaking and entering, e.g.
52 Helicopter blade
53 Gestation stations
55 Beat painfully
58 Speedway competition
59 Type of cabbage
60 Heron cousin
61 Rescue
62 "Don't delete this"

66 Bring It

by Tyrone Bass
Edited by Timothy E. Parker
Answers in back

ACROSS

1 Dispose of, informally
5 Rain cloud
11 Junior reporter
14 Jai ___
15 Believe to be true
16 Anecdotal assortment
17 Be infamously unusual
19 Some lead to forks, briefly
20 Message boat
21 Outdoor warning
22 Have misgivings about
23 Pampered one?
25 Progressively declined
27 Imminent danger warning
32 Pocket sandwich bread
33 They may hold pencils
34 Pig product
36 Basic security device
39 Lifting device
40 Hordes
42 Israeli-designed weapon
43 Saxon start
45 Blood components
46 Go off the deep end
47 Riverbank component
49 Some are at the helm
51 Like many soft drinks
54 Zodiac name
55 Bobby of the Bruins
56 Bumbling
59 Artifices
63 Kimono cincher
64 Suffer a sports-related injury
66 Goose egg
67 American songbird
68 Assuage
69 Venusians, e.g.
70 Annoy
71 Choreographer's creation

DOWN

1 Sheffield farewell
2 Name of several Norwegian kings
3 Pseudonym of H.H. Munro
4 Noonday naps
5 "Ixnay"
6 Cinches or clinches
7 1,201, to Tiberius
8 Mountain goat feature
9 Maintenance
10 Lettering tools
11 Display one's ability to sing well
12 Inordinate
13 Situated
18 Word with "kit" or "around"
24 Prompter's beginning
26 Words with "distance" or "glance"
27 Country queen McEntire
28 Command a salary
29 Places to burn rubber
30 Scott Joplin's legacy
31 Essays
35 Extremely uncool person
37 Kaiser kin
38 Rose fruit
40 It gets a good licking
41 It's hit on the head
44 Torched
46 Wedding acquisitions
48 Professor's goal
50 South American nation
51 Fall off the wagon
52 Path that the whole world follows
53 Some are kosher
57 Conspirator's creation
58 Imaginary narrative
60 "Amscray!"
61 It may follow something
62 Penetrate slowly
65 Sea, to Monet

by Pearl Anderson
Edited by Timothy E. Parker
Answers in back

ACROSS

1 Like "Lady Chatterley's Lover"
5 Mom-and-pop store grp.
8 Home of the flamenco
13 Letters from Calvary
14 First number in season records
16 It has a long neck
17 Getting-years connector
18 Sport played on a 2-meter by 14-meter strip
19 Feeder of the body's organs
20 '70s TV detective series
21 Destitute
23 Put one's signature on a contract
25 Spring ahead letters
26 Birmingham-to-Huntsville dir.
27 Paris newspaper, Le ___
29 Fresh response?
31 Advertiser's target
32 One in the game
34 At quite an incline
36 Extravagant show
41 "The Phantom Menace" planet
42 Professor's milestone
43 Party animal?
46 Raison d'___
48 Changes comodity to commodity, e.g.
49 Some conjunctions
50 Words with "jam" or "hurry"
51 Turkish coins
53 Once in a while
56 Zinger
59 Type of squash
60 Roof part
61 ___ about (legalistic phrase)
62 Wine region of France
63 Herding dog's name, commonly
64 What happens when the sun rises in S. California?
65 Honduran honorific
66 Crumb carrier
67 Ball-bearing items

DOWN

1 Very funny fellow
2 Word on a cornerstone
3 Malefactor
4 Chinese principles
5 Kronor owner
6 Rifle supports
7 De novo
8 Few and far between
9 Cattle motivator
10 Burr and Hank
11 Without a sour note
12 More in order
15 Mails
22 Put forward as truth
24 "I couldn't ___ straight face!"
27 Sticker abbr.
28 Pay stretcher?
30 With respect to
31 No longer bedridden
33 Fix, as a paper clip
35 Islamic prince (Var.)
37 Takes turns?
38 Dennis, to Mr. Wilson
39 PC screen, possibly
40 Some shoe widths
43 Submarine detection systems
44 A medicated candy
45 Out, temporarily
47 One after another?
50 Word with "circle" or "ear"
52 Like Inspector Clouseau
54 Florence is on it
55 Guffaw sound
57 Hollywood handout
58 Some unmentionables

68 Look Out Below

by Carl Cranby
Edited by Timothy E. Parker
Answers in back

ACROSS

1 Seemingly forever
5 Burnoose wearer
9 Fleshy medicinal plants
14 Brilliant display
15 Turkey club?
16 Dried meat of the coconut
17 Bit that's visible
20 Uncut
21 Filled with a great quantity
22 Pilfered
23 Sharpen by rubbing
25 "Antiques Roadshow" network
28 Rocky peak
29 Like organza or chiffon
31 When repeated, a Western city
33 Traditional will?
34 Address for a countess
35 Where heads may come together
38 One-dimensional
39 The black ball
40 Well-developed muscles
41 Valuable stringed instrument, for short
42 French connections
45 A Bush
46 Become prominent
47 Drive in Beverly Hills
49 Another time
52 Big name in telephony
53 In seventh heaven
57 They may be round and pound
58 Component used as fertilizer
59 Seaman's saint
60 Marsh plant
61 Spacek biopic role
62 No longer waiting for the doctor

DOWN

1 Most likely to
2 Select, as a career
3 Buyer, in legalese
4 Rain on a parade
5 Pot part
6 Shout of support
7 Corroded
8 Vessel in a steam vessel
9 More than passed
10 Occipital ____
11 It consists of few dividing partitions
12 Commit a faux pas
13 Mattress problem
18 Certain newbie
19 Jazz aficionado
23 Raised stripe
24 Knight caps
26 Super's concern (Abbr.)
27 Two cents' worth
30 Minuscule margin
31 Back out
32 Got off a broomstick
33 Diving bird
34 Prefix for bucks
35 Man o' War, to War Admiral
36 With continued force
37 Kerry's country
38 "Great Society" monogram
41 Iniquitous
42 '20s English Channel swimmer
43 "Spill it!"
44 Convinced of
46 Former capital on Guanabara Bay
48 Some woodwinds
50 It may be hit with a hammer
51 Choir recess
52 Plebeian
53 Photo ____ (picture sessions)
54 Name separator
55 Determine judicially
56 Natural incubator

69 Under Sail

by Alex Henry
Edited by Timothy E. Parker
Answers in back

ACROSS

1 With the wherewithal
5 Stylishly elegant
9 "Hundred" prefix
14 Close hermetically
15 Sari-clad royal
16 Declared strikes?
17 What a captain may command
20 Sound of a belly laugh
21 What you may set a camera on
22 Assumes the role of
23 It can be upped
24 Hymn "Dies ___"
25 Avoid that sinking feeling?
29 Shoe with a puckered seam
32 Like magma
33 32,000 ounces
34 Astronomical sighting
35 Light reflector
36 Small intake
37 Brave legend
38 Impose, as a tax
39 Pester for payment
40 Color in an Alice Walker title
41 Obsolete palindromic preposition
42 Prepare to sail
44 When it's saved, it's taken
45 Pangolin's diet
46 Joust combatant
49 Sparkling wine spot
50 A dinger is at least one
53 It may be said from the bridge
56 Start of a classic literary title
57 Get to
58 ___ breve (music)
59 Did ranch work
60 Sinus, e.g.
61 Match makers

DOWN

1 Like a post-eruption landscape
2 Steady guy
3 Escapade
4 The past, in the past
5 Bit of fried bread
6 Expedite
7 Word of division
8 Org. with moles
9 Auto part often found along the road
10 Play to the back row
11 Yr.-end visitors?
12 Trillion prefix
13 They're put on some horses
18 Bicycle type
19 ___' to go (eager)
23 Nervously impatient
24 Chain with links?
25 More than enough
26 Auger or destructive bug
27 Kicking partner?
28 Police leader
29 Change, sci-fi style
30 Rounded molding
31 One administering corporal punishment
34 They look for bad deals?
36 With sweat or wet
37 Mame, for one
39 Honeybun
40 American feline, for one
42 Pulled dandelions
43 Inconvenience
44 Cliche-ridden
46 Pre-Soviet royalty
47 "Sock ___ me!"
48 One way to tackle a hurdle?
49 Words with "happens" or "seems"
50 Play thing?
51 Asteroid area
52 "… your goodness ___ a morning cloud" (Hosea)
54 "Exodus" character
55 Energy source

70 You Don't Say!

by Kyle Gray
Edited by Timothy E. Parker
Answers in back

ACROSS

1 Fetched
4 Rice dish
9 Thin, fibrous bark
14 Old preposition
15 Dunne of "I Remember Mama"
16 West Indies sorcery
17 Freely communicating
20 Investor's goal
21 Some undergraduates
22 One of the Brady kids
23 Nautical position
25 Deplete (with "up")
28 Where beauty is, to the beholder
29 Seek to replace current tenants
31 Pro ____ (in proportion)
32 Some have boards
33 Check the books
34 Enunciation challenge
38 Moth stages
39 Pal of Potsie and Richie
40 Help when one shouldn't
41 Victor's share
43 Iniquity
46 It gets steamrollered
47 Great time or great noise
48 Vaudeville dancer's prop
49 Brilliant achievement
51 Aid to digestion
53 How natives communicate
57 One receiving womb service?
58 Who might be to blame
59 Poem of devotion
60 Rock layers
61 Works the bar
62 Kind of tag or tape

DOWN

1 First name of three U.S. presidents
2 Like a mule, stereotypically
3 Exam taker
4 Mooring spot
5 Zagros Mountains locale
6 Albanian currency
7 Hangman request
8 Good ones make good neighbors
9 Tribal symbol on a pole
10 Tucked in
11 Twist someone's arm
12 She was Mindy to Robin's Mork
13 Exclamations of contentedness
18 Small toy dog
19 Zodiac animal
23 On the sheltered side
24 Modest cafes
26 Mix with a spoon
27 Break bread
29 Bad thing to fly into
30 Outback creature
31 Baseball Babe
32 Punkie, e.g.
33 Racer relatives
34 Orchestral heavyweight
35 "Trouble in Tahiti," e.g.
36 Bide one's time
37 Prepared introduction?
38 Like some answers
41 Croat or Bulgar
42 Inventor's document
43 Salt
44 Intrude on
45 Got close
47 Word of grace
48 Oater actor Gulager
50 Fisherman's lure
51 Ocean liner?
52 The best pair?
53 Stipulations
54 Genealogy word
55 Preschool components?
56 Prefix with "dairy"

by Joy M. Andrews
Edited by Timothy E. Parker
Answers in back

ACROSS

1 Sauce of chili peppers and tomatoes
6 1991 Wimbledon champ
10 Spin after logging on?
14 Nobel chemist von Baeyer
15 Kinks' lady of song
16 Theatrical halls
17 First five books of the Bible
19 Some pens
20 Beginning of a young couple's lament
22 Sound caused by an involuntary spasm
23 Plato's mentor
24 Hallucination drug
27 Long, narrow inlet
29 Pt. of USDA
30 Young couple's lament (Part 2)
37 Biblical twin
38 Winning tic-tac-toe line
39 Women's magazine
40 Young couple's lament (Part 3)
45 Group of relatives
46 Place to shoot from
47 "That feels g-o-o-o-d!"
48 Unwavering
53 Zero
55 End of the lament
60 "The Cosby Show" son
61 Aggressive taunt
62 Type of tube
63 Cpls. and such
64 Like the Leaning Tower of Pisa
65 Sciences partner
66 Documentarian Burns and Griffey of baseball
67 Vietnam site in 1969 news

DOWN

1 Margarita enhancement
2 Spouse of 37-Across
3 "St. Elmo's Fire" actor Rob
4 Wade through mud
5 "De coeur" starter
6 Unappetizing fare
7 Parks, Bonheur and Ponselle
8 Oldsmobile model
9 1988 Tracy Chapman hit
10 Longtime "The Price is Right" host
11 Numskull
12 Give actors a second signal
13 Survives from start to finish
18 1,602 another way
21 Jason's mythical ship
24 MGM co-founder Marcus
25 Capital of Elam
26 "Fiddlesticks!"
28 Shakespearean "soon"
31 Pellets aimed at birds and ducks
32 ___ and Magog
33 The two of them
34 Zeno's origin
35 "Casablanca" character
36 Cain's second brother
41 Noted sexologist Shere
42 Quick as lightning
43 Gandhi, for one
44 Short, witty saying
48 Terra ___
49 "… by a jury ___ peers"
50 Bikini experiment, for short
51 Immediate occasion
52 Check a jacket for fit, e.g.
54 High as a kite
56 Profit's opposite
57 Bondsman's security
58 California campus
59 Tibetan snowman

72 Quiet Down!

by Wesley Holman
Edited by Timothy E. Parker
Answers in back

ACROSS

1 AC capacity units
5 Canyon edges
9 Type of book
14 Emanating glow
15 "Heavens to Betsy!"
16 Expunge
17 Amtrak stops (Abbr.)
18 Implement
19 Second airing
20 Cornmeal cakes, in the South
23 Needing a lift
24 Indefinitely long periods of time
25 Spur parts
27 Blew over
30 Fatuous
32 Sort
33 Hammett pooch
35 To be of use to
39 1966 Simon & Garfunkel album
43 "___ of Two Cities"
44 Den outburst
45 Big score on the floor
46 Escapade
48 Orchestra member
51 Letter abbr.
54 Become unhinged
55 Queen's subject
56 They often run deep
62 Raccoon relative
64 "I ___ bad moon ..."
65 Cortex product
66 Sacrifice site
67 Anatomical canal
68 Parts of newly-weds' cars?
69 They have narrow waists
70 Fill beyond full
71 Jolly Roger crewman

DOWN

1 Big blowout
2 Multilayered garment
3 Some servers
4 They hug beauty pageant winners
5 Large, circular rooms
6 Flapjack places, familiarly
7 Alphabet quartet
8 Arias, e.g.
9 Intimate
10 Metal-in-the-rough
11 Analyze, grammatically
12 Like some suspects
13 Awaits action
21 "The Bells" poet
22 It's full of periods
26 "___ Only Just Begun"
27 Galileo's hometown
28 Frequently
29 Gull-like bird
30 "Let's Hear ___ the Boy" (Denise Williams hit)
31 Houston gp.
34 Harboring a grudge
36 Knock opener?
37 Cold confections
38 Ash Wednesday follower
40 It puts a team in the World Series (Abbr.)
41 A letter opener
42 Pots, kettles, etc.
47 Clock setting at LAX
49 Rambouillet remark
50 Field of vision?
51 Avian chatterbox
52 Name on a famous B-29
53 Sports figures
54 Driving hazard
57 Egyptian fertility goddess
58 "___ Smile Be Your Umbrella"
59 Imported cheese
60 Philosopher Descartes
61 Letter enc.
63 Dancing specialty

by Alice Walker
Edited by Timothy E. Parker
Answers in back

ACROSS

1 Deli side dish
5 Photo ____ (media events)
8 Celery starter?
13 Fervent wish
14 Great quantity
16 "My Cherie ____"
17 Sched. entry
18 Yours, in Burgundy
19 Gambling game
20 Fennel, e.g.
21 Passionate or virile
23 City on the Allegheny
25 Battery size
26 ____ Day (May 1 in Hawaii)
27 Collection of poems
29 Pt. of IRA
31 "____ la vie!"
32 Agent of the Vietnam War?
34 "Billy, Don't Be ____" (1974 hit)
36 What the cautious tightrope artist did?
41 Ignore in pronunciation
42 Bum out
43 Talk casually
46 Throw carelessly
48 C sharp equivalent
49 Kind of chamber
50 Challenge for a hairstylist
51 "My Dinner with ____"
53 Cold gin with vermouth
56 Unnamed people or things
59 The-near link
60 Larger-than-life
61 Lets touch them
62 Punch back instinctively
63 Show excessive affection
64 Romanov ruler
65 Infections of some sebaceous glands
66 Land of Damascus, briefly
67 They used to turn down their noses

DOWN

1 Exile of 1979
2 Run of the ranch?
3 Thumbs-up
4 Hardly a live wire
5 Hold 'em variation
6 Words with "pedestal" or "happy face"
7 William Wallace, for one
8 American or Western follower
9 Melville sequel
10 Touch lovingly
11 Private students
12 Type of card or union
15 Cooking device
22 Approaches dawn
24 Georgia of "Everybody Loves Raymond"
27 Jones' financial partner
28 Bit of tax planning
30 Trendy eateries
31 They'll give you chills
33 Marginal worker?
35 Double-check the check
37 Voted to accept
38 Inaction
39 Cultural grant giver, for short
40 Suffix with "differ" or "insist"
43 Halloween beverages
44 It stings
45 Very soon
47 Mental equilibrium
50 Mizzens
52 Comparatively congenial
54 They may squeak by you
55 New stock issuances, for short
57 Coup d'____
58 The Baltics, once (Abbr.)

74 Cowboy Up

by Henry Quarters
Edited by Timothy E. Parker
Answers in back

ACROSS
1 Political sphere, e.g.
6 Ornamental attire
10 Ming artifact
14 Kind of cake
15 Dramatic presentation
16 Woeful expression
17 This and this
18 Modicum
19 Some square dancers
20 Hang in there
23 Got into the swing?
25 Dos Passos trilogy
26 He cometh
27 "Don't say a word!"
30 Little soldier
31 One watching the figures?
32 Frankenstein monster feature
34 Boring tools
38 Endure defeat
41 Put through the paces
42 Oft-twisted snack
43 Correspondent's request
44 Personal
45 Stew in one's juices
46 Ogden native
50 Unproductive commotion
52 Poetically always
53 Face the music
57 Geishas' accessories
58 Site of tiny orbits
59 Opposite of deject
62 "It's good for what ____ ya"
63 It could be in your throat
64 Type of flu
65 British museum
66 Ad-____ (improvises)
67 Attacks with snowballs

DOWN
1 Keyboard key
2 "Yay team!"
3 Features of a lobster's anatomy
4 Arboreal abode
5 Wall-to-wall measure
6 Barbecue accessories
7 Wahine's welcome
8 Fill to full
9 Garden plant
10 Ambiguous
11 Smoke signal?
12 Dance or dip
13 City near the Ruhr and Rhine
21 "Uh-huh"
22 Antepenultimate mo.
23 "Ivanhoe" writer
24 Birdbath gunk
28 Assemble
29 Israeli mentalist Geller
30 Voice below soprano
32 Word with "loser" or "free"
33 Letterless phone number
34 One of the back forty
35 Deer feature, perhaps
36 Gracefully limber
37 Display disdain, in a way
39 Place of public assembly
40 "You" homophone
44 Breakfast grain
45 Fa-la link on a musical scale
46 German war vessel
47 Knee-to-ankle bone
48 Not perfectly upright
49 "Steppenwolf" author Hermann
50 Enola Gay's payload
51 One may be down in them
54 Holder of combs, perfumes, etc.
55 Bound
56 Alternative word
60 Rat-a-____
61 The two for tennis?

by Alice Walker
Edited by Timothy E. Parker
Answers in back

ACROSS

1 Schooner feature
5 Miro, Miro on the wall?
8 Cleverly avoid
13 Eastern nanny
14 Clash of clans
16 Elementary particle
17 Middle Eastern potentate (Var.)
18 Chancellor von Bismarck
19 Shot put, for one
20 Kissing disease
21 Spanish-American War figure
23 Starchy veggie
25 Slyly reticent
26 Site of the first stroke?
27 Mosquitolike insect
29 Assemblage of Bears
31 10 cc, perhaps
32 Hello and goodbye
34 ____-Roman wrestling
36 Crash, e.g.
41 Determinant of utility charges
42 Superlatively wise
43 Air passageway
46 Campus recruiting grp.
48 Word with "Entertainment!" or "Amore"
49 KJV suffix
50 Defeat at bridge
51 Gave ___ (inspired)
53 Cold comfort?
56 Egyptian menaces
59 Interrupted breathing
60 Hipbone sections
61 "Fargo" director
62 Found pleasant
63 "Babel" star
64 Coin of the Continent
65 Disrespectful, in a way
66 Alliance org. founded in 1948
67 Bit of a pencil

DOWN

1 Palindromic form of address
2 Pistol pellets
3 Elizabeth Ann Seton's status
4 Production in a given period
5 Archaic "prior to"
6 Sharp reply
7 Dancing garment
8 Certain board material
9 "Christ Stopped at Eboli" author
10 Familiar with
11 Beneficiaries
12 Main selection
15 Two-wheeled, horse-drawn vehicle
22 They leave the park
24 They come to court
27 Country singer Davis
28 UN agcy.
30 Plumed wading bird
31 Northerners who once sympathized with the South
33 Looked impolitely
35 Raccoon's kin
37 Self-motivated journey?
38 Edges
39 "Saving Private Ryan" carrier
40 "Independence Day" assailants
43 Model kit extras
44 Perfect world
45 Thick masses
47 Per follower
50 Of ill repute
52 Atty.-to-be exams
54 Gibbs, in a group name
55 A little of this, a little of that
57 Andean nation
58 Persnickety one

76 Made in What Shade?

by Pearl Anderson
Edited by Timothy E. Parker
Answers in back

ACROSS

1 Address in colonial India
6 Dull pain
10 Disgraced gardener
14 Shopper's mecca of old
15 High seas
16 Its flag features a vicuna
17 Shy person
20 Third-generation Japanese-American
21 Add water
22 Like uncirculated air
25 Eyelid inflammations
26 Opera that opens in Memphis
30 Livestock abode
32 Wrist bauble
35 Surprise attack
41 Like Prince William
43 Supreme Court, for one
44 Religious recluses
45 Get as a reward
47 Pantheon figures
48 "Carrie" portrayer
53 Question type
56 Twelve-year-old
58 Pinpoint
63 Alec Guinness film (with "The")
66 Bullet point
67 Fjord explorer?
68 Barbecue cube
69 Change for a hundred, perhaps
70 "I need it yesterday!"
71 Ladybug features

DOWN

1 Lip service
2 Khan's title (Var.)
3 ___ of plenty
4 Tennessee's state flower
5 Thoms in one's side
6 "___ making myself clear?"
7 Recyclable item
8 Swinger's plea
9 Green feeling?
10 Toward the left, on a ship
11 Airport worry
12 Ragged mountain ridge
13 Does a muffler's job
18 Baby beaver
19 Air travelers' requirements
23 Assist in malfeasance
24 Tizzies
26 Ex of Cugie
27 Frequently pumped item
28 "Fooey!"
29 Benzoyl peroxide treats it
31 Tag irritation point
33 Greek letter
34 Mineral deposit
36 Fall bloomer
37 Seagoing slammer
38 As many as
39 It may cause spills on hills
40 Amoco rival
42 Airborne fish-eaters
46 Virgilian hero
48 Alley "oops"
49 Steamed
50 Good roll, for starters
51 Hollyhock features
52 It's tender to the Japanese
54 Fatima's husband
55 Cholesterol part of eggs
57 Viking reading
59 Show appreciation, in a way
60 Church desk
61 Tugboat sound
62 Is retrocessive
64 Genetic material
65 With it

ACROSS

1 Some claim they're terrible
5 Stationed
10 Binary system elements
14 Kind of wave
15 "The Violent Land" author
16 Academic figure
17 Dog dreamed up by Dashiell
18 Hogwash
19 "Whip It" group
20 Tenacious bug of rhyme
23 "Take it easy!"
24 Comment off the main point
25 Made a cartograph
28 Tease playfully
30 Abraham's grandson
31 Haughty response
33 551, to an ancient Roman
36 Fibs
40 Dickensian epithet
41 Words on a Dickens cover
42 Whitaker's Oscar-winning role
43 Fly in the ointment
44 More than dislike
46 One place to be lost
49 Absconded with
51 Nightgown wearer of rhyme
57 Word in the a.m.?
58 Arizona tribe members
59 Geologists' times
60 Part of Ripley's title
61 Gander's mate
62 Word with mail or time
63 8,000 pounds, for four
64 Queen ____ lace
65 Minus

DOWN

1 Cuisine choice
2 Needle point?
3 Muesli base
4 Refuses to budge
5 Mollycoddled
6 Cordiality
7 Lively dance
8 Showing strain
9 Leporine females
10 Queer
11 "____ say more?"
12 Like chalet roofs
13 Sleep soundly?
21 Spell-off
22 Dupe's diamond
25 Scary Spice
26 Atlas section
27 Way to go
28 ____ de vivre
29 Crumb
31 Ill-gotten gains
32 Art Ross Trophy org.
33 Bit of change
34 Tourist accessories, in a state
35 Does not exist, in brief
37 Hawaiian veranda
38 In-flight info, for short
39 Vice principal's concern
43 Wasteful things?
44 Searches for water
45 "Boola Boola" singer
46 Anticipate
47 11:50, vis-a-vis midnight
48 Not vacillating about
49 What he says goes
50 Fluff hair
52 Links org.
53 Share holder?
54 Kind of nut
55 Words with "move" or "cash"
56 Ballpark figs.

78 Joking on the Farm

by Kyle Gray
Edited by Timothy E. Parker
Answers in back

ACROSS

1 Chow ____ (Chinese dish)
5 "Darn it all!"
9 Act of fraud
13 Ten square chains
14 Some are dramatic
16 ____ Nostra (crime syndicate)
17 Start of a farm riddle
19 "Do you have Prince Albert in ____?"
20 Seaport in the European part of Russia
21 Nickel in a pocket?
22 Disorganized crowds
23 "The Rome of Hungary"
25 Time filler?
27 Farm riddle (Part 2)
31 French one
32 Not genuine or real
33 Asian river and range
37 Hightail it
39 Certain youth orgs.
42 "Leave this alone"
43 Tea type
45 Father of Art Deco
47 Greek "T"
48 Farm riddle (Part 3)
52 So deep as to be unmeasurable
55 Sorcerer
56 Satisfy, as demands
57 Craggy peak
59 In the money
63 "I've Got the Music ____"
64 End of the farm riddle
66 Forward-looking person
67 Astronomer Hubble
68 River celebrated by Burns
69 Worker IDs
70 Safecracker, slangily
71 Bacon sizzle

DOWN

1 Bryn ____ (Pennsylvania college)
2 Rebounding sound
3 Retirement accts.
4 Cleared, as profit
5 It leads to home
6 Staff without personnel?
7 Type of sax
8 1943 conference site
9 Runs like a rabbit
10 Type of bean or butter
11 Easy ____
12 Church residence
15 Apple trees, once
18 "A ____ Flanders" (1960)
24 Baba au ____
26 Moo ____ pork
27 Crescent point
28 Without repetition
29 Debilitated
30 Shine
34 "____ boy!" ("Nice going!")
35 Pastoral expanses
36 Actors Gilliam and Erwin
38 Some wedding guests or gifts
40 Calla lily, e.g.
41 It's a crime
44 Little green men
46 Prod
49 Wonderland cake words
50 Obviously injured
51 Double-checks the math
52 Out of sorts
53 "Seinfeld" character
54 Land on the Red Sea
58 T. ____ Price of finance
60 "Vaya con ____"
61 Freudian subjects
62 Mafia bigwigs
65 Use a mattock

by Matthew J. Koceich
Edited by Timothy E. Parker
Answers in back

ACROSS

1 Football infraction
5 Former European coin
10 What's done is this
14 Superior rating
15 American chameleon
16 Like arson evidence
17 Indian dignitary
18 Electrician, at times
19 Practice with a palooka
20 Flightless fowl
21 ... the beginning of a spy?
23 A"natural" dice toss
25 On the double, poetically
26 Extended (out)
28 Scruffs
30 De Mille specialties
31 DNA structure
32 Part of FWIW
35 Every relative?
36 Place of safety
37 Your largest joint
38 Map abbreviation
39 Monica of tennis
40 Doha is its capital
41 They're unassisted
42 Crescent-shaped area on a fingernail
43 Consume or enjoy immensely
45 Hispaniola country
46 ... the beginning of a gridiron scheme?
49 II
52 Olfactory perception
53 Without a connection
54 Edict
55 Borrowed without permission
56 Empty shipping container weights
57 Lightning unit
58 Sugar bowl team?
59 Wear away, as earth
60 Keen on

DOWN

1 Give a darn
2 Fertile soil
3 ... the beginning of fairness?
4 Edible green seed
5 Occurred to (with "on")
6 Lincoln's concern
7 Business name abbr.
8 Away from the wind
9 Diamondback turtle
10 Fettuccine and lasagna
11 Savory jelly
12 Remove stubble
13 Ancient seaport of Phoenicia
21 He told the story of Rudolph
22 Highest point
24 Make a photoengraving
26 Scoff or boo
27 "___ the crack of ..."
28 Upper part of glaciers
29 Fermented beverages
31 Angel's trademark
32 ... the beginning of college costs?
33 Blue-green
34 Without moisture
36 Better half
37 "Critique of Pure Reason" philosopher
39 Like some grapes
40 English stage actor James
41 Wading birds
42 Chinese philosopher
43 Conclude with
44 Currently in progress
45 Added to the staff
46 Smidgen
47 On ___ with (equal to)
48 Edible tuber
50 Whitman the poet
51 Von Bismarck
54 Starling's agency

by Timothy E. Parker
Edited by Timothy E. Parker
Answers in back

80 En Route

ACROSS

1 California alternative?
5 It's on the parson's parcel
10 Conks on the head
14 On the Red or the Dead
15 "The Tempest" character
16 Environs
17 Security problem
18 Customary observances
19 Silver coin of Iran
20 Displays precision in every detail
23 Right of final decision
24 It has gutters to the left and right
25 Just talk, nothing more
28 Rather suggestive
30 Crucifix inscription
31 Go from two or more to one
33 Soft serve it's not
36 Endorsement
40 Sauce on many dishes in the Orient
41 Parting of the Pacific?
42 Flat, circular plate
43 Comes to the rescue
44 Places to call home
46 Adjust wheels precisely
49 It may be added to the bill
51 Exceed normal boundaries
57 "To Live and Die ___" (1985 film)
58 Calculators of yore
59 It may come before after?
60 Quite a while
61 Magic word
62 Disrespect verbally
63 Group of vipers
64 Cavern
65 ___ gin fizz

DOWN

1 Island in Indonesia
2 "1,001 ___"
3 Barking mammal
4 Prepares to shoot
5 Willing sacrifice
6 Ovine sign
7 It's dynamite stuff
8 Ooze through a porous substance
9 Last word in a threat
10 More than just a pub regular
11 Bay window
12 Inner contentment
13 Coarse, as language
21 Mai ___ (rum cocktail)
22 Toy on a track
25 Vent sound
26 Able to see right through
27 High chair feature
28 Philbin cohort
29 Tennis tour letters
31 Extraterrestrials' fleet
32 Lazy refusal
33 Ardent
34 Matter of grammar
35 Benevolent and protective order
37 House coat?
38 The kind of friends that go way back
39 Like argon
43 Filled with sudden fright
44 Consult
45 It is entirely dependent on flowers for food
46 Like 45-Down
47 Epeeist's thrust
48 Florida Keys, e.g.
49 Take countermeasures
50 Become liable
52 A couple of laughs
53 Black, to a bard
54 Zero-shaped
55 Tijuana tender
56 Scots Gaelic

by Tyrone Bass
Edited by Timothy E. Parker
Answers in back

ACROSS

1 Houston player
6 Drive
11 Doo-wop song syllable
14 "Apocalypse Now" actor
15 Nigerian money
16 Trail the pack
17 Speech fit for a King
19 Rose-rose link
20 Casual carpeting
21 Loren's hubby
23 "Citizen ___" (1941)
24 Mount Hood locale
25 Famous spinach eater
28 Bishops' headdresses
30 Hertz alternative
31 Brown of song
32 Cynical laugh
35 Favorite, as a theory
36 The Baltimore Sun and Kansas City Star, e.g.
38 Metallurgist's material
39 Jump a gap, as electricity
40 Key chain?
41 Headliner
42 '60s nonconformist
44 At a rapid tempo, in music
46 Forces back
48 One end of a hammerhead
49 Dispatch boat
50 Requirements for logging on, sometimes
55 A small drink of liquor
56 Cloisters
58 Had a fast break?
59 Scrap the mission
60 Actress Claire
61 ___ in turkey (part of a kindergarten lesson)
62 Uses a stopwatch
63 Some members of the mil.

DOWN

1 "... ___ is in heaven"
2 "Be quiet!"
3 Sign of sorrow
4 Rescinds
5 Sign with an arrow
6 ___ course (soon)
7 Helgenberger of "CSI"
8 Humble and shoo-fly
9 Noteworthy time
10 Eel look-alikes
11 Weapons of old
12 Can't help but
13 From the top
18 "Comus" composer Thomas
22 "___ the land of the free ..."
24 Platte River tribe
25 He was a rolling stone in song
26 Word with "lord" or "board"
27 Instrument tuner's supply
28 More than a scuffle
29 Part of the eye
31 1953 Leslie Caron film
33 The E of QED
34 Apt sandwich for Superman
36 One with immunity and tact
37 Egyptian cobras
41 They're not single in Seville
43 Y pluralized
44 Aphid, to a gardener
45 Ties the knot once more
46 Charged, as a bull
47 Andrew Lloyd Webber musical
48 Attention-getting sounds
50 ___ Penh, Cambodia (Var.)
51 Bern is on it
52 Frodo's burden
53 Insect-repelling chemical
54 Sound of air escaping
57 Kimono sash

by Alice Walker
Edited by Timothy E. Parker
Answers in back

ACROSS

1 Form of writing
6 It's secured in an orbit
9 Charmingly spritely
14 Stop worrying
15 The south of France
16 Like the Vikings
17 "Dreams from My Father" author
18 Old shipping nickname
19 Like some bank accounts
20 Frantic pusher's target?
23 Remove vitals
24 Words with "distance" or "disadvantage"
25 Discounts considerably
27 Theatrical
32 Opposite of "yippee!"
33 "The King and I" star Brynner
34 Brief piece of writing
36 Broncos legend
39 Airport approximations, familiarly
41 Bad thing to wreak
43 Floor square
44 Measure of dignity?
46 Marner of fiction
48 Tibetan gazelle
49 Hailed one
51 Drunken reveler
53 Bald helper around the house
56 Met display
57 "You've got mail" co.
58 Crack assault group
64 Times of a.m.-p.m. changeovers
66 One of the "Rocky" films
67 First name of a "The Color Purple" cast member
68 Host at a roast
69 M and N, in D.C.
70 Margaret Hamilton role
71 Nursery denizens
72 No alternative
73 Submission encls.

DOWN

1 Theatrical object
2 Country queen McEntire
3 Buck heroine
4 Seuss character
5 Some track bets
6 Genesis hunter
7 Mongolian tent
8 Trims, cuts, pastes, etc.
9 Rope in
10 Dispirited
11 Halloween wear
12 Point in question
13 They're for the birds
21 Cookie amount
22 Prehistoric
26 Sodium chloride
27 They may provide highlights
28 It includes Naomi's story
29 Feature of some radios
30 They're sometimes rolled over
31 Municipal
35 Negri of silent movies
37 Shower gel ingredient
38 Time for a worldwide revolution
40 Tamperer hamperer
42 Lapidary's measure
45 Little black numbers
47 Woes
50 "Fargo" affirmative
52 Ideal place
53 "Olympia" painter Edouard
54 Commodious
55 Unpleasantly loud
59 Provide with a summons
60 Made-up rock group?
61 Food morsels
62 Walk like a worrywart
63 Movie theater admonitions
65 Formerly known as

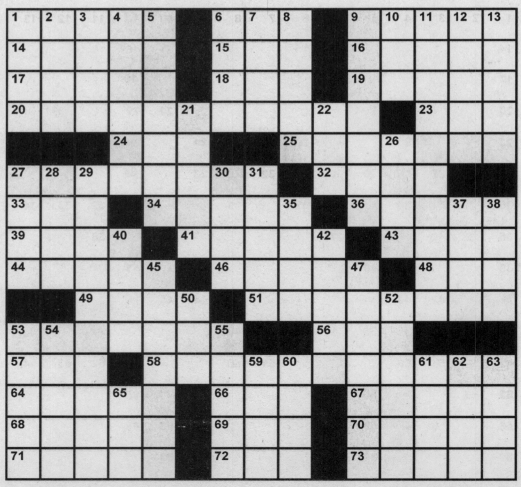

83 Chinese Mustard

by Kyle Gray
Edited by Timothy E. Parker
Answers in back

ACROSS

1 Doesn't keep up
5 Recipe amts.
10 Cheat, in a way
14 It's something else, in Madrid
15 ___ once (suddenly)
16 It can lead to raises
17 Word on a check you won't cash
18 Certain Arab
19 Edinburgh miss
20 Morning side
23 Singer Blige
24 Eggs ___ Suisse
25 Emmy winner Ruby
28 First name in gins
29 Furrow, as the brow
33 Blown flies, say
35 Lessen one's exposure?
37 Immature newts
38 Popular import
43 Comment of the despondent
44 Doesn't tip
45 No longer tired
48 "___ of Flanders"
49 They go around the block, briefly
52 One tippling too much
53 Vein glory?
55 Dig for squares?
57 Pizza topping
62 Nuncupative
64 Young lady
65 Custom auto accessories
66 Fairy tale villain
67 Sharp or severe
68 It may be electrical or red
69 Gwen Verdon role
70 Mar. 17 figure
71 "The Call of the Wild" vehicle

DOWN

1 Elvis Presley or Fats Domino tune
2 Hardly melodious
3 An African amulet
4 One way to be mistaken
5 Old Soviet news agcy.
6 Uninteresting
7 It needs renewal
8 "The Taming of the Shrew" locale
9 Archie Bunker's command
10 Notorious drug cartel
11 Like some relationships
12 Barnum and 109, e.g.
13 Unambiguous response
21 Alphabetical run
22 "___ from the Madding Crowd"
26 Big name in Art Deco
27 To be, to Caesar
30 San Francisco hill
31 Medical suffix
32 "Is ___ fact?"
34 Some whistle-blowers
35 Part of any profit calculation
36 "National Velvet" author Bagnold
38 What a lot may have
39 Product in a tub
40 Barkeeper's yell
41 Corp. money handler
42 Gift ___
46 Many, many millennia
47 Soap operas, e.g.
49 Kind of climber
50 Visual deception (with "l'oeil")
51 Heard, smelled or tasted
54 ___ of Nantes, 1598
56 Pub game
58 ___ Romeo (sports car)
59 "The jig ___!"
60 Celluloid terrier
61 Muscovite's negative
62 Nocturnal creature
63 Eeyore's bookmate

by Pearl Anderson
Edited by Timothy E. Parker
Answers in back

ACROSS

1 Bustle
5 Musketeer motto word
8 They're in a league of their own
13 Genesis setting
14 Stick around the kitchen?
15 Once around, to an astronaut
16 Small insectivorous mammal
17 Half of CCCXII
18 First name among "American Idol" judges
19 One with money to risk
22 Comply with orders
23 Intense anger
24 Unconventional physician
27 Blazer, e.g.
29 Litter critter
33 Big name in petroleum, once
34 Grand Canyon transport
36 Kanga's tyke
37 You may exercise a right in it
40 Historic period
41 Slender fasteners
42 Put on a hair-raising display?
43 Not easy to find
45 U.K. honor
46 Prepares spuds, in a way
47 1/6400 of a circumference
49 Bowl for baptismal water
50 What a young slugger dreams to play one day
58 Muse of love poetry
59 Queens stadium name
60 Et ___ (and other men)
61 It'll make you pull over
62 Evening hour, in Madrid
63 Dear partner
64 Smart-alecky, in a way
65 Atlantic City casino, familiarly (with "the")
66 Drought-stricken

DOWN

1 One without benefits
2 It comes out in the wash
3 Poor boy provider
4 What a unified group speaks with
5 Place for pinheads?
6 Jacob's third son
7 Type of cloth
8 Hard drinker
9 Corrections agent?
10 Border on
11 "Venus de ___"
12 Grade-schooler's reward
14 Composition for eight
20 Incorporate
21 Joie de ___ (joy of living)
24 Viking of the comics
25 The last of any series
26 Hardly a people person
27 Glove material, perhaps
28 Addresses that are often underlined (Abbr.)
30 Fictional clerk
31 Featured item in a necktie party
32 Vocal inflections
34 Give everything away
35 Gas range?
38 On ___ (doing well)
39 Some detente issues
44 Plays to the balcony
46 Pouting grimaces
48 O. Henry technique
49 Alphabetic quintet
50 Kettle of fish
51 Oratorio highlight
52 Honey holders
53 Point in the right direction?
54 On open waters
55 On the calmer side, nautically
56 Unreliable witness
57 Italian units of money, once

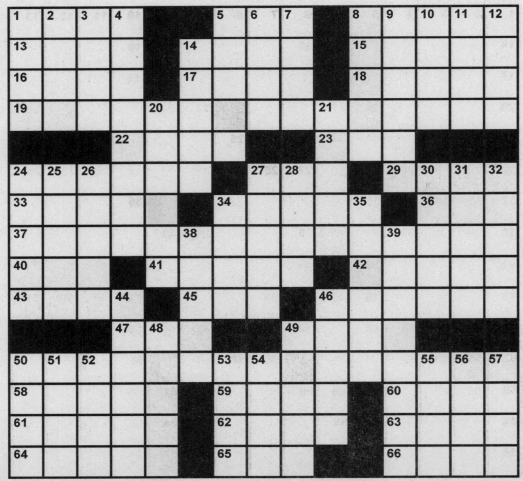

85 Jewelry Box

by Carol Lachance
Edited by Timothy E. Parker
Answers in back

ACROSS
1 Big tip, slangily
6 Potluck item
10 Needle source
14 "My Friend Flicka" author
15 ___ snuff (adequate)
16 Like some ports
17 Extreme quietness in an office that leads to stress
20 Sal's canal
21 Dropped name preceder
22 Lemonlike fruit
23 Authoritative order
25 Grub
26 James Farrell's subject in his 1930s trilogy
32 Ghostly greeting
35 Conjectures
36 The Magi, e.g.
37 German seaport
39 Itinerary word
40 Garden hazard
41 Diva's big moment
42 EE and EEE, e.g.
44 It's N of Colo.
45 Good place to catch the punches
48 Hard-to-swallow verbiage
49 Works in progress
53 Police officer's badge, e.g.
56 "Go on"
58 A good one is usually square
59 Hitchcock's trademark
62 "You, there, on the boat!"
63 Story or tale
64 Hero of Castile
65 Lawn tool
66 Love god
67 Sugar sources

DOWN
1 Got through the hard times
2 Hobbit's home
3 Button type
4 Selects from the menu
5 Roofing goo
6 Easy mark
7 ___ dixit
8 Place to wallow in mud
9 Bosses
10 Hand over
11 Dr. Frankenstein's assistant, in film
12 Animated fish
13 Adam's arboretum
18 Winning 3-2, e.g.
19 Singer Celine
24 James Bond's school
25 Athletic footwear
27 Split
28 Derogatory, as a remark
29 "... how does your garden___?"
30 Well-ventilated
31 Inadvisable action
32 Shoulder, as a burden
33 Father of Ahab
34 Cosmos creator, in myth
38 Sharpshooter
40 Ivan IV was Russia's first
42 Archer's concern
43 Gossipy Hopper
46 Minuteman's home
47 Mexican dish
50 It's about a yard
51 Indicated by a nod
52 Seasonal gliders
53 Former stitch location
54 "Got you!"
55 Post-accident reassurance
56 Lhasa ___
57 Court partitions
60 MPG part
61 Grayback

by Wesley Holman
Edited by Timothy E. Parker
Answers in back

ACROSS

1 "Chop-chop"
5 You answer to him or her
9 Three Stooges actions
14 Hemingway's handle
15 Informal affirmative
16 Monthly bill, for many
17 Downright evasive
20 Twelfth of a subscription, often
21 Bony
22 Extremely arid
25 It may be bitter
26 Liquid measurement
28 Carefree gait
32 Owen Davis' Pulitzer drama
37 Turn, as food
38 In the altogether
41 "Zorba the Greek" setting
42 Plane class?
43 Player in the Shell game?
44 Back in the navy
46 Homer Simpson shout
47 Accountants may work them
53 Gets hitched with
58 "Gentleman Jim" portrayer
59 Recalcitrant
62 "Spider-Man" star Maguire
63 Hibernia
64 Alphabetical run
65 Cushy class
66 "Don't change this!"
67 Dumbarton denials

DOWN

1 Astronomical point
2 Dance or condiment
3 Given to servile imitation
4 ___ New Guinea
5 "Sayonara!"
6 Poetic contraction
7 Word with "he" or "she"
8 Mover partner
9 Burn with steam
10 Half of a road, often
11 Assist in malfeasance
12 Court statement
13 Owner's option
18 By order of
19 In the mail
23 Blue tinged with green
24 Wimple wearers
27 "Look before you leap," for example
28 Occipital ___
29 Brief notice of departure
30 Wife number VI for Henry VIII
31 Swirling current
32 Type of worm
33 Upkeep
34 Just makes (with "out")
35 What some pools consist of
36 Metrical homage
37 Workout facility
39 Weightlifter's maneuver
40 Top-of-the-line
44 Worth a C, perhaps
45 "___ no place like …"
46 Presidential nickname
48 Vocal support
49 Image maker
50 Caribbean Eden
51 Gabbana's partner
52 Winter coasters
53 Noble Italian family
54 Greek portico
55 Pint places
56 Follow commands
57 Angry mood
60 Is for more than one
61 Complete collection

87 Man in Charge

by Lucille Evanstone
Edited by Timothy E. Parker
Answers in back

ACROSS

1 Some cover-ups
5 Elevator pioneer
9 Famous commercial flop
14 Winter woe
15 Famous literary bear
16 Gladiatorial milieu
17 Carrot, on occasion
18 Dark, poetically
19 Vegas casino razed in 1996
20 Some arachnids
23 Compass dir.
24 Anthem preposition
25 Fielder's stat
28 Expired, as a subscription
30 Wheel part
32 Physique, in brief
33 Reach, as one's goal
35 Goes public
37 Some parental substitutes, psychologically
40 Rapture
41 Does a carpenter's task
42 "___ Day Will Come"
43 Squiggly shape
44 Popular computer game
48 Take up, as liquid
51 Touchy subject, to some
52 Sawbuck fraction
53 Noted New England music group
57 Some wall hangings
59 Prefix for "scope"
60 Exam for an atty.-to-be
61 "The Purple Rose of ___"
62 Mattress type
63 Raison d'___
64 Classified, as blood
65 Plan impediment
66 Laundry holder, briefly

DOWN

1 Son of Odin and Frigg
2 Tennessee Williams title critter
3 Unwanted baggage
4 Provide capital for
5 Folded dish
6 Drum that often accompanies a fife
7 Springsteen's "___ Fire"
8 Imitated a bird
9 Alleviates
10 Pulls along
11 Rational
12 Bitter part?
13 "Viva ___ Vegas"
21 Juveniles
22 Scientist's milieu
26 Some music scale notes
27 QB or RB successes
29 Mare fare
30 They played Elvis
31 Squad car, e.g.
34 Supplies with weapons
35 Soup holder
36 Beginning for "while"
37 Bungle
38 Landing field
39 Start moving
40 Burlesque accessory
43 Recede to the sea
45 Abodes for biddies
46 One way to spend idle time?
47 Last six lines of a sonnet
49 Chicago stopover
50 Greenkeeper's task
51 Indoor courtyards
54 Decides
55 Fastened with thread
56 One of the common folk
57 Step into character
58 Flat fish

88 Ultimate Favorites

by Tyrone Bass
Edited by Timothy E. Parker
Answers in back

ACROSS

1 It may need stitches
5 Arbiters of plays
9 Shoe shapes
14 Lay eyes on
15 Like some advanced exams
16 Focus of worship, in Islam
17 Bring in the sheaves, e.g.
18 Mystical emanation
19 Bird of paradise feature
20 Ultimate Fighter's favorite side dish?
23 Give off, as radiation
24 Sodom survivor
25 "This instant!"
28 Small progression
30 Bitty bark
33 Stiff hairs or bristles
34 Compost place
35 Counter offer?
36 Ultimate Fighter's favorite entree?
39 Shrink's statement
40 Cogito, ___ sum
41 General vicinities
42 It's spoken in Berlin (Abbr.)
43 Not occurring naturally
44 Offensive, in a way
45 Styling substance
46 Some say it's for boobs
47 Ultimate Fighter's leafy dish?
54 Demanding payment, in a way
55 It's sold in bars
56 Lake feeding the Niagara River
57 Nostalgic tune
58 Decent plot
59 Bar mitzvah, e.g.
60 It may have a brand name
61 Cold War participant
62 Malamute's burden

DOWN

1 Cold cause
2 Making a crossing
3 Reducing resorts
4 Break one's word?
5 John's employee
6 Spew lava
7 One-time Vegas game
8 Jalousie unit
9 Common airline carry-on
10 Divvy
11 Swing around
12 Glaswegian headgear
13 Start of a memorable tongue twister
21 Presiding personality
22 First Hebrew letter
25 Comparable to a barn
26 Display poor sportsmanship
27 Mink relative
28 Umbrella plant, e.g.
29 Cantina fare
30 Jethro Bodine, e.g.
31 Standard of perfection
32 Flower from the violet family
34 Drover's charge
35 Some radio talk show employees
37 Ruled territory
38 Metric poetic feet
43 Deficient in amount
44 Word in the title of a da Vinci painting
45 Barbara Eden played one
46 Nicholas and Alexander, e.g.
47 Branch Davidian sect, for one
48 Get carried away?
49 Hairy twin of the Bible
50 Medicos, briefly
51 Seed appendage
52 Quote, as an authority
53 Lend an ear to
54 Distress signal

ACROSS

1 Vise parts
5 Salzburg setting
9 Duelers' distances
14 Colliery opening
15 Disastrous defeat
16 Economize on the wedding
17 Aft antithesis
18 Nearly unique
19 Glass component
20 VCR feature
23 "The Partridge Family"co-star
24 Amati of violin-making fame
25 Artist's theme
27 Mailbag attachment
30 New Zealand natives
33 Young Darth Vader's nickname
36 Review, as damage
38 Bustle
39 Creator of 33-Across
41 Coolly aware
42 Group of judges
43 Jumped bail
44 Cub reporter's dream
46 Thomas Lincoln, familiarly
47 Guanaco kin
49 Word in many university names
51 Root used as a substitute for soap
53 Option for the inn crowd?
57 Bosom buddy
59 Film directed by Ingmar Bergman
62 Mutual of ___
64 About a third of the world's land mass
65 End to be attained
66 Return to the mind
67 Dessert trolley
68 You may find a judge in here
69 Word with "knock" or "weak"
70 "K-i-s-s-i-n-g" place
71 Falco of "The Sopranos"

DOWN

1 Sweet variety of orange
2 Bejewel, e.g.
3 Like some undercover cops
4 Mans the helm
5 Back payments
6 Bread in the oven
7 Contented tabby sound
8 Propellent for Casey Jones
9 Bronze coin of Spain, formerly
10 Legendary boxing champ
11 It can make one wear heavier clothing
12 Sword with no cutting edge
13 Extremely alluring
21 Followers of epsilons
22 TLC purveyors
26 Whit
28 White as a ghost
29 Loses a sunburn
31 It may be half-baked
32 Realtor's favorite sign
33 ___ Romeo (imported auto)
34 Empty, as a set
35 Richard Burton film or Ferber novel
37 Meat skewer
40 Garden party?
42 "She loves me" unit
44 "___ Ha'i"
45 Provide commentary
48 Yellow-bellied one
50 Political escapee
52 Carry through legislatively
54 Put in ___word for
55 Sheikdom, Abu ___
56 Former British prime minister
57 "The other white meat"
58 Grace period?
60 Alexandra's husband, e.g.
61 Dublin's land
63 Color property

by Lucille Evanstone
Edited by Timothy E. Parker
Answers in back

ACROSS

1 A freelancer may work on it
5 "Young Frankenstein" co-star
9 Something amazing?
14 Western wolf
15 Prelude to a solution
16 Showing effortless grace
17 Effluvium
18 Something the euro replaced
19 More than occasionally
20 Is worse than ever
23 Major inconveniences
24 Offensive expression
25 Dogcatcher's quarry
26 Slowly become bald
28 Rug texture
31 Attested
34 Clothes line?
35 Boxer's cue
36 Question a plumber may ask of noisy kids?
39 From the beginning
40 Soak up the sun
41 Hops kilns
42 Neither partner
43 Allot
44 Hightail
45 Old Testament book
47 Party supplier
51 Demonstrate great affection
54 Like Hermes' sandals
55 Advocate forcefully
56 Nod neighbor
57 Observant one
58 False god mentioned in Judges
59 Delivered by post
60 Parts of hospital bills, often
61 Getting around well
62 Chronic imbibers

DOWN

1 Trudge through melting snow
2 Lecture hall platforms
3 Black hues, in old poems
4 Wine bottle accessory
5 You don't want to be out of this
6 See you in the Sierra Madres
7 Juno's Greek counterpart
8 Indian flatbread
9 Shone brightly
10 Cartridge holder
11 They keep practicing
12 Consider (with "over")
13 Suffix with "velvet"
21 Swung around
22 Tree resin
26 Have a premonition of
27 It preys from above
29 What little things mean?
30 "Not only that ..."
31 Bridge length
32 Port authority?
33 Formal headgear for men
34 The Sultan of ___ (Ruth's moniker)
35 Completely innocent
37 Beyond plump
38 Antipathetic
43 Blade cutters
44 In the recent past
46 Short choral composition
47 Panatela, e.g.
48 One place to see clowns
49 Momentous occasion
50 Charges for use
51 ___ gin fizz
52 Ointments
53 End of shooting
54 Emmet or pismire

ACROSS

1 Henry VIII's sixth
5 Concealed
8 Like some bank accounts
13 Common fertilizer ingredient
14 About intro
16 Postulation
17 Republic in SE Europe (Abbr.)
18 La ___ Tar Pits
19 Word for a statesman
20 Plan impediment
21 Marginal
23 Character in "The Gondoliers"
25 Establishment with staying power?
26 WWII dogfaces
27 "___ lift?"
29 Its very existence is an open-and-shut case
31 Fibers to the medulla oblongata
32 Some Mozart works
34 ___ resemblance to (look like)
36 Animated redhead
41 Fruit of the vine
42 Emulate Thomas Crown
43 Awe-struck expression
46 Place for fresh eggs
48 "___ Pretty" ("West Side Story" tune)
49 Time-wasting bother
50 "The Star-Spangled Banner" contraction
51 Fix the end of a pool cue
53 Exurb, e.g.
56 Their days are numbered?
59 Comprehensive test
60 Soho socials
61 ___ avis (one of a kind)
62 Invitation on a Wonderland cake
63 Canoer's threat
64 Gross
65 Contemptuous expression
66 Explorer/filmmaker Johnson
67 Imbroglio

DOWN

1 Taprooms
2 Make ___ for it (flee)
3 Empathize with
4 The brink, as of a cliff
5 "The Natural" baseball star Roy
6 Tactical advancement
7 Couch potato's opposite
8 Rudder's place
9 Water source
10 Blue dye
11 Greeted and seated
12 Emphasis
15 Wirelessly transmitted
22 Mesmerized
24 Woodland deity
27 Without further delay
28 "The Island of the Day Before" author
30 Krummhorn cousins
31 Far East countries, collectively
33 Foster's river of song
35 Go up to bat again
37 Surgeon's decision
38 Not fall behind
39 Morn counterpart
40 Short kinsman?
43 Campaigners' bloopers
44 Mrs. Rocky Balboa
45 Tiptoe, in ballet
47 They leave tracks
50 Lustful looker
52 High mark with low effort
54 Anthroponym
55 Edit menu command
57 Slow-moving vessels
58 Shows, as a watch

92 Stately Meals?

by Casey Rumblach
Edited by Timothy E. Parker
Answers in back

ACROSS

1 Bean or capital
5 RNA component
11 Best way to get it down
14 Bus. course
15 Promised Land
16 "Honest" president
17 Stately meal?
19 Beaver's exclamation
20 "Candle in the Wind" John
21 Refuse to acknowledge
22 Barracks' beds
23 Hole for a shoelace
25 "The Lion and the Mouse" writer
27 Stately meal?
32 Marched on
33 Money motto starter
34 First fratricide victim
38 Bars on wheels
41 Jellystone Park resident
42 Amazon ungulate
44 Muslim chief
46 Stately meal?
51 Good roll, for starters
52 Bring to a boil
55 Some Indochinese
57 Alphabetical run
60 Volcanic landslide
61 Familiar, as friends
62 Stately meal?
64 Maiden name intro
65 Fancy
66 Loving son of myth
67 Wide shoe widths
68 Reply to "Am too!"
69 Have the gumption

DOWN

1 Robert E. Lee waiting spot
2 In a very unfriendly way
3 Post follower
4 Neighbor of Namibia
5 A third of a movie dog
6 Goddess of fertility
7 Breakfast cereal ingredient, sometimes
8 Certain Hawaiian islander
9 It has a wet floor
10 "A Nightmare on ___ Street"
11 Capital of American Samoa
12 Sanction misdeeds
13 Ball holders
18 Sluggish by nature
22 Hokey, as a joke
24 One-time runway model Banks
26 ___-fi
28 Bagel topper
29 Perform without preparation
30 Where to find cranberries
31 Star Wars research prog.
34 Cash dispenser, briefly
35 Lamb's call
36 Soap installments
37 Crow's-feet, e.g.
39 They're worth three points in Scrabble
40 Fill completely
43 Accelerate, briefly
45 ___ Park, California
47 Front-runner
48 Important percentage for leadoff hitters
49 Like many violent films
50 "The English Patient" setting
53 Burt Reynolds film
54 Irregular, as leaf edges
55 Like Tonto's masked friend
56 On the sheltered side
58 Cleft locale
59 Stella ___ (biscuit brand)
62 "Sweet as apple cider" girl
63 Animal kept for companionship

ACROSS

1 No neatnik
5 Jewish month before Nisan
9 It may be cradled
14 Participate in a child's game
15 Battering wind
16 Of the kidneys
17 Coffee choice
18 Auditory
19 Literary technique
20 Weekly since 1955 (with "The")
23 Country album?
24 Perception
25 Deadly reptile
28 Moneymaker
30 Shortsightedness
32 Raised-eyebrow remarks
35 Tiniest amount of rice
38 Casting requirement?
39 Washington memorial dedicatees
43 "The African Queen" screenwriter James
44 Pie flavor
45 Round Table knight
46 Pummel
49 Regular trips
51 Suffix with lion
52 Roundup need
55 Serviceable
59 Flame-tender of myth
61 Some 1940s internees
64 Double-reed woodwind
65 ___ Romeo (Italian auto)
66 More than passing
67 Exhort
68 Coffeehouse attraction, maybe
69 Pullman accommodation
70 Is profitable
71 Holding a grudge

DOWN

1 Partner of Brahma and Vishnu
2 Authorized
3 Digby "Digger" ___ of "The Life of Riley"
4 Sheer chaos
5 Eagerly expectant
6 Receiving clerk's gadget
7 Still with us
8 Scouting job, briefly
9 Expensive
10 Homeroom response
11 Words of protest from Yoko?
12 Bert Bobbsey's twin
13 Culbertson of bridge
21 "And this shall be ___ unto you" (Luke 2:12)
22 A certain doctrine or theory
25 Vertical, nautically
26 City near Assisi
27 Buddy-buddy
29 Gun lobby, briefly
31 Bruin whose #4 jersey is now retired
32 Egg-shaped
33 Euphoric states, slangily
34 Crystal ball users, e.g.
36 "___ Gotta Be Me"
37 Obituary
40 Herbal brew
41 It's after sigma
42 Lethargy
47 Winter conveyance
48 Is down with
50 Subway car danglers
53 Basin for holy water
54 Tel Aviv native
56 Arctic dwelling
57 Permanent cell occupier
58 Akin on Mom's side
59 Air duct
60 Letters featured in this puzzle's theme
61 Capture, as a criminal
62 Hotel sign
63 Title for Arthur Conan Doyle

94 Dress for the Occasion

by Cole Cooke
Edited by Timothy E. Parker
Answers in back

ACROSS

1 Put ___ on (limit)
5 Get the pot going
9 Allow entrance to
14 Asian desert
15 Fastidious
16 Ruth's mother-in-law
17 Gillette brand name
18 Moat menace
19 Bellyache
20 Pompous types
23 Conciliatory offering
24 Onager
25 It may be beaten or bucked
28 Unbroken
30 Part of a crater
32 Stereotypically blind official
33 Leave stranded
35 Dismissive gesture
37 Prudish type
40 Run out
41 Academic achievement
42 Clairvoyant's forte
43 Prevailed
44 Equestrian activity
48 Armstrong's program
51 Storage space
52 Gazelle of Tibet
53 Aristocratic types
57 Thick-skinned grassland beast, briefly
59 Sandwich filler, perhaps
60 Clothing
61 Good-looker (Var.)
62 Sanction misdeeds
63 Canal of renown
64 Change for the better
65 Show fully
66 The "M" in YMCA

DOWN

1 Tennis great Andre
2 Ginned product
3 Precipitous
4 "The Little Sparrow" Edith
5 Lineage
6 Social misfits
7 Art colony of New Mexico
8 Draw with acid
9 Incensed
10 Game room activity, perhaps
11 Dew, e.g.
12 Tiny terror
13 Suit partner
21 Pretense
22 An end to alcohol?
26 Birds raised for food
27 Car ad abbr.
29 Tori or Wally
30 Aftermath
31 Party to
34 Football great Graham
35 Doctor with a couch
36 Broke some ground
37 Fight for air
38 Night, to day
39 Mongoose kin
40 Ewe's milieu
43 Chinese frypan
45 Pay no attention to
46 Bean or noodle
47 Neon and argon, for two (Var.)
49 Flax product
50 Bridges of "Airplane!"
51 Big goof
54 Wild guess
55 March instrument
56 Part of a list
57 NBC's former owner
58 Engine sound

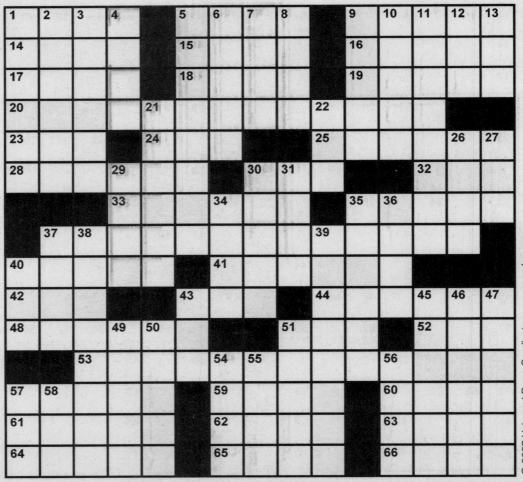

95 Move It or Lose It

by Tyrone Bass
Edited by Timothy E. Parker
Answers in back

ACROSS

1 Selling point
6 Tipsy
10 With the wherewithal
14 The Gold Coast, now
15 4,047 square meters
16 "Just ___" (Nike slogan)
17 Sprinter's event
20 Feelings of dread
21 "Frasier" setting
22 Penny Black was the first one
25 Short straw drawer, e.g.
26 God of war
30 Healthy, wealthy follower
32 Transportation-sharing arrangements
35 Whopper competitor
41 Event at the company picnic, perhaps
43 Looked for fingerprints
44 Suddenly attacked, in a way
45 Telephone button
47 Chromosome occupant
48 Paris subway system
53 Green tea
56 Transferee, in law
58 Summer month
63 Tougher competition than you thought
66 Whetter's concern
67 Roman greetings
68 Tobacco pipe
69 Divination practitioner
70 Withering
71 Heated conflict

DOWN

1 Turkish bigwig
2 Avoid deliberately
3 Ratted
4 They can be made to meet
5 Queen of Hearts' specialty
6 "If I ___ a Hammer"
7 Hardly gregarious
8 Gets the picture
9 Where the buck stops
10 Expand upon
11 Regatta entrants
12 Tightly twisted cotton thread
13 Old sleep inducer
18 "To the max" indicator
19 Lentil sauce
23 Shoemaker's tools
24 Make a fielding error
26 Breezed through, as an exam
27 Sauce brand
28 Divisions of joules
29 Bit of marital friction
31 Dark, poetically
33 Wee hour
34 They may be against you
36 Gerund maker
37 A Brady boy
38 Not occurring naturally
39 Open ___ of worms
40 Group of badgers
42 What belongs to us
46 Plural contraction
48 Some equines
49 Escape the notice of
50 Glimmer of color
51 Give someone the business
52 Lennon's widow
54 Gear for a galley
55 Loses feeling
57 Mesozoic and Cenozoic, for two
59 Skirt insert
60 Army outfit
61 Musical chairs goal
62 One wet behind the ears
64 "___ the fields we go"
65 Play for a sap

by Wesley Holman
Edited by Timothy E. Parker
Answers in back

ACROSS

1 Plumb loco
5 Bakery purchase
9 Lunkheads
14 Prefix with "phobia" or 1-Across
15 Grandson of Abraham
16 Watch for
17 Flabbergast
18 "SportsCenter" network
19 Odorize by burning
20 Part of a horse race
23 J.E.B. Stuart's outfit
24 Clear the board
25 Unprofessional one
27 Certain ID
28 Some cigars
32 Chrysler Building architect William Van ___
33 She can be lazy or black-eyed
34 Obey the dentist
35 Accountant's software
38 Allocation
40 Hardly refined
41 Hockey great Gordie
42 Moves along quickly
44 West end of L.A.?
47 It borders Georgia
49 In ___ (in the womb)
51 3-D diagnostic machine
52 Vegas spread?
56 Type of bear or cap
58 Rush job letters
59 "A Death in the Family" novelist James
60 Heraldic bands
61 Voyager insignia
62 Hungarian sheepdog
63 Davis of "Do the Right Thing"
64 Hardly ruddy
65 Bear's cry?

DOWN

1 Wild parties
2 Some Oscar recipients
3 33rd U.S. president
4 Sound units
5 Borscht vegetable
6 Former Olympic team
7 Neck feature
8 Beach bum's hallmark
9 Home on the Black Sea
10 Have liabilities
11 Round Table member
12 Cold comfort?
13 The "S" in T.S. Eliot
21 Safe and sound
22 1 in. = 2.54 ___
26 Entertaining anecdotes
29 Press into service
30 Rambouillet remark
31 Wds. in some business names
33 Bout of indulgence
34 Admit to everything
35 Lumber processors
36 Full house sign (Abbr.)
37 Magician's stock item
38 Beauty shop offering
39 Atrocities
42 "To ___, With Love" (1967)
43 Changing place
44 National or American
45 "Animal Farm" author
46 Cirque du ___
48 Sip slowly
50 Pitfalls
53 Hutchinson and Gray
54 "A Beautiful Mind" subject
55 Fix, at the vet's
57 Vowel-sequence start

© 2007 Universal Press Syndicate www.upuzzles.com

by Lucille Evanstone
Edited by Timothy E. Parker
Answers in back

ACROSS

1 Fly in the ointment
6 They're handled by people with handles
9 Silver salmons
14 Drop by
15 Fond du ___, Wisconsin
16 Electric terminal
17 Meeting room prop
18 Garment of camel's hair
19 Pullman berth
20 Missing person alert
23 Pseudonymous surname
24 Persian or Siamese
25 Human beings
27 Of imposing height
32 Flower with a floating pad
33 "That's the spot!"
34 Approximates
36 Murmured amorously
39 "___ she blows!"
41 Sitting Bull or Crazy Horse
43 Simple partner
44 Plant products?
46 Glittery fabrics
48 Numbered cube
49 British submachine gun
51 Orchestral composition based on literature
53 Show the ropes
56 Sculling instrument
57 Cut off, as branches
58 Classic baseball comedy routine
64 It may be in a stew
66 Kind of sister or story
67 Capital before Lincoln
68 "___ a Parade"
69 Nobel-winning U.N. agency
70 Miscellaneous collections
71 Spanish national hero
72 Before marriage
73 There are 100,000 in one newton

DOWN

1 Emit
2 He put two and two together?
3 Area next to an ambulatory
4 Menacingly wild
5 Get out of the habit of
6 Hammer part, perhaps
7 "Open, Sesame" man
8 Place for a massage
9 Heat-related
10 Noted Japanese-American
11 Pleasant greeting
12 Start of a Keats title
13 Ecological stages
21 Farmyard enclosures
22 Key on a keyboard
26 Trough fare
27 "Be seein' ya"
28 Waikiki Beach locale
29 Classic cartoon question
30 Detect and expose
31 Fourpence
35 Clash of heavyweights
37 Port in Pennsylvania
38 Exercise judgment
40 Group marching around campus
42 Gas used in tubes
45 Kelp, e.g.
47 Type of restaurant
50 Unspecific degree
52 In a proper fashion
53 Jock Ewing's spouse
54 Factotum
55 Gasoline colorant
59 Dover specialty
60 An orchestra tunes to one
61 Farmer's necessity
62 It's all about a foot
63 Old Soviet news agcy.
65 56, to Caesar

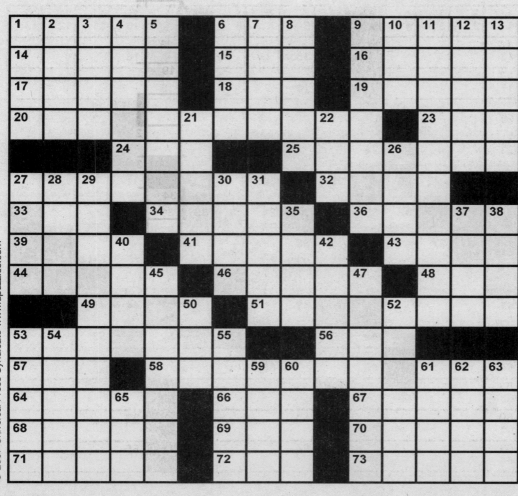

ACROSS

1 Marsh hens
6 An ump is paid to make it
10 Elementary studies
14 Blessing prompter
15 China setting
16 "Dies ___" (mass hymn)
17 Fab Four member
18 Occupies a table for one
20 Trouble, so to speak
22 Pick on playfully
23 Smog-monitoring org.
24 Srta. after marriage
25 Lobster eggs
26 Compass dir.
27 CD component
29 "Jewel Song" or "Flower Song"
31 ___-in-the-bone (deeply ingrained)
32 Hightail
34 Basic commodities
37 Like an hourglass form
39 Former German state
40 ___ Mateo, California
41 Dos y uno
42 301, Roman-style
44 "Doggone it!"
48 Sinbad's transportation
49 "'Tis a pity"
51 Verb or malt ending?
53 Book between Gal. and Phil.
54 Ugh cousin
55 Intelligent insect?
58 Rushed headlong
60 Battle depicted in "The Last Command"
61 Nero's robe
62 "If all ___ fails …"
63 Easier on the eyes
64 Part of a palindromic phrase
65 Unnatural blonde, e.g.
66 Diminutive

DOWN

1 Converted a check
2 Some mollusks
3 "Gone With the Wind" family
4 Of two minds
5 Hurting spots
6 He asked, "Et tu, Brute?"
7 Dumb ___ ox
8 Educated ones
9 Bronco catcher
10 Feel malaise
11 Talked terms
12 Pound fillers
13 Like most fruit
19 Absorbed, as an expense
21 Vagabonds
28 Christmas name
30 Father of Jacob
31 Amalgamation
33 Sure-footed work animal
35 St. Francis' birthplace
36 "Harper Valley ___'
37 Tornado aftermath, typically
38 In a decidedly evil manner
39 Supervise, as an exam
41 "Valse ___" (Sibelius work)
43 More frigid
45 Manufacturer's payback
46 Knuckle-dragging sorts
47 More than a hypothesis
49 1/6 fl. oz.
50 Make it harder to stop?
52 Create a statute
56 ___-majeste
57 Collagist's need
59 ___ tai (cocktail)

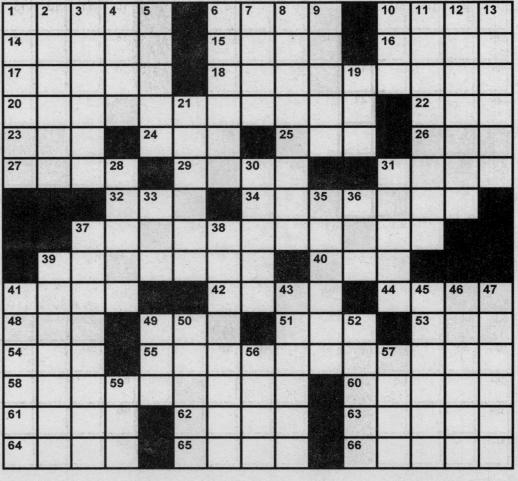

99 Making Bacon

by Candice Everly
Edited by Timothy E. Parker
Answers in back

ACROSS

1 Vintner's valley
5 Parker's music
10 Well-briefed about
14 Difficult burden
15 Mrs. Rob Petrie
16 Common transport
17 Political patronage
19 Storybook giant
20 He's second to Jordan in Sports Illustrated covers
21 Clear, as a drain
22 Jelly for germs
23 Make a comment
25 Aesthetically pretentious
27 Nipponese immigrant to the U.S.
30 Restaurant employee
33 Earthy pigment
36 Davidic verse
38 Arab cloak
39 Salty greeting
40 "Odyssey" enchantress
41 Kind of leopard or goose
42 Mulberry fruit
43 Diamond side
44 Kind of resistance
45 Fishy gathering
47 Market section
49 Peerage title
50 Vlad the Impaler, e.g.
54 Capone's distinguishing mark
56 Fit to be farmed
60 Princeton greenery
61 Founder of one of the 12 tribes
62 Overacted
64 Arabian Sea gulf
65 "I am just ____ boy ..."
66 Clinton's opponent of 1996
67 Bullet-against-metal sound
68 Some undercover cops
69 Anonymous people

DOWN

1 Without face value, as stock
2 Arboreal lizard
3 Jewish festival
4 Pump or grill
5 They may be loaded
6 Cornstalk features
7 Actor Reynolds
8 Popular cookie
9 Tangible
10 Maritime hazard in WWII
11 Where some savings are deposited
12 Cajun veggie
13 Do-well intro
18 Eucharist container
24 Well-ventilated
26 Pina colada ingredient
28 "Beowulf" is one
29 Looks embarrassed
31 Philharmonic instrument
32 Display boredom, in a way
33 Lummoxes
34 Stylishly elegant
35 Sheer bliss
37 Official records
40 Eastwood role
41 Some beans
43 The "F" in FYI
44 Cornered
46 Paddling
48 Slackers and couch potatoes
51 Climber's aid
52 Seed source
53 Uses the keyboard
54 Palm whack
55 Basic monetary unit of Ghana
57 ____ Nui (Easter Island)
58 Roman god of love
59 College VIP
63 Words at the altar

100 Bill Me

by Ezrem Hollis
Edited by Timothy E. Parker
Answers in back

ACROSS

1 Teamster's truck
5 Barn denizens
9 Choice word
14 Esau's father-in-law
15 Basketball target
16 Blow it in the last seconds, e.g.
17 Unproductive exercises
20 "Leave It to Beaver" character
21 Most alarming
22 Feels hurt by
25 Steamed state
26 United (with "up")
28 Oscar winner Celeste
32 Tchaikovsky ballet
36 Slow primate
37 Schoolbag item
40 Algerian money
41 It's easy as pie
42 Cancellation notation
43 She has more fun, supposedly
45 Variety of whale
46 Light detectors
51 McClellan battle site
56 Conspicuous success
57 Noted circumnavigator
60 Brown ermine
61 Words with "thanks"
62 Divisible by two
63 Camp shelters
64 The deadly seven
65 Exxon's former name

DOWN

1 Where Ed Norton worked
2 Ignore in pronunciation
3 Shapes and forms
4 Non-studio film, for short
5 "So that's your game, eh?"
6 Try to win over
7 Negative entry
8 Coins collectively
9 Earth pigment
10 East Asian
11 Vacuum feature
12 Makes do (with "out")
13 Take a load off
18 Less severe
19 It's cheaper than a gift
23 Sign of remorse
24 Hector Hugh Munro
27 "The Evil That ___" (Bronson flick)
28 Sweeties and dearies
29 Word on a greenback
30 In ___ of (replacing)
31 Car sticker abbr.
32 Benchmarks (Abbr.)
33 Least bit
34 "Rule, Britannia" composer Thomas
35 Litter-free
36 Compared
38 Spear and squirt
39 Alphabetic quartet
43 Alpha follower
44 Woody vines
45 Some Rockefeller Center murals
47 Sloping mass of rocks
48 Several Norwegian kings
49 Deals with the fall fall
50 Shorthand specialist
51 Type of coach (Abbr.)
52 Evening, in adspeak
53 1982 cyberfilm
54 "___ first you don't ..."
55 Mid 12th-century date
58 Charged particle
59 Ave. crossers

101 Party Time

by Alice Walker
Edited by Timothy E. Parker
Answers in back

ACROSS

1 "Dynasty" actress
6 Rhino's zoo cousin
11 Kentucky Derby month
14 Belief in sorcery and magic
15 Dental filling
16 Model of honesty
17 Type of party
19 Mariner's "Mayday!"
20 Have a bun in the oven
21 Highly embellished style
23 Caesar's hail
24 "___ Little Indians" (Christie classic)
25 Party snacks
26 Generous gift
30 Contentment
32 Steak partner
33 Came apart at the seams
35 Do some waiting
38 Microwave's nemesis
41 Warbucks henchman
42 Far from flighty
43 Brown family member
44 Restrain
46 Follow relentlessly
47 Campus military org.
49 Barely
52 He sincerely flatters
54 Unusually intelligent
56 It's tired
57 Island in western Indonesia
59 Squire carrying the armor of a knight
63 Eminent leader?
64 Type of party
66 Night of poetry
67 Half-diameters
68 State one's stance
69 Invoice word
70 Tartan pattern
71 Units of force

DOWN

1 Something to break into
2 Have ___ in one's bonnet
3 Litter noises
4 Employer of an idle repairman
5 Grooved pulley wheel
6 "Fire" antonym
7 Incumbents
8 Academy newcomer
9 Stately court dance of the 16th and 17th centuries
10 Hearing in open court
11 Type of party
12 It's-time link
13 Positive feedback
18 "This is only ___!"
22 Early stages
24 Least verbose
26 Exemplar of innocence
27 Away from the salty spray
28 Type of party
29 Head for the heavens
31 Braying beast
34 On a grand scale
36 Old orchestral string
37 Experiencing jitters
39 Aesop's shopping place
40 Fail to prevent
45 Mollusk creation
48 Relating to the flesh
50 Cleaner for gun barrels
51 Like fresh potato chips
52 Tree or resort
53 Turn to mush
55 Bamboo muncher
58 Waterproof canvas
59 Dyed-in-the-wool
60 Dieter's dread
61 Long-winged sea eagle
62 Certain grains
65 Second-sequel indicator

ACROSS

1 Perceive
6 String necktie
10 Generic dog name
14 Course of travel
15 Played for a sucker
16 Seascape color
17 "Abbey Road," e.g.
18 Hearty party
19 Diamond sacrifice
20 Weekend events
23 You may break it with guests
24 Umbrella component
25 Adept entertainers
27 Toy in a groove
31 Garment often made with six yards of silk
32 Take a bead on
33 Heartburn cause
35 Wanders
39 Sign of eccentricity?
44 "Show Boat" author Ferber
45 Sunbathing risk
46 Parliamentary vote
47 "I Heard It Through the Grapevine" singer
51 "Stay alert!"
53 Lamp oil
57 It's Big in California
58 To the ___ degree
59 Highly contentious situation
64 Bounty bellow
66 Camouflage
67 "Anybody home?"
68 Hobbler's support
69 Chills and fever
70 Writing assignment
71 Fathomed
72 Penury
73 Some rack bearers

DOWN

1 Court notable
2 Tape unit
3 Cote-d'Or's neighbor
4 "Little" mouse
5 North American Indian dish
6 Veep who had a duel
7 Japanese metropolis
8 Casino arms?
9 One-named folk singer
10 Beatles adjective
11 "Uncle!"
12 Fool's-cap wearer
13 Author Joyce Carol
21 Bahamas' Great or Little
22 Salutation for Edmund Hillary
26 Catcher's putdown?
27 Kemo ___
28 Bent the truth
29 Handwriting on the wall
30 First name in dog stars?
34 Girl at a ball
36 Novelist Seton
37 Boy Scout's undertaking
38 Command to 10-Across
40 "Aladdin" parrot
41 Long sandwich
42 Port in western France
43 Military tactics
48 Bat wood
49 Beefeater, e.g.
50 Bring to a boil
52 Writer Hemingway
53 Natural talent
54 "Training Day" actor Hawke
55 River through Lyon
56 Come after
60 ___ out a living (scraped by)
61 Lohengrin's love
62 Smelting dross
63 Kiddy litter?
65 Bowmaker's wood

by Pearl Anderson
Edited by Timothy E. Parker
Answers in back

ACROSS

1 Deck post
5 Bakery offering
10 Persia, now
14 Mean-tempered fellow
15 "My Cherie ___" (Stevie Wonder song)
16 Prefix meaning "one-billionth"
17 Slots
20 Unruly situations
21 Black gold
22 Schubert's "The ___-King"
23 "___ live and breathe!"
24 Pitfalls
27 Odd couple or dead ends?
29 Renaissance instruments
32 Nibble for a nag
33 Well-preserved king
36 Party site, sometimes
38 Characteristics of fixated people
41 Like many bagpipes
42 Place to be pampered
43 "… yadda, yadda, yadda"
44 Alcohol variety
46 Moore poem starter
50 On dry land
52 It goes through withdrawals
55 Need to pay the piper
56 Allen wrench shape
57 Qualified fellow's boast
60 Cyclopes
63 No great shakes
64 Uplift spiritually
65 "The Neverending Story" author Michael
66 Cows and sows
67 Stylist's creations
68 Sounds from a snake pit?

DOWN

1 Increased significantly, as the economy
2 Deliberately not notice
3 Increase by 200 percent
4 Ceylon and green, e.g.
5 Brings under control
6 Third sequel of a Gregory Peck classic
7 Hectored
8 Some like them hot
9 Memorable time
10 Second-most-populous country
11 Convict unfairly
12 Amazon, for one
13 Uncooperative votes
18 Panasonic competitor
19 Type of mats or surfaces
24 Pares pounds
25 Word that stops some trucks?
26 Jeanne d'Arc's short title
28 Editor's override
30 "The Simpsons" mouse
31 Common deciduous tree
34 Downright
35 Hackneyed
37 Pesky insect
38 Opal mos.
39 Fast food or deli request, sometimes
40 Fire proof?
41 View from the deck, perhaps
45 Unemploy, in a way
47 Type of NCAA basketball
48 Some arbitration decisions
49 Has a hunch
51 Bread spreads
53 Theater prizes
54 Greek letters
57 "___ Anything" ("Oliver!" song)
58 2002, in old Rome
59 66 and I-95
60 CIA predecessor
61 Classic Japanese drama
62 Common Market initials

by James Sajdak
Edited by Timothy E. Parker
Answers in back

ACROSS

1 Parts of some ER charts
5 Stroller wheelers, often
10 First Christmas visitors
14 Booty
15 Where to find heaven
16 Wild way to run
17 Jackknife, e.g.
20 Pencil of a sort
21 Guadalajara gala
22 It might result in a change of title
23 Second-highest U.S. Army award
24 Lighter or writer
27 Send to seventh heaven
30 Gold purity unit
35 "The Time Machine" race
37 Alibi ____ (excuse makers)
38 Jagged
39 Ageless quest
42 "Mon ____" (French comedy)
43 Jacques of 42-Across
44 Kind of molding
45 Cartoonist Wilson
46 Mixing with
48 Before, in poesy
49 Some WKRP characters
51 It takes two
53 Beethoven work
57 Breeding horse
62 Think tank, e.g.
64 Basso Pinza
65 Botanist's interest
66 "...slithy toves / Did ___ and gimble" ("Jabberwocky")
67 Was for a few?
68 Direct-sales giant
69 Iditarod necessity

DOWN

1 If not
2 Radio response
3 "An Inconvenient Truth" author
4 Long-billed bird
5 Tree of the South
6 Ecclesiastic title
7 Drop anchor
8 One of eight for Mickey
9 Landless laborers
10 Crafted
11 Cherbourg chums
12 Political syst.
13 Home furnishings megastore
18 Victory personified
19 Faux collar
23 Mississippi River explorer
24 Muddle
25 Actress Massey
26 Comfortable furnishing
28 Japanese watchdogs
29 Brunchtime, perhaps
31 Buck tail?
32 Baton end?
33 Blossom of autumn
34 Bit of laughter
36 "To Live and Die ____" (1985 film)
40 Take care of
41 Be resourceful
47 Sea bird
50 Former Israeli port city
52 Cosmonaut Atkov and designer Cassini
53 Eject forcefully
54 Move like flood mud
55 Dark film genre
56 Emollient yielder
57 Blanket material
58 ____ Bora, Afghan region
59 Pastoral composition
60 Fairy-tale baddie
61 Welfare state?
63 Airline to Amsterdam

by Fred Jackson III
Edited by Timothy E. Parker
Answers in back

ACROSS

1 It runs in veins
4 Make the transition
9 Monteverdi opera
14 Teachers' org.
15 Passageways in the brain
16 Stuck in muck
17 GENESIS
20 Exhausted
21 Terse verse
22 Lascivious look
23 Additions to a bill
26 TV watcher?
29 Newspaper staffers, for short
30 Request more Money?
31 Snowball
32 Feline nine
33 Decline an invitation
35 GENESIS
38 Type of cord
39 Job-related moves, for short
40 Bailiwick
41 Elaine of "Seinfeld"
42 Ball belle
45 Conservative leader
46 Discharges
48 Massive volume
49 "Long time ____!"
51 Some horses
52 GENESIS
57 Buddhist monk
58 Utility company's measurement
59 Give permission
60 "Doe" follower in song
61 Candidate of 1992 and 1996
62 Middle of summer?

DOWN

1 Priced to move
2 Staggered
3 An NFL team
4 Zodiac unit
5 When you might come down (Abbr.)
6 Tanzanite, e.g.
7 Moist add-on
8 Stay clear of
9 Old Dodges
10 It may be calculated
11 Frilly decoration
12 It can be found in a conger line?
13 Lofty tribute
18 Word with "field" or "strike"
19 Something in the water
23 Variety show
24 Feminine suffixes
25 Hopes
27 ____ d'etat
28 100 lbs.
30 Wintry coating
31 Pontiac muscle cars
32 Org. where ladies drive?
33 Keeps an eye on the figures?
34 Those in favor
35 Simple partner
36 Like most tutoring
37 Loafer insert
38 Outlaw
41 Add muscle
42 Possible
43 Allegory
44 Attacks from every angle
46 Glacial ridge
47 Logical start
48 Prefix for "age" or "angle"
50 Slimy substance
51 Look out for a looter, e.g.
52 Org. for attys.
53 Physique, informally
54 Deadly fly, when doubled
55 Laugh syllable
56 Id associate

ACROSS

1 Peninsula lost and recaptured during WWII
7 "Raising Arizona" director
11 Hazardous for driving
14 Squirreled-away things
15 "Man __Mancha"
16 Long of "Boyz N the Hood"
17 1948 Olivia de Havilland drama
19 Demolitionist's charge
20 Prepares apples for baking
21 Board with a planchette
22 Extra-ample shoe width
23 Unicorn feature
24 Elementary warning devices?
26 "… ___ penny earned"
28 Carrot-top creator
29 There's no escaping it
35 Some Morse code clicks
37 Fifth scale tone
38 Ridiculous
41 "Not my error" notation
42 Shoemaker's tools
44 Like some efforts
46 "Sun," "star," or "cloud" follower
49 Abbr. after a telephone number
50 Assembly hall
54 College booster, usually
58 Poetic form
59 Gather, as details
60 Oligarchy
61 Some gridiron positions, briefly
62 Hippie archaeologist's query?
64 Hue holiday
65 Suffix with "usher"
66 It can raise spirits?
67 ___ Z (everything)
68 Baseball's "Walking Man" Eddie
69 Supreme Court or baseball team, e.g.

DOWN

1 Cookie amount
2 Sound that might elicit a blessing
3 Start of a saying on forgiveness
4 Poisonous atomic number 33
5 Actresses Sothern and Jillian
6 Code-breaking govt. group
7 ___ d'Alene, ID
8 "Have another slice ___"
9 Chariot of fire passenger
10 Christmas in Rome
11 Many a doctor
12 Fit for the big screen
13 Eastwood's "Rawhide" role
18 Colorful form of the common carp
24 King of Saudi Arabia
25 Up-coming link
27 Kind of jump
29 "Be Prepared" grp.
30 Like a film made on a shoestring
31 Hints at
32 Jed's discovery
33 Mauna ___, Hawaiian volcano
34 Martians and such
36 UCLA or USC, e.g.
39 Newspaper clipping
40 CCV x II
43 Indian title of respect
45 Ranch alternative
47 Actress Dash of "Clueless"
48 Plum, beefsteak or cherry
50 Principal artery
51 Harangues
52 "The worst ___ to come!"
53 Wartime entertainers
55 Linear unit
56 Neighbor of Syracuse
57 Distributed (with "out")
60 Place at the start?
63 Bring into play

by Allan E. Parrish
Edited by Timothy E. Parker
Answers in back

ACROSS

1 Unfitting
6 R&B singer Bryson
11 Chucklehead
14 Like yesterday's culture, today
15 Negatively-charged particle
16 Link between home and school
17 It's cured in brine
19 Mythical monster
20 "You Bet Your Life" host
21 Second Amendment word
23 Elvis was born here
26 Dirk Nowitzki, e.g.
27 The "Fat" in "Fat Tuesday"
28 "The Art of Love" poet
29 Willing to agree
32 Clinton or Kennedy, briefly
33 Some bombs, briefly
34 Boardinghouse guest
37 Saguaro and prickly pear
39 Real finish?
41 Word in a Yale yell
42 On the beach
44 Mr. Kristofferson
46 Relative of "i.e."
47 Event scheduled for 2008 in Beijing (with "The")
49 Relinquish
50 Knotts character
52 Club of diamonds
53 Germ cells
55 They performed before kings
57 Sierra Club co-founder
58 ____ pro nobis
59 Copier snafu
64 Beneficiary of nepotism, briefly
65 Woody's "Annie Hall" co-star
66 Nancy Drew's Carolyn
67 Morse sound
68 "When ____ said and done …"
69 U-shaped curve in a stream

DOWN

1 Bread collector, for short
2 Like F.D.R.'s Deal
3 Went to Wendy's
4 Certain collegiate major, informally
5 The sum of all parts
6 Paris' Rue de la ____
7 Business letter letters
8 MVP of Super Bowl XXVII
9 General dubbed "The Liberator"
10 Scott Turow work
11 Dry cleaner's supply
12 Open-ceilinged rooms
13 Nocturnal rodents
18 Kind of golf tournament
22 Arctic abode
23 Puccini opera
24 Eye layers
25 Recipe phrase
26 Canteen cousin
30 1,501, Roman-style
31 Moves up and down
33 Like shortstops before Ripken
35 Slur over
36 Levels
38 Words on an apartment-window sign
40 Richie's dad, to Fonzie
43 Draw into an argument
45 Put out
48 Computer language
49 Outer layer of the brain
50 Narrow Norwegian inlet
51 Center of a well-known palindrome
54 One name Archie called Meathead
56 Icelandic epic
57 Short French mesdames
60 Prefix with "corn"
61 Civil War general Stuart
62 Yucatan year
63 Kitten's cry

108 Busy People

by Clifford Barnes
Edited by Timothy E. Parker
Answers in back

ACROSS

1 Astronomical sighting
5 Get bent out of shape
9 Atmospheric balloon probe
14 Metallurgist's materials
15 Therapeutic plant
16 Instructor
17 Some "Dear" ones
18 Network of veins
19 Old anesthetic
20 They go after men they shouldn't
23 Elijah's successor
24 Exudation
28 Homey room, typically
29 Chemical compound
32 Tailgater's need
33 Type of saint
35 Type of cabbage
36 Uninvited guests
40 Type of "cop" portrayed in a 1987 film
41 Ape or monkey
42 More thoughtful
45 Parodied (with "up")
46 Cookbook abbr.
49 Case that's not grammatical
51 Japanese hostess
53 Classic comedy film
56 Formerly Portuguese territory (Var.)
59 Rock, to a sea otter
60 "It's OK after all" in editing
61 5 1/2-point type
62 11,000-foot Italian peak
63 "... ____ forgive our debtors"
64 Some winning margins
65 Target of a swift kick
66 Trueheart of the comics

DOWN

1 Had some munchies
2 Bird popular in Baltimore
3 Flies, mice, etc.
4 Ancestors of domestic donkeys
5 Quality assurance?
6 On the sheltered side
7 Campus military org.
8 Looks from concealment
9 Typical introduction?
10 Blunt
11 To the ____ degree
12 Nanny goat
13 Misadd, e.g.
21 Flour grain
22 Continental trading org.
25 Former apple application
26 Thickens
27 Palindromist's preposition
30 Horrid giants
31 Nocturnal, tailless mammal
33 Engender
34 Implicate
36 Donne, for one
37 "Not on ____!" ("No way!")
38 Unique
39 Can't stand
40 Abbr. on a nutrition panel
43 Alpine sounds
44 Letter after pi
46 Fly from Africa
47 They have sharp tongues
48 Hits hard
50 Fragrant organic compound, often
52 Where ____ (trendy place)
54 Schlep
55 ____ fide (Latin)
56 Word that sandwiches "oh"
57 It comes after many moons?
58 ____ in Charlie

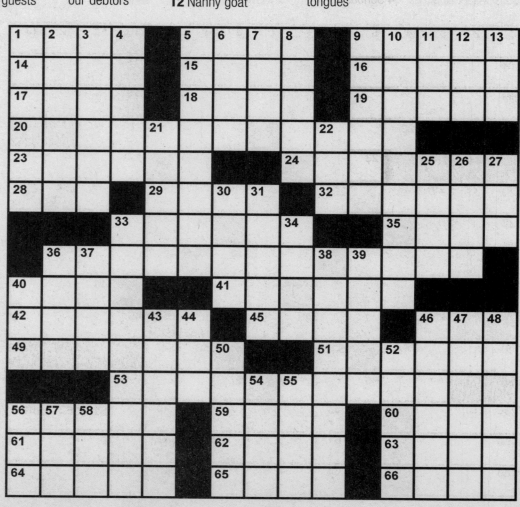

by Alice Walker
Edited by Timothy E. Parker
Answers in back

ACROSS

1 Dilapidated dwelling
6 "Jungle Book" star
10 Movie pooch
14 Betray one's awareness
15 Big-elephant link
16 AC capacity units
17 "I ___ Walrus"
18 Belgrade inhabitant
19 Doggie bag morsels
20 Award presentation site
23 Tarzan's swinging kid
24 Procure
27 Spent
31 Disapproving sounds
33 School in E. Lansing
34 Kofi, of the U.N.
35 Riot-subduing stuff
36 "Put ___ on it!"
37 Gary Lewis and the Playboys hit
40 World Heritage Pueblo site
41 Muscovite's negative
42 Annuity, in France
43 Room offerer
44 "Sweet" vegetables
45 Leisurely strolls
46 Infamous Fords
48 "The One I Love" group
49 Stun
56 Like the Kalahari
58 Narrow inlets
59 Thin bark
60 Calcutta queen
61 Ye ___ Shoppe
62 "… bombs bursting ___"
63 Put through the paces
64 Serious troubles
65 Four-time Australian Open champ

DOWN

1 Barbecue offering
2 Engine type
3 Mailroom abbr.
4 Mindy of "The Facts of Life"
5 Exercise of a sort
6 Full of lip
7 "Wait just ___!"
8 City on the Adriatic
9 Complete
10 Like ___ from the blue
11 Make more efficient
12 Well-preserved king
13 Palm Sunday mount
21 Lightning attractor
22 "60 Minutes" network
25 Loves
26 Prods along
27 Flat peppermint candy
28 Available to purchase now
29 Gazpacho preparers' discards
30 Move on ahead
31 Emulates a horse whisperer
32 Robert Burns, for one
35 Poet Angelou
36 "Iliad" figure
38 Held by a third party, as money
39 Personae leader
44 Party to a 1993 peace accord
45 By order of
47 Break up, informally
48 Tea and cabbage, for two
50 Metric weight, briefly
51 Lose color
52 It may be fast, slow or in a bowling alley
53 Certain gemstone
54 Mayberry resident
55 Strokes of luck, sometimes?
56 Lord's Prayer verb
57 Sally Field role

by Pearl Anderson
Edited by Timothy E. Parker
Answers in back

ACROSS

1 Delicate color variations
6 Sound projectors
10 Indian tourist mecca
14 Be smitten with
15 Have feelings
16 East Azerbaijan is a province in it
17 Laundered
18 Settled onto a branch
19 Precious vase
20 Tabloid fodder
23 Israel's southernmost city
24 Dawning
25 Damaged
28 It's the word on the street
31 Ovid's bird
32 Had in mind
33 Back in time
36 Tabloid fodder
40 Old preposition
41 Lorenzo of "Falcon Crest"
42 Mythical king of the Huns
43 Development developments
44 Inflame
46 Moisten in the morning
49 Sweatshirt part, perhaps
50 Tabloid fodder
56 One of an Iraqi minority
57 Resident of the funny farm
58 Muscle Beach dudes
60 Risky place to live?
61 Busy one in Apr.
62 Shopper's mecca, way back when
63 Closing document
64 Tony Fifth Avenue store
65 Temperamental

DOWN

1 "Hollywood Squares" square
2 Wait curbside, e.g.
3 Christmas season
4 Cross over
5 Beyond mere forgetfulness
6 "With ___ of thousands!"
7 French Sudan, nowadays
8 Holier-than-thou type
9 Third man from the first man
10 Intending
11 Shows happiness, in a way
12 The Andes, e.g.
13 Dread
21 Bummed out
22 Scout's master
25 Armor-busting weapon
26 Affirm confidently
27 Bug
28 ___ an example
29 Is a valuable hen
30 "Hulk" director Lee
32 Silent performer
33 Sparkling wine spot
34 Gold in color
35 Bee's nephew
37 Revealed, as an identity
38 Battering tool
39 Home for a famous chicken
43 Paid attention to
44 Gp. overseeing the Summer Games
45 The Big Apple
46 Made like bricks
47 Outwit, as a posse
48 Gloomy tune
49 Tries to get a buck?
51 Word of woe
52 ___ Raton, Florida
53 Berth place
54 Sequel to "Typee"
55 Brainy, socially inept sort
59 Thumbs-down vote

by Carrie Hansome
Edited by Timothy E. Parker
Answers in back

ACROSS

1 Paving block
5 Computer dialing device
10 Carton contents, for short
14 Linen hue
15 Mormon settlement
16 Emulate couch potatoes
17 Start of a popular saying
20 Bulgarian capital
21 It'll keep you out of a scrape or two
22 Transgresses
25 "Leave as is"
26 This may sting
29 Suffering partner
31 Parsley units
35 "___ be an honor"
36 It may be in judgement
38 City in Uttar Pradesh
39 End of 17-Across
43 You may feel it pass
44 Bubble-headed
45 Harvest goddess
46 Rapscallions
49 Global septet
50 "What have we here!"
51 Abacus feature
53 Con's home
55 Monotony's result
58 Where the Gurkha reigned
62 Theme of this puzzle
65 Similar to others
66 Tenement arrangement
67 Inter ___ (among other things)
68 Tricky play
69 English earldom
70 Zoom or contact

DOWN

1 Hems but doesn't haw
2 Lovelorn nymph
3 Not conforming to dietary laws
4 Capital of Tunisia
5 Speed measure, briefly
6 Pitchblende, e.g.
7 Deduct from
8 "Dynasty" star
9 Polyphonic choral pieces
10 Pretentious talk
11 The 29th state
12 Delighted
13 Vulpine in wit
18 Taiwanese city
19 Escape slowly
23 DEA officer
24 Had a horse
26 Vertical ship posts
27 Work ___ (code of the dedicated)
28 Tomato trouble
30 "___ not the time!"
32 Hemispherical home
33 Place for a sine curve
34 Authority to decide
37 Baptism and others
40 It might be permeable
41 Future attorney's exam, for short
42 Essential amino acid
47 One end of a hammerhead
48 Jockey's need
52 Features of some stadiums
54 Befitting a monarch
55 Azerbaijan's capital
56 "Miss ___ Regrets" (Porter tune)
57 Extinct kiwi relatives
59 "A Whiter Shade of ___"
60 Whitaker role
61 Pastoral expanses
62 Monopoly game piece
63 Employ
64 Type of education

ACROSS
1 Pay for everyone's dinner
6 Made ___ of things (botched the situation)
11 Dr. Mom's remedy
14 Kind of dressing
15 Ship's load
16 Microscopic
17 Concern for your own interests and welfare
19 One-million connectors
20 Flush beater
21 Finishes a book?
23 Senior's org.
24 Prophetic shrine
25 Premier Khrushchev
28 Tune from "The Sound of Music"
30 "___ sure you know ..."
31 Shrink in fear
32 "Hollywood Squares" square
35 Chess pieces
36 The Moor of Venice
38 NASDAQ abbreviation
39 Brain waves measurer (Abbr.)
40 Skating couples
41 Speak humorously
42 Advisories
44 Uses the backspace key
46 Some baseball statistics
48 Nail puller
49 Espresso with hot milk
50 They have hives
55 "Sorta" suffix
56 Brilliant feat
58 Alphabet sequence
59 Cold-weather forest
60 Tie ___ (get smashed)
61 Cerumen locale
62 On the say-so of
63 Harness parts

DOWN
1 Nonkosher
2 Spaghetti sauce brand
3 Hydroxyl compound
4 Plaudits
5 Last part of a Dr. Seuss title
6 Be mischievous
7 Fourth rock from the sun
8 New York canal opened in 1825
9 Koop and Elders, briefly
10 Tijuana topper
11 St. Paul and Minneapolis
12 U.S. Open tennis finalist eight straight years
13 Desist partner
18 Asta's mistress
22 "___ the Walrus" (The Beatles)
24 City south of Moscow
25 Moniker
26 Words said with a nod
27 Spumador's rider
28 Movers and shakers
29 Birds that may be spotted
31 Debt voucher
33 Vaulted area
34 Barracks beds
36 Bernstein's "Trouble in Tahiti," e.g.
37 ___ and feathers
41 Weapon for Samson
43 Choosing unit
44 Robert ___ (Civil War general)
45 Sought the office of
46 "Fur ___" (Beethoven)
47 Member of a Jamaican religion
48 Moth-repelling wood
50 Funny comment
51 Primal impulse
52 "s saw Elba"
53 Supply and demand subj.
54 D.C. VIPs
57 Successor to the Pan-American Union

113 Home Addition

by Arthur Groom
Edited by Timothy E. Parker
Answers in back

ACROSS

1 Colors slightly
7 Online journal
11 "So" homophone
14 "Relax, and that's an order!"
15 Of the highest quality, informally
16 Eminent introduction?
17 Addition to the family
19 Plant appendage
20 They're paid to make trades, briefly
21 "Go to the right, jackass!"
22 Log-on requirement
24 Arrival of 17-Across, e.g.
27 Gateway Arch site
30 Wading bird
31 Have ___ (enjoy yourself immensely)
32 Roar of a Spanish crowd
33 Three of a kind?
36 "Et tu, Brute? Then fall, Caesar!," e.g.
41 Obsolete palindromic preposition
42 Razor-billed diving bird
43 "...not ___ mouse"
44 "What a way to ___ living!"
47 Incites or pushes
49 17-Across, in a joke
52 Moderated
53 Early second-millennium date
54 Dipstick word
57 Coin of little worth
58 What 17-Across is
62 ___-80 (classic computer)
63 ___ about (approximately)
64 Up until now
65 "Get my drift?"
66 Brewski barrels
67 Had in common

DOWN

1 Apollo quaff
2 Agendum, e.g.
3 Latest scoop
4 Semi front
5 General of Chinese chicken fame
6 Fedorov of the NHL
7 Toyland visitors
8 Mauna ___, Hawaiian volcano
9 How some films are delivered to the studio
10 Old Faithful, e.g.
11 Autos' emergency replacements
12 Stu of old films
13 Peterson portrayer on "Cheers"
18 "The Untouchables" character
23 Garden party?
24 Heavy Philippine knife
25 Humdinger
26 Sushi servings
27 Yegg's target
28 Alpine elevator
29 "My dog ate my homework," e.g.
32 Tree with yellow ribbons?
34 SSN, e.g.
35 "No man ___ island"
37 Desert formation
38 Waikiki feast
39 "And away ___!"
40 Type of mitt or rack
45 Suffix with "lemon" or "lime"
46 Nike competitor
47 Gas or elec.
48 Holds spellbound
49 Blood and acid, e.g.
50 Martin's "That's ___"
51 Nautical offs.
54 Allowing a draft
55 Show excessive fondness
56 Not the original color
59 Christmas quaff
60 "___ la la!"
61 Food safety agcy.

by Fran & Lou Sabin
Edited by Timothy E. Parker
Answers in back

ACROSS

1 Let through the turnstile
6 Usher's request
10 Bellicose deity
14 "You can __horse to water …"
15 Throw a walk-off homer, e.g.
16 Hans Arp genre
17 Gossip
19 It'll take the cake
20 Prepping for inspection, as a weapon
22 Old-English letter
23 Cave dweller
24 Mental sharpness
28 Print shop employee
33 The Wizard of ___ Park (Edison)
34 Rip
35 Latin I word
36 Estimates
40 Malt finish?
41 Dismiss unceremoniously
42 Frankie who sang "Mule Train"
43 One political entity among 50
46 Sticky situation
47 Shot put's flight path
48 Stephen of "V for Vendetta"
49 Audience convenience
57 Bit of help
58 They're in no hurry
60 "American ___"
61 State name adopted in '37
62 Star-crossed lover
63 Sheet of stamps
64 Large number
65 "The ___ of Kilimanjaro" (1952 film)

DOWN

1 CTRL-___-DEL
2 Hearing-impaired
3 Niger neighbor
4 ___ fixe (obsession)
5 Site for chicken dinners
6 Reduce, as prices
7 Suit material, perhaps
8 Mac owner
9 Lack of vitamin B causes it
10 Accepts, as a resolution
11 Sitar player Shankar
12 Opening scene?
13 Ratted
18 Hot tub swirl
21 Ballet step
24 Fossil resin
25 Desist companion
26 Proceeding independently
27 "___ Be There" (Jackson 5)
28 Black tea
29 White water sight
30 "West Side Story" tune
31 Congregants' responses
32 Wine characteristics
34 Walk beater
37 You can count on them!
38 Bad winners
39 '50s Middle East initials
44 Tack room item
45 Three, in combinations
46 Essence
48 Keep a subscription
49 Transport
50 "How about that!"
51 Soon, in the past
52 It may be certified
53 Doubt-free
54 Age after Bronze and Stone
55 "Finding ___" (film)
56 Reached maturity
59 Scary signal

by George Keller
Edited by Timothy E. Parker
Answers in back

ACROSS

1 Use the left lane
5 Health centers
9 Spread around
14 Microwave device
15 Advocate
16 Cool South American country?
17 Office transmittal
18 Like church mice
19 "To err is ___ ..."
20 Booking for a monk?
23 Bakery pastry
24 Speaker's cousin
25 Wet spongy land
28 Place alone
31 Did some noshing
34 Hong Kong housemaids
36 Nobel-winning U.N. agency
37 Image on a radar screen
38 1955 Frank Sinatra song
42 Movie player?
43 Oater affirmative
44 Be on the same page
45 Charged swimmer?
46 Dealt with too lightly (with "over")
49 Bride's title, briefly
50 Dove cry
51 Sills specialty
53 Classic comedy series
61 Roof overhangs
62 Cord contents
63 "True ___" (John Wayne movie)
64 Crop up
65 Scots Gaelic
66 One of six for a hexagon
67 Defrosts
68 Nautical seven
69 Be overabundant

DOWN

1 Brilliant display
2 Affirm positively
3 Teamster's truck
4 Condescending type
5 Bldg. custodians
6 "Stat!"
7 Overly eager
8 Part of Doris Day's theme song
9 Crook's plan
10 Sound a stethoscope detects
11 Hoarfrost
12 Distinctive flair
13 Traveled
21 Madame Gorbachev
22 Big snapper
25 What "F" could mean on a test
26 Be actorish
27 Like some forces
29 Favors one side?
30 In the manner of
31 Word with "smoke" or "fire"
32 Woods with a wood
33 Dueling swords
35 Feminine pronoun
37 Oversized
39 Hose material
40 Half a quartet
41 Easy-listening medium
46 Pinches the buttocks
47 Delhi stuffed pastry
48 Decays gradually
50 Place for toys
52 Feeling of anxiety
53 League constituent
54 Rodentlike mammal
55 Bad to the bone
56 They like to gambol
57 "... golden days of ___"
58 Lake, city or canal
59 Roller coaster, e.g.
60 Rosebud support

by Fran & Lou Sabin
Edited by Timothy E. Parker
Answers in back

ACROSS
1 Fall guy
5 Fictional elephant king
10 Partially open
14 Clip contents
15 "Kate & ___"
16 Western Nevada city
17 Jimmy Carter had one
19 Gifted with the gift of gab
20 About half the people in revolving doors
21 Coral rings
23 Put aboard
24 Sidekick
25 First victim
27 Type of shark
28 Early jazz
31 Geisel's pen name
32 It has its reservations
33 Cassowary kin
34 Some are fine
35 Exercised one's wanderlust
36 Unlikely, as chances
37 Torched
38 Pivot bar
39 Triangular Greek letter
40 It's only one until you cross it
41 Pre-owned
42 Basker's delight
43 Autumn sight in suburbia
45 Valedictorian's platform
47 Distinctive badge
49 Rudolph or Santa, notably
53 It may follow a shuffle
54 Spreader of the theme answers
56 The younger Guthrie
57 French waterway
58 Pot addition
59 Cheese concoction
60 Broke off
61 Minus

DOWN
1 Stare in astonishment
2 Warning sign
3 "Amo" follower
4 Lacking in expression
5 Like a whisperer's breath
6 Woodard of "Beauty Shop"
7 "Gil ___ de Santillane" (Le Sage work)
8 Broadcast
9 Said something
10 Vacuum tube gas
11 Santa Claus feature
12 Indigo source
13 Pulls a heist
18 Russian range
22 "Home Improvement" prop
24 Supply the reception
25 Condor's home
26 Turkey brand
27 Brought to tears
29 Skips over
30 Nike competitor
31 Dash in the kitchen
32 Hang up?
35 Appear like
36 Like Christmas and Hanukkah
38 Book of the Gospel
39 Prohibition prohibition
44 Divvy
45 "The Wreck of the Mary ___"
46 Stirred in
47 Dutch export
48 Type of formality
49 The Lone Ranger's real name
50 ___ qua non
51 Immature newts
52 Middle's middle
55 Ex-jockey Turcotte

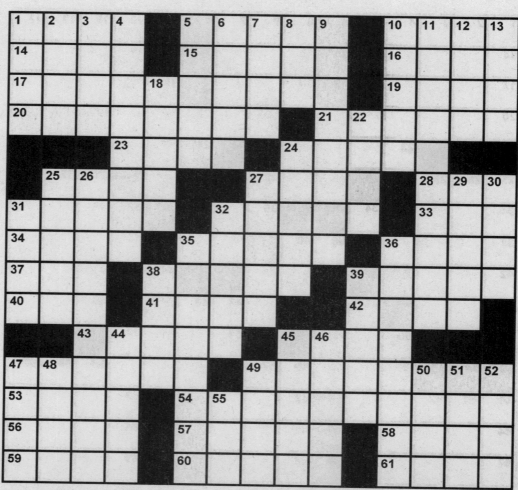

by George Keller
Edited by Timothy E. Parker
Answers in back

117 How Do You Do?

ACROSS
1 Cinch belt's cousin
5 Refer to, as a research paper
9 Like khaki
13 Duly distribute
15 Shakespearean "soon"
16 Go back to square one on
17 Weather forecast word, sometimes
18 Cartoon dog
20 Among stars
22 Desire strongly
23 Russian city or oblast
27 All fired up
30 Salad ingredient, perhaps
33 Frosted
35 Peer of the realm
36 "___ tu che macchiavi" (Verdi aria)
37 Slugger of 70 homers in one season
40 Views furtively
42 One-time connection
43 Drudgery
45 Pal of Potsie and Richie
46 Google.com, e.g.
50 Requirements at some restaurants
51 "Give it ___!"
52 Woman of refinement
54 One stirring up a hornet's nest
60 Hero's forte
63 Freshman course word
64 Popular cookie
65 Buck heroine
66 Paradisiacal places
67 Index card attachments
68 Become prominent
69 Peter Fonda title role

DOWN
1 Indian garment
2 Shepard in space
3 Oriental dress feature
4 Sweet melon
5 World leader since '59
6 Make furious
7 Die partner
8 Organic compound containing a hydroxyl group
9 Wood deck trouble
10 Color that suits Santa?
11 Hullabaloo
12 Sound of disapproval
14 Ancient seaport on the Mediterranean
19 Combatant
21 Cul-de-___
24 Granola cousin
25 Minor injury
26 Rock's Richards and Moon
27 Fleet of fighting ships
28 Spoils taker
29 "Sure, count me in"
31 Drink from a dish
32 Before, in rhyme
34 Conductor Mitropoulos or composer Tiomkin
38 Howard of "American Graffiti"
39 German 101 word
41 Himalayan capital
44 Kappa followers
47 Houston nine
48 Danson's role on "Cheers"
49 City near Arnhem
53 Parisian lady friend
55 ___ about (approximately)
56 Aptly named fruit
57 Record label in some TV ads
58 Beach bird
59 Banished baseball legend
60 E-mail address element
61 Stage of history
62 CSA soldier, for short

118 Keep It Moving

by Frances Burton
Edited by Timothy E. Parker
Answers in back

ACROSS

1 Nonsense
6 Doorframe upright
10 Quickly, quickly
14 "Fraud" novelist Brookner
15 Succulent plant
16 Collagist's need
17 Makeshift punishment device
18 Stringed instrument
19 Acquire through merit
20 "To the max" indicator
21 Rick Nelson song
24 Shepherd's, for one
25 Legally binding command
26 Poisonous element
30 Eats between meals
34 Michael Jackson song
37 Swelling soother
38 Heckelphone's cousin
39 Leatherworker's tool
40 Run in neutral, perhaps
41 Cat sound
42 Johnny Preston song
46 Out like a light
48 Pedants
49 Virtue
52 "__the season ..."
53 Nat "King" Cole song
57 Actress Lupino
60 Muslim prince
61 Kind of rags
62 Skywalker's father
64 Refuse to admit
65 Strong and healthy
66 Put up
67 Aware of
68 "__the night before Christmas ..."
69 Newsroom array

DOWN

1 March animal
2 Cross to bear
3 Scottish attire
4 Shoshonean
5 Bond's drink
6 Coffee, in slang
7 Still in the game
8 Used a Jersey expression?
9 Italian composer of operas
10 Some airline employees
11 Cutting criticism
12 Nimbus
13 Quaker colony founder
22 Horse-and-buggy handful
23 Graphic symbol
24 Small dog
26 Subject for a wine connoisseur
27 Terry cloth garb
28 Expression of displeasure
29 Capacity unit
31 Skins
32 Enthusiastic approval
33 Forward-looking group?
35 Possess
36 Dot on a radar screen
40 Wading bird
42 Tape measure part
43 Kind of piano
44 Streisand film
45 Had a broken heart
47 Life, in the early days
50 Relative by marriage
51 Carefree song syllables
53 Make over
54 "Lilies of the Field" song
55 After-dinner candy
56 Lyric poems
57 Caesar's bad day
58 Nautical platform
59 Crafts partner
63 Fill spaces

ACROSS

1 First name in spydom
5 Last word from Rhett Butler
9 Bowed instrument
14 Wetlands bird
15 Buck's tail?
16 Sidestep
17 "Land ho!" site
19 Basil-flavored sauce
20 Turkish state, once
22 Google alternative
23 Argus-eyed
24 Hazard starter?
27 One of a short seven
29 Stands in art class
31 "Rumor ___ It"
34 Makes waves, in a way
38 "Goodbye, old chap!"
39 Battle critic
42 Unreliable gossip
43 Chamomile tea, e.g.
44 Dickensian kid
45 Overnight bag
47 Egyptian boy king
49 Wing that can't flap
50 Arrangement
54 Double-check the check
58 Good doctor's attribute
61 Use leather on a diamond?
63 One taking the law into one's own hands
64 Utopian
65 Brain tests, for short
66 Peeples and Long
67 Carried, as by the wind
68 Reddish-brown
69 Vietnamese celebrations

DOWN

1 The real thing?
2 Arterial vessel
3 Fairy of childhood
4 "The Handmaid's Tale" author
5 Agent Scully of "The X-Files"
6 Rock concert venue
7 German wine valley
8 "I didn't do it!"
9 Per ___ (for each person)
10 Grimm word
11 Become discouraged
12 Snockered
13 "ST: DS9" shapeshifter
18 Part of the make up or make out
21 Here and now
25 Mongolian mountain range
26 One of 150 in the Bible
28 Moon hollows
30 Jeanne d'Arc, for one, briefly
31 Split evenly
32 Type type
33 Trivial
35 Square root of IX
36 Doubtfire or Miniver
37 Org. with no hackers
40 Dernier ___ (latest fashion)
41 Affecting the brain and spinal cord
46 Order to a cowboy (with "up")
48 Walk-up resident
51 Ohio or Missouri
52 Bye-bye, in Burgundy
53 They perform safe jobs
55 Photographer Leibovitz
56 Coup ___
57 Rebuke with ("down")
59 Pizazz
60 Rain forest feature
61 Wee whopper
62 "Deep in my heart, ___ believe ..."

by Alice Walker
Edited by Timothy E. Parker
Answers in back

120 Pass It to Me

ACROSS

1 Specialized vocabulary
6 Film brand
10 Alfred E. Neuman's smile feature
13 Noted Helmsley
14 Emulated a hen
15 Top-drawer
16 It may be loaded
17 Noted nickname in hoops
19 Cast aspersions
21 Make lovable
22 Gallivant
25 Mr. Bumble's metaphor for the law
26 Don't waste words
29 Aptitude for note-worthy creations?
30 Blows before the derby
31 Like rough-cut logs
32 Course with good greens?
35 Tingling with excitement
37 Word in a Nicole Kidman film title
38 Coxswain's order
39 Certain African inhabitant
41 Short mornings?
44 Things people do to get their kicks?
46 Make untidy, e.g.
48 Intense fighting at close range
51 Engagement ring choice
53 Cheese town near Rotterdam
54 Famous movie river
55 Condescender
56 Key key on the keyboard
57 Koizumi's cash
58 Troublemakers at meetings
59 Oracles

DOWN

1 International Tennis Hall of Fame's Gibson
2 Classic TV enthusiast's delight
3 Decorations seen with cornstalks
4 "Mon ___" (Tati film)
5 Go by Greyhound, e.g.
6 Kyrgyzstan range
7 Make up ground
8 Philatelist's collectible
9 Make a solemn request
10 "Have a safe journey!"
11 Literary collection, e.g.
12 Sword trumper
15 A freshman humanities course
18 Scandinavian saint
20 Bottom-of-the-barrel stuff
23 Observed
24 Eagle surmounting a wave
27 Causing flaws in
28 French painter Odilon
30 Quagmire
31 Solo on film
32 Municipal development guideline
33 What March may go out like
34 Pedigrees
35 Certain eyebrow shape
36 Indian area formerly annexed with Daman and Diu
39 Intl. commerce pact
40 Take from the crate
41 Sharp as a tack
42 Fox on "The X-Files"
43 Some primitive weapons
45 103, in old Rome
47 Fourteen pounds, in Brighton
49 Switch add-on
50 They come out at balls
51 Optimist's limit
52 Have a liability

ACROSS

1 After-hours money sources, for short
5 Actors Grey and McCrea
10 Jellicle Ball attendees
14 Actor Diggs
15 Stinking, old-style
16 Fly on a hook, perhaps
17 A narrow fissure in rock
18 Kind of silence
19 ___ about (approximately)
20 Some savings accts.
21 Musical featuring "I Like the Look"
23 Comrade
25 Went in haste
26 Stool pigeons
27 Broadway angels, for example
31 "Rocky" actress Shire
33 Hounds' prey
34 "___ Crazy" (Paul Davis hit)
35 Airline to the Middle East
36 Invents, as a word
37 "Time ___ My Side" (Stones hit)
38 "The Tonight Show" announcer Hall
39 ___ plume
40 "Johnny Angel" actress Signe
41 Parts of a baseball schedule
43 Donaldson and Cooke
44 Part of a checklist
45 Respectful bows
48 Musical featuring "It Takes a Woman"
52 100 dinar piece
53 "___ Three Lives"
54 They climb the walls at some colleges?
55 Grimm fellow
56 Bestow
57 Buenos ___
58 Nursery rhyme King
59 Fuzzy Wuzzy's lack
60 "Outta sight!"
61 Break off

DOWN

1 Take ___ down memory lane …
2 Japanese city, now called Iwaki
3 Musical featuring "You Did It"
4 Goes to sea
5 Robards and Lee
6 Prefix with "pedic" or "dontic"
7 Job rights agcy.
8 She played Glinda the Good in "The Wiz"
9 Superman's views
10 Weather Channel forecast
11 Female in the family
12 Run without rushing
13 Repeated word in a Doris Day hit
22 Some grades
24 One-time connection
27 Domestic help
28 Musical featuring "The Movie in My Mind"
29 They can be boosted or inflated
30 Off-limits word
31 Positioned a golf ball
32 Benjamin Franklin Pierce portrayer
33 Amateur production
36 One who gives a hoot?
37 1966 Simon & Garfunkel hit
39 Alliance est. in 1949
40 Linden of "Barney Miller"
42 He lays gold on thin
43 Gives the OK
45 Another Weather Channel forecast
46 One of the Donald's exes
47 Stop counting sheep?
48 It's linked to mighty
49 "The Last Tycoon" director Kazan
50 One of Jacob's sons
51 Former cash on Capri

122 Gold-ie Record

by Arthur Groom
Edited by Timothy E. Parker
Answers in back

ACROSS
1 From scratch
5 Handwoven fabric with pictorial designs
10 A crow's-nest tops it
14 Genesis son
15 Sports authority?
16 Lotion ingredient
17 Goldie Hawn film
20 Commit a faux pas
21 Break in friendly relations
22 Plays with Lego blocks
23 Pool table success
24 Diddley, Jackson and Derek
25 Type of room in cyberspace
26 Country on the Caspian
28 Lemon candy
29 Chicken-king center
32 Jammed with the band
34 Wolf's stare?
35 "East of ___"
36 Goldie Hawn film
39 On the quiet side, nautically
40 Amtrak transportation
41 Notched, as a leaf
42 Plea at sea
43 "The ___ Days of Disco" (1998)
44 Director of "Marty"
45 Clio, Erato or Urania
46 Japanese title
47 Suffix for "bull" or "fool"
50 Sneak attack
53 Kicker's target
54 Alphabet sequence
55 Goldie Hawn film
58 Perry Mason's creator Gardner
59 Observe Yom Kippur
60 Honest-to-goodness
61 Can't live without
62 Was visibly awestruck
63 They may be against you

DOWN
1 Daisylike bloom
2 Indira Gandhi's father
3 Endless time periods
4 Doctor of sci-fi
5 Director's shout
6 They're raised in revelry
7 Inflatable floater
8 Make a scene?
9 Footwear seller's implement
10 French impressionist artist Edouard
11 Actor Guinness or Baldwin
12 Prepare the laundry
13 1979 Nastassja Kinski title role
18 University of Illinois locale
19 Stop making a scene?
25 Trout tote
27 Tear asunder
28 Accounting entry
29 Chastised
30 Luau loops
31 Singer Murray or author Rice
32 Mineral springs
33 "Alice's Restaurant" singer
34 Landlord's guarantee?
35 Rightfully deserve
37 Dumpster item
38 Actress Tripplehorn
43 Luxuriant
44 Severely injured
45 Turned down the sound
46 Stood out in the crowd
48 Word before "fast" and after "home"
49 Flings
50 "... have made it ___ of thieves" (Matt. 21:13)
51 A ___ formality
52 Cotton unit
53 Old English bard
56 Aristotle's seventh letter
57 Sign of stage success?

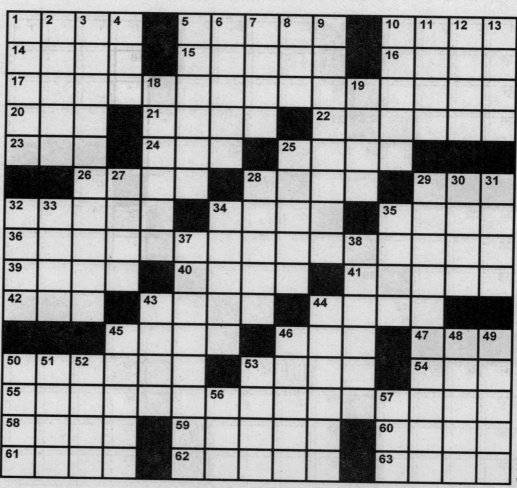

by Gayle Dean
Edited by Timothy E. Parker
Answers in back

ACROSS

1 Twenty-one gun salute, e.g.
6 Cough up for a kitty
10 Mackerel shark
14 A good way to leave Vegas
15 Academic, as an arguable point
16 First name in the "Doctor Zhivago" cast
17 Take no risks
20 Wallach in "The Two Jakes"
21 Rain forest feature
22 Happenings
23 Closed tightly
25 It has its reservations
27 Anatomical pathway
29 "Of Mice and ___"
30 "Peter ___" (Disney film)
33 Dome-shaped dessert
36 River through Opole
38 Vocal inflection
39 Take no risks
42 Inner Hebrides island
43 "Star Trek" producer Roddenberry
44 Shoelace part
45 Spearheaded
46 Rocky hill
47 Domesticated
49 Poker player's ploy
51 Bounded
55 Fluttering trees
58 Throb
60 "I cannot tell a ___"
61 Take no risks
64 Pinball violation
65 Aftermath of a brainstorm
66 Establish a law
67 "___ and Janis" (comic strip)
68 Monetary unit
69 Recipient

DOWN

1 Bread boxes?
2 Sinatra film "___ in the Head"
3 George Sand novel
4 Kilmer of "The Saint"
5 You'll travel far before it turns over
6 Bands' accessories
7 What's up with Rand McNally?
8 Type of hold
9 Catchall phrase
10 Tyra Banks, once
11 Congregational response
12 "Critique of Pure Reason" author
13 Table scraps
18 "Eyes ___ Shut"
19 Neck and neck
24 Tripoli's country
26 Brunch order, perhaps
28 Astaire's dancing partner
30 "The Color of Money" game
31 Mrs. Shakespeare
32 Digs of twigs
33 Cookbook instruction
34 Shawm's follower
35 Repair
37 Demand payment of
38 Type of lily
40 Devoted to one's own interests
41 Fiddled (with)
46 Propane holder
48 New York City stadium name
49 Right-hand page
50 Corroded
52 Detective Pinkerton
53 Extended family member
54 "Beau ___"
55 "The Thin Man" pooch
56 Show signs of life
57 Rx unit
59 Gabfest
62 "___ to Psyche"
63 Crazy Eights cousin

124 Looking Good

by Randall J. Hartman
Edited by Timothy E. Parker
Answers in back

ACROSS
1 Mount Olympus residents
5 California wine region
9 Beaten, a la Bobby Fischer
14 Teenage heartthrob
15 Kind of exam
16 Similar
17 ___ Lisa
18 Like an NBA player
19 No-show at a mixer
20 Notorious gangster of the early 20th century
23 He lost to D.D.E.
24 Whistle blower
25 Sticky note
29 Border on
31 Sharp turn
34 "The Cherry Orchard" playwright Chekhov
35 "Batman" actor West
36 Story told around the campfire
37 Tabloid TV topics
40 Safe haven
41 Brazen boldness
42 Bounds along
43 Over the hill
44 Trumpeter Al
45 Lighter liquid
46 Mazel ___
47 Lend a hand
48 He entered the ring to "Pomp and Circumstance"
56 Fortuneteller's card
57 Make bootees
58 "The First Wives Club" co-star
59 Valuable violin
60 Hardly chivalrous
61 Eloquent equine of '60s TV
62 Thick as a brick
63 Mass assent
64 Hankerings

DOWN
1 Hobbling gait
2 It comes out in the wash
3 Wrapped up
4 Louver feature
5 "Hold your horses!"
6 Many Al Jazeera viewers
7 ___ Alto, California
8 Comrade in arms
9 Croquet striker
10 Standoffish
11 Like Tim Cratchit
12 Barely managed (with "out")
13 "___ Rosenkavalier"
21 Contaminate
22 Dowdy dresser
25 Cellist Casals
26 Shaquille of the Heat
27 Prim and proper
28 Take the show on the road
29 Chaperon, typically
30 Event attended by Cinderella
31 "Burnt Weeny Sandwich" composer Frank
32 Type of wrench
33 Gaggle gang
35 In the distance
36 Honk the horn
38 "Uncle!"
39 Give the slip
44 Immobilize, at a rodeo
45 Where to find Badgers and Wolverines
46 Home run runs
47 Stage whisper
48 Ready for anything
49 Algerian seaport
50 Creole cookery item
51 E pluribus ___
52 "Goodness gracious!"
53 Seldom seen
54 Broadway star Verdon
55 They justify the means
56 Smidgen

125 Musical Fruit

by Matthew J. Koceich
Edited by Timothy E. Parker
Answers in back

ACROSS

1 Jenny of diets
6 "___ Louise"
10 Bausch's partner
14 Former rival of Prudential
15 Ornamental bag
16 Organic compound
17 Aired "The Jackie Gleason Show"
18 Mountain lake
19 Blind trio of song
20 Fruity group?
22 Aahs counterpart
23 Female chicken
24 Some Toyota models
26 Choice of words
31 Hearth residue
32 Turkish military leader
33 Philbin's sidekick
35 Badger
39 Lunchtime, for many
40 Pig's nose
42 On the ocean
43 Exam type
45 High-strung
46 Metal-stamping items
47 Catch a crook
49 Envoy
51 Egyptian tourist attraction
55 Compass point
56 Den
57 Venue for 20-Across, 10 and 29-Down?
63 ___ mater
64 Milkshake additive
65 Popular morning show
66 It's on the agenda
67 Fencing sword
68 Electric introduction?
69 Spaceship builders
70 Plant starter
71 German metropolis

DOWN

1 Sugar or starch, to a marathoner
2 Stagger
3 "The Bell of ___" (Longfellow)
4 Words with "instant" or "uproar"
5 Nonviolence advocate
6 Airplane component, often
7 And others, briefly
8 Monetary unit introduced in 1999
9 Brightly colored flower
10 Fruity group?
11 Pungent bulb
12 Starbucks order
13 Sanctify
21 NASCAR's Casey
25 N.Y.C. clock value
26 Windmill blade
27 Centers of pride
28 17th letters of an alphabet
29 Fruity group?
30 Kind of lyric poem
34 Added to
36 Major market for U.S. exports
37 Oracle
38 Like taking candy from a baby
41 Binding things together
44 Sweet potato, familiarly
48 Large ecosystems
50 Get hot under the collar
51 Obvious
52 Scene of the 1945 Allied conference
53 Singer LeAnn
54 Furnishing
58 Toward shelter
59 Clothing-store section
60 Probability
61 "Silver" or "soft" ending
62 French city

126 Stop, Thief!

by Carl Cranby
Edited by Timothy E. Parker
Answers in back

ACROSS

1 Mamie Eisenhower trademark
6 Kind of station
9 Videos
14 Tornado siren, e.g.
15 It's unsmelted
16 It may help you see an error
17 Chef's implement
18 Baby's "piggy"
19 Old calculators
20 Make a run for it
23 Modern collectible
24 Prompter's offering
25 Hits nothing but net
27 Estimates
32 Popular New Age singer
33 Replayed tennis shot
34 Everly Brothers hit
36 Architectural wing
39 Football holders
41 Meal starter
43 Dulles designer Saarinen
44 Stand up and speak
46 Yale, Brown, etc.
48 New homophone
49 Russian spacecraft series
51 French appetizer
53 No-goodnik
56 Had a little something
57 Reindeer's kin
58 Make an effort
64 Ignore in pronunciation
66 Cyberspace initials
67 ___ aves (unique individuals)
68 Submission encs.
69 Part of a cell nucleus
70 Be over the top, while acting
71 Obstinate equines
72 CBS forensic drama
73 "Love Story" author

DOWN

1 Starr of the gridiron
2 Part of et al.
3 Place to plant a kiss
4 Where Euboea is
5 "Vienna Blood" composer
6 Words with "jail" in a popular board game
7 "Pretty maids all in ___"
8 Pinecones, essentially
9 Alexandra Feodorovna, for one
10 Clerical gown
11 Make breakfast, illegally?
12 Game show host
13 Agronomists' study
21 Chihuahua cash
22 Lamb source
26 Year's last word
27 Certain sax range
28 Omen examiner
29 Buss illegally?
30 Actor Morales of "La Bamba"
31 Medicinal ointment
35 Banquet spot
37 Cube designer Rubik
38 Strike from a list
40 Floor
42 It won't keep you up
45 Lasting forever
47 "Saturday Night Live" features
50 Do-say connection
52 Change handles?
53 ___ ghost (hallucinates)
54 Earthen water jars
55 Joan ___
59 Some cargo weights
60 Jai ___
61 Pirate's potation
62 "I could ___ horse!"
63 Virginia's dance?
65 Gidget portrayer Sandra

127 Take It Off

by Joy M. Andrews
Edited by Timothy E. Parker
Answers in back

ACROSS

1 Isn't serious
6 Slender-waisted stinger
10 McCartney and John
14 Boat used in Alaska
15 Adenauer moniker "Der ___"
16 It might be skinned in the fall
17 "Winnie-the-Pooh" author
18 It may be subject to modification
19 Current status?
20 JFK takeoff
23 "___Kick Out of You"
24 "Bravo, bullfighter!"
25 Physique, informally
26 "The Star-Spangled Banner" preposition
27 The "Y" in BYOB
30 Tonsorial offering
32 Cinch
33 More debatable
34 It's made by taking off the bun
38 Like a six-year celebration
39 Brewer's oven
40 Cultural dish for a microbiologist?
41 They're seen in waves of grain
42 Scrooge word
45 Eruption fallout
46 Unannounced, as a quiz
48 First of the year in Mexico City
50 Takeoff on Broadway
55 Wetlands amphibian
56 Word with "eight" or "fast"
57 "___ Got Mail"
58 Southernmost Great Lake
59 Eye part
60 Nudged, dog-style
61 "Jurassic Park" star
62 Editor's catch
63 Salad green

DOWN

1 Use a pogo stick
2 "The Mighty Ducks" star Estevez
3 Stored fodder
4 Roscoe of tennis
5 Clay-target shooting
6 Tinker Bell prop
7 Skin-soothing ingredient
8 Daze
9 Certain code
10 Three-handed card game
11 Sit on eggs
12 Team game played at recess, perhaps
13 One leaving the union
21 Vote no
22 Vacation place
28 Long propeller
29 Violinist's notation
31 Road boor
32 Lines for a movie
33 Paella ingredient, sometimes
34 Downwind side of the river
35 Broadcasting
36 All-out hostility
37 Proscription
38 Engaged in a petty argument
41 Home to a queen
42 Exist indigently
43 Stir up
44 Feet of an ungulate mammal
47 Elliptical path, typically
49 "Bye Bye Bye" band
51 Arabian peninsula port
52 Movie teaser
53 "The Sun ___ Rises"
54 "The Untouchables," e.g.

128 Lovey-Dovey

by Elizabeth C. Gorski
Edited by Timothy E. Parker
Answers in back

ACROSS
1 Italian fashion designer Miuccia
6 Kind of improvement
10 Gorgeous legs, to a guy in a zoot suit
14 Consume
15 Magazine items?
16 Mosque leader
17 Jazzy dance
18 Table section
19 Type of formality
20 English dandy
23 Time zone letters
26 Calliope power
27 Also-ran in '96
28 Soporifics
30 Tag pursuers
32 Half a city?
33 Shepherd's place
34 The lady of the Haus
38 Special business offerings
42 Some Giants
43 Not a particular
44 "West Side Story" role
45 Bro counterpart
46 Spaniel, for one
48 Trail closely
52 Slab of chocolate
54 Chicago-to-Miami dir.
55 Post-reception status
58 Fully avenged
59 Decade components, in Mexico
60 Words of dismay
64 Bivouac element
65 Hurt all over
66 Suspended
67 Foundations may support them
68 O'Casey or Connery
69 Office dispatches

DOWN
1 Foot, in Latin
2 Snitcher
3 From ___ Z
4 Stupid
5 Hunger trigger
6 Attaches importance to
7 Biology 101 subject
8 Like a snake oil salesman, and then some
9 Protein-rich health food
10 Greedy person's demand
11 Middle Eastern ruler (Var.)
12 Phil's wife
13 Small silvery fish
21 Pigged out
22 AWOL-hunters
23 Search for water, in a way
24 Salmon do it
25 Like some floors
29 Brewpub quaffs
31 End of an exchange?
33 Not of the cloth
34 Manage independently
35 Bookies' nightmares
36 Some chorus girls
37 Application
39 "Bali ___" ("South Pacific" song)
40 Settle snugly
41 Developer's site?
45 You may reach for it
46 Burner designer
47 Suffix with serpent or elephant
48 Eighth letter of the Greek alphabet
49 Generic dog name
50 With regard to
51 Word on a nickel
53 Foofaraw
56 "Serpico" author Peter
57 Year's last word, often
61 Vitality
62 Author Umberto
63 It's an OK word

129 Piece of Cake

ACROSS
1 Marine mollusk
5 Explosive device
9 Test type
14 Capital of Peru
15 Unwritten
16 Woodland deity
17 Dark black
18 Title word in a Doris Day song
19 Attempts
20 Mixture of slices and dices
23 Wife of Abraham
24 Take in food
25 Caustic matter
28 Mea ____
32 Firm engaged in trading
34 Close friend
37 Large northern deer
39 Trace the shape
40 Popular morning stop
44 Italian river
45 Studio sign
46 Three for nanny?
47 Like covered jars
50 ____ first (diamond call)
52 Barker and Kettle
53 Propel with oars
55 Large books
59 Child's drink option
64 Hoax
66 Brief written reminder
67 Ankle bones
68 Tree or syrup
69 Report or maintain
70 Arabian Peninsula country
71 Lieu
72 Baseball club
73 Young woman

DOWN
1 Like C & G
2 Seventh sign of the zodiac
3 Love in Lyons
4 Song from "Flashdance"
5 Pear variety
6 Cream-filled treat
7 Latin singer Anthony
8 British poet William
9 Beverly Hills home, typically
10 Hindu dress
11 Painting of inanimate objects
12 Uh-huh
13 365 days, over and over
21 Hitch a ride
22 Slight amount
26 Arabian republic
27 European sea eagles
29 Costello or Gehrig
30 Somewhat, musically
31 "And ____ other dowry ..." (Shakespeare)
33 The Tanners' alien guest
34 One of 150 in the Bible
35 Indoor courtyards
36 Expanse of scenery
38 "Hairy man" of the Bible
41 "The Twilight Zone" creator Serling
42 Op ____ (in the work cited)
43 Employ a silver tongue
48 Worn away
49 One of seven dwarfs
51 Drum with a small head
54 John Lennon song
56 South Beach locale
57 Fitzgerald and Grasso
58 Pickup game team
60 Dance performed in grass skirts
61 Strauss the jeans maker
62 Prayer ending
63 Ruptured
64 AM alternatives
65 Long-tailed rodent

by Casey Rumblach
Edited by Timothy E. Parker
Answers in back

ACROSS

1 Jane Austen heroine
5 Subway Series player
8 IHOP offering
14 Extinct birds of New Zealand
15 Gardner of Tinseltown
16 Domiciles
17 Shipboard bed
18 Piece of Walt Disney art
19 Practice site for the Partridge family
20 Mel Brooks' spouse
23 "Maggie May" singer Rod
24 It does a bang-up job?
25 Fizzled firecracker
28 "To ___, With Love" (1967)
29 Monopoly purchases
31 Words of approximation
32 "By all means!"
33 Med. school subj.
34 In regard to
35 Big name in etiquette
38 Country estate
41 Sonny boys
42 Business equip. co.
45 Twistable cookie
46 Beehive or afro
48 "Cakes and ___" (Maugham novel)
49 Candle material
50 Booking agent?
51 Made filthy
53 "Diff'rent Strokes" actress
55 One of Santa's reindeer
58 Singer/songwriter DiFranco
59 PBS science program
60 Virgil's hero
61 Society page word
62 The fourth person
63 Literary family of this puzzle's theme
64 Kildare and Quinn, e.g.
65 "Gorillas in the ___"

DOWN

1 Diplomat's building
2 Dudley Do-Right was one
3 Things you should mind
4 Twisted to one side
5 What Yankee Doodle called the feather
6 Happening someday
7 After-bath powder
8 Chuck and station
9 Rearward, at sea
10 Setting for "F Troop"
11 Pharmaceuticals watchdog agcy.
12 Lamb serving
13 Linguistic suffix
21 Freeport's "Grand" island
22 AAA info.
25 Eminem's mentor
26 J.F.K.'s service branch
27 Part of an e-mail address
30 Phonograph needles
31 Toronto prov.
34 Arrange by categories
35 "Don't Bring Me Down" grp.
36 Governor, at times
37 Curiosities
38 Promise
39 Gershwin or Levin
40 Superman's foe Luthor
42 Kenya capital
43 Splits
44 Passed out the cards again
46 Surprise head of "The Godfather"?
47 Spring mo.
50 Ignore the rules
52 Coffee break time, perhaps
53 "Big Brother" host Julie
54 Touch down
55 Light touch, as with a paintbrush
56 ___ Lingus
57 "Cone" or "Cat" intro

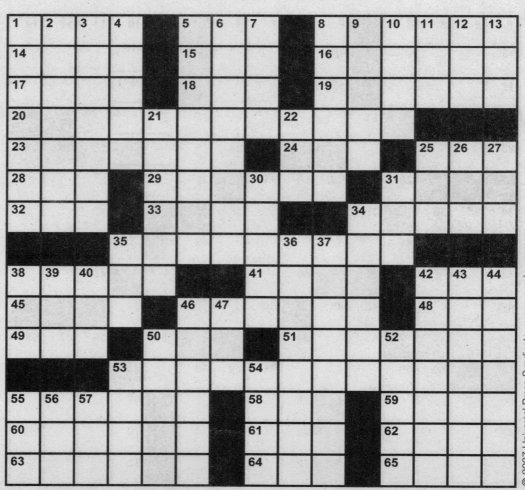

131 Filmed Animals

by Gregory Pace
Edited by Timothy E. Parker
Answers in back

ACROSS

1 Settings for many sci-fi films
5 Went out, as the tide
10 "Name That ___"
14 Chills and fever
15 Girl in Byron's "Don Juan"
16 Put in an overhead bin, say
17 1,760 yards
18 Mailed a tax return
19 Laid-back quality
20 100 percent
21 Peter Sellers film (with "The")
23 Detroit iceman
25 Hastens
26 Coffee brewers
27 Skillful
31 Shopaholic's binge
33 Private languages
34 Popeye's approval
35 Actress Madeline
36 Legal wrong doings
37 Thoroughly awed
38 "I'd like to buy ___, Pat!"
39 Actors Jamie and Felicia
40 Adhere closely
41 Chutzpah
43 Blessing
44 French Sudan today
45 Fast, in music
48 Owl partner, in a film title
52 Emulate Sugar Ray
53 Semitic deity
54 Sticks out one's bottom lip
55 Asinine
56 Lowest female voice
57 Body of water
58 Margarine
59 Like Santa's cheeks
60 Lists of basics
61 Candle's light

DOWN

1 Texas university
2 Like gymnasts
3 Kevin Costner film
4 "We're off to ___ the wizard ..."
5 Pixies
6 Human or alien
7 Defraud
8 Pachyderms
9 Arp and colleagues
10 Dangerous fly
11 2002 Winter Olympics site
12 Jimmy Durante's prominent feature
13 Decorative pitcher
21 Wood type
22 New Jersey NBA team
24 "Beau Geste" author
27 Join in wedlock
28 Film about Jake La Motta
29 City on the Rhone
30 Safecracker
31 Three-hand card game
32 Sheet of glass
33 Shot a baseball pitcher may take
36 Dangerous dive
37 Medicinal plant
39 German Mrs.
40 Filly counterpart
42 Hire
43 Uses TNT
45 Performed in a film
46 Gentleman of Verona
47 "The ___ Incident" (Fonda Western)
48 Ski lift
49 Angelic symbol
50 Greasy spoon sign
51 Holiday log
55 Man's best friend

by Fran & Lou Sabin
Edited by Timothy E. Parker
Answers in back

132 Makes Sense

ACROSS

1 High-flying reindeer
6 Shore washer
10 "Do you mind?"
14 Cut down
15 ___-friendly
16 Garr of "Tootsie"
17 Measure of quality
19 "What's that I hear?"
20 Endangered whale
21 Worn and torn
22 Bard's medium
23 Place for a grilling
24 Series starter
25 Free people?
28 Audience to the King of Id's speeches
32 Mother of all battles, to Ajax
33 Relinquish, as an office
34 Garner
35 Magician's command to a person tying ropes
38 Oblivious
40 Butt end
41 Diarist Nin
43 Engage one's services
44 Disappoints
46 Web-ster
48 Genuine
49 Nobody's fool
51 Comedy club reactions
53 Frasier's lost love
54 Speedy Atlantic crosser, once
57 Carter and Vanderbilt
58 Fashion arbiter
60 At times, it's a stretch
61 Money to play with
62 The best of the best
63 High school soph, most likely
64 Predicament
65 "The Divine Comedy" author

DOWN

1 Tabbies
2 Reed under Ozawa
3 Hawaii's second-largest island
4 And so forth
5 Capital near the Caspian Sea
6 ___-frutti ice cream
7 Physicist's atom
8 Turn down
9 "Able was I ___ ..."
10 Minerva's counterpart
11 Sound enhancer
12 Misspells or misspeaks
13 Sound enhancer
18 Pre-college exams, for short
22 Postcard's allure
23 Ritzy
24 Water carrier
25 Kind of detector
26 Come about
27 Poet's creation, like "have" and "shave"
29 Big birds
30 ___ Haute, Ind.
31 Drive critter
33 Oater challenge
36 Words said with a flourish
37 Organic compound
39 Just a jot
42 Won't take no for an answer
45 One of four in a year
46 Level-headed
47 Future M.D.'s course
50 Karpov victories
51 "Don't take another step!"
52 Friend of Deneuve
53 Copenhagen resident
54 Bones' other half?
55 Paving block
56 Genealogist's map
58 Scot's cap
59 In the manner of

by Randall J. Hartman
Edited by Timothy E. Parker
Answers in back

ACROSS

1 Media for Monet
5 Writes a brief note
9 American buffalo
14 Piece of cake
15 Troop group
16 Stage whisper
17 Hidalgo home
18 Author Jaffe
19 Drew a line in the sand
20 Conversation between Carney and Linkletter?
23 Makeshift tools of punishment
24 Penultimate playoff game
25 Middle of summer?
28 Slob's abode
29 GPS heading, perhaps
31 Number 2, for one
33 Des ___, Iowa
36 Cry of disbelief
37 Insurance company commercial?
41 They're better than kings and queens
42 Norman athlete
43 "Really?"
46 Playground game
47 Carlsbad Caverns inhabitant
50 Chippendales dancers
51 Word in reference to Yorick
54 It's yet to come
56 Schedule for a Budweiser plant?
58 Requiring assembly
61 "___ Told Me (Not to Come)"
62 Fairy-tale beast
63 Hope chest material
64 Pub potables
65 Bohea and hyson
66 Fantasy league activity
67 Partner of Crosby and Stills
68 Blues singer James

DOWN

1 Prestigious statuettes
2 Going nowhere fast
3 "As my final point …"
4 Outpouring
5 Time of the dinosaurs
6 ___ about (approximately)
7 Salon jobs
8 Washington, but not Washington, D.C.
9 Predicament on the links
10 "Out of Africa" pseudonym Dinesen
11 Elton John or Paul McCartney, e.g.
12 Pindar poem
13 Nancy Drew's boyfriend
21 Welles of "Citizen Kane"
22 It was for the Byrds
25 Canyon comeback
26 Wis. neighbor
27 ___-mo
30 Son of Seth
32 Word with "cafe" or "film"
33 At least 50.1 percent
34 "Xanadu" band
35 Part of a piggy bank
37 Tylenol target
38 University big shot
39 Chop-chop
40 Smooth transition
41 Place to enter a PIN
44 Author who declined the Nobel Prize
45 Cheer for Manolete
47 Spending plan
48 Landing place of Noah's Ark
49 Mother of Calcutta
52 "Dude, gimme a break!"
53 La ___ (Milan opera house)
55 Govt. security
56 Pitt of "Fight Club"
57 Brothers who sang "Rag Mop"
58 Play the part
59 A pop
60 Oral surgeon's org.

134 Cheese It!

by Lynn Lempel
Edited by Timothy E. Parker
Answers in back

ACROSS

1 Brilliant successes
6 Sami, formerly
10 "No ___, no foul"
14 Kind of committee
15 On open waters
16 Village Voice honor
17 Sandpapery
18 St. Bernard's beat
20 Lord's Prayer opener
21 Feline film heroine
23 Accentuate
24 Awfully long time
26 Bundle of money
27 Factor in beauty?
28 Don Corleone, for one
32 Watch for
35 Trade punches
37 IRS shelter
38 Small at-home business
42 Prefix with "pod" or "angle"
43 It may be irresistible
44 The "necktie" in a necktie party
45 Emancipate
48 Brandi's one-time soccer teammate
49 Occupational suffix
50 Blunt criticism
55 Arcade classic
58 Nautical start
59 Dylan's "I ___ Lonesome Hobo"
60 Vanilla-flavored drink
62 Boat launches
64 "Saved by the ___"
65 Washstand pitcher
66 Blue blood
67 Merchandise mover
68 Cravings and Japanese coins
69 Winter Olympics participant

DOWN

1 Chocolate alternative
2 Two-time batting champ Lefty
3 Robert Ruark novel
4 Collectible cap, once
5 Diagrammatic representations
6 Catch by the neck, in a way
7 African city near dams
8 Chinese-born architect
9 Identity verifier
10 Stockpiles
11 Qualified
12 Splits sans scissors
13 Barracks break
19 Attempt
22 Cured salmon
25 Send forth
28 Gnu feature
29 Man who once backed Michael Jackson
30 Calls Mary Larry, e.g.
31 Comedian "Colonel Maggie" Martha
32 Legislative decisions
33 Modeled
34 Squabbling
35 Like leaves in late autumn
36 Glutton
39 Cheese source
40 Mythical beasts
41 Overcharge mightily
46 Title IX beneficiary
47 Paper pack
48 Space station
50 Southwest area of Germany
51 Brings up, as a child
52 Animated film of 1942
53 Plentiful
54 Police weapon
55 EPA-banned chemicals
56 Square measure
57 Hive compartment
61 Be beholden to
63 NASA thumbs-up

135 Don't Hurt Me!

by Carl Cranby
Edited by Timothy E. Parker
Answers in back

ACROSS

1 Floor or roof squares
6 Show signs of life
10 Starting place for all of us
14 Oak, in a nutshell
15 Pitch
16 Side by side?
17 Roberts of "The Mexican"
18 Circle components
19 Not left out (Abbr.)
20 "Call a time-out"
23 "___ the Good Times Roll"
26 "Some ___ It Hot" (1959 Marilyn Monroe film)
27 Amphitheaters
28 Slip away, as time
30 Opinionated equine
31 Snooty attitudes
32 Respond to stimuli
34 First name among soccer legends
37 "Get the music playing!"
41 The Say ___ Kid (Willie Mays)
42 Jennifer Garner series
43 Compressed data
44 Type of muffin
45 More tense
47 Like this clue
50 Cold coat
52 It can follow you
53 "Surf the big wave!"
56 Starting gate at Pimlico
57 Shakespearean character
58 Taxpayer's dread
62 Cleveland's lake
63 "Braveheart" group
64 Become used (to)
65 "___I say more?"
66 "The ___ of Katie Elder"
67 Ditched cargo

DOWN

1 ___ Mahal
2 Hospital area, for short
3 "Ha ha!" on the Internet
4 "CHiPs" actor Estrada
5 Slow-moving mollusks
6 Celery stem
7 Rich cake
8 Rainfall measure
9 Scientific inquiry
10 Imitated a siren
11 "Smoking ___?"
12 Spiritual center of Islam
13 Pitchers' illegal moves
21 Tell it like it isn't
22 Largest Greek island
23 Spot's tether
24 The best and the brightest
25 Lollygag
29 23rd Greek letter
30 Wrestling pads
32 Completely botch
33 Fed. smog watchdog
34 Beatle suffix
35 Surmise
36 Think the world of
38 Limestone terrane
39 Rubber bands
40 Oversized
44 Started, as a computer
45 Figure on an Australian stamp
46 Get off track
47 Where many go downhill
48 Laundry, e.g.
49 Famous riveter or O'Donnell of talk
50 A daughter of King Lear
51 Elvis and Marilyn, e.g.
54 Angel costume accessory
55 Moon goddess
59 Thought it was groovy
60 Tax-deferred nest egg
61 Bo Derek, numerically

by Fran & Lou Sabin
Edited by Timothy E. Parker
Answers in back

ACROSS

1 Carmine and cerise
5 Mining nails
10 MBA's major, perhaps
14 Fail to mention
15 Plant again
16 Of the first water
17 Vintner's unit
19 Breathalyzer test flunkers
20 French student
21 Yankees star, for short
22 Fight enders
23 Harps for Zeno
24 German mythical siren
26 Ultimate degree
28 Unruffled
31 Cartographer's collection
34 Jacob's twin
38 Waiter's parting word after serving
39 Grounded bird
40 Half-sleeps
42 "You ___ here!"
43 Before now
45 Pod pieces
46 Venus de Milo's lack
47 Unknown to many
49 Sidekick
51 Went yard
55 Bunch of bushes
59 Depression figure
61 Campbell of "Scream"
62 Vietnam's capital
63 Waist-length jacket
64 NHL's top prize
66 "St. Elmo's Fire" actor
67 Dada artist Max
68 "Anything ___?"
69 Pinochle play
70 Drugstore designations
71 White-tailed animals

DOWN

1 Spur part
2 Poet Dickinson
3 Burger stop
4 Spielberg et al.
5 Hit indicator
6 Flower part
7 Houston player
8 Poetic grief
9 Norwegians' neighbors
10 Part of EDT
11 Snack stop
12 Catch ___ (start to get)
13 Costner role
18 Overthrow
25 Pinky and Peggy
27 Feminine pronoun
29 General level
30 They may be black or blue
31 Unkempt state
32 French friend
33 Site of a spiking
35 Bribe
36 Impress deeply
37 Springsteen's "Born in the ___"
40 Consider
41 Mental gift
44 Sang softly
46 Toned down
48 Was uptight
50 Yearning
52 Style comeback
53 Dame Edith
54 Compact
56 Cry of surrender
57 Computer device
58 Kilted musician
59 Bridge position
60 Sooner State tribe
65 Some commissioned offs.

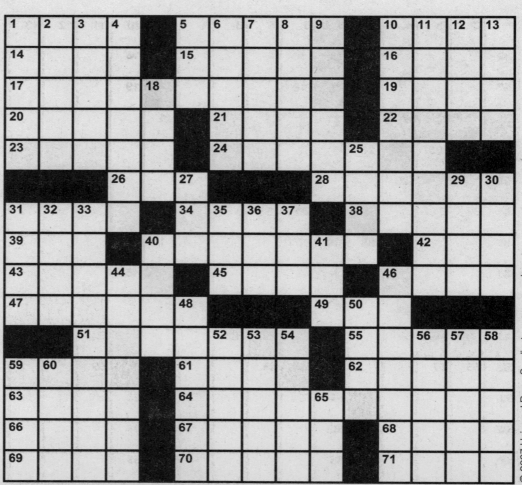

ACROSS

1 Problems for parents
5 Chocolate source
10 Ho-hum
14 Wry expression
15 Containing gold
16 Womanizer
17 Fashion, music, sports, film, e.g.
19 Get by labor
20 Cause for Steinem
21 Grub
22 Andes dwellers
24 Landlords, e.g.
26 Take for every penny
27 Chi Omega connection
28 Donna Summer song
32 Chutzpah
35 Cleft locale
37 "In a row" number
38 Now partner
40 Fertility clinic needs
41 Clinches
42 Cupid's leader?
43 Action word
45 Troubles
46 Acts as president
48 Anita Brookner's "Hotel du ____"
50 Downright rotten
51 Problematic situation
55 Teeth straighteners
58 Sign of engine trouble
59 Driller's quest
60 It may be a stretch
61 Warm up the crowd, in a way
64 Emeril's appliance
65 Merge
66 Friendly opening?
67 Give a little
68 Type of bar or fork
69 Kind of pattern

DOWN

1 Drive
2 Melodious Melba
3 Insect stages
4 Big Board overseer, briefly
5 Pertaining to heat
6 Carbon monoxide creators
7 Grunge
8 Melodic tune
9 Tamable cat
10 Get a party going
11 The good earth
12 Invisible vibes
13 Layers in the barnyard
18 Strange sightings
23 Stays to the conclusion
25 Kind of timing
26 Submarine apparatus
28 Homes for drones
29 River to the Caspian
30 Went from bull to bear
31 Parker of "Old Yeller"
32 Recover from a sprint
33 Lab gel
34 Lovers' place
36 Small, crude dwelling
39 Unsuspecting
44 Missed the action, in a way
47 Track-and-field item
49 Birdbath organism
51 Formal statements
52 Riverdale High jock
53 Wallace and Myers
54 Vigilant
55 Shapeless movie monster
56 Tear asunder
57 Worshipper's word
58 It'll hold water
62 Cell substance
63 Extend outward

by Fran & Lou Sabin
Edited by Timothy E. Parker
Answers in back

ACROSS

1 Not very promising, as chances
5 Darth of sci-fi
10 Pulls back, as water
14 Etna output
15 Fred's onstage partner
16 The Pineapple King
17 Meal preceder, perhaps
18 Street kid
19 Develop
20 Diner serving
23 Roy at the bar
24 Variety of whale
25 Suit-of-lights wearers
30 Crams full
35 "Congo" villain
36 "Mr. Watson … I ___ you!" (A.G. Bell)
38 "___ Beverly Hills" (1989)
39 Diner serving
43 Diamond flaw?
44 Woody's boy
45 Gumshoe
46 WWII prison camp
48 Ruth, Bonds, Mantle et al.
51 ___ chi ch'uan
53 Easter preceder
54 Diner serving
63 Something sensed
64 Row in a bar
65 "The Times They ___-Changin'" (Bob Dylan)
66 Toledo toddler
67 Weapons supplier
68 Anna Leonowens taught here
69 What you must do when the trade falls through
70 Approximates
71 Harvard rival

DOWN

1 Duel preceder
2 Tibetan monk
3 Currier's partner
4 Chanted incantation
5 Knight of the road
6 First place resident?
7 Moore of "A Few Good Men"
8 Inventor Howe
9 Capital in Brittany
10 Barely beat
11 Wimbledon champ, 1976-80
12 Online diary
13 Sutures
21 "Do Ya Think I'm Sexy?" singer Stewart
22 "Likewise, I'm sure!"
25 Spiked clubs
26 Toward a plane's left side
27 Earth, in sci-fi
28 Country singer McEntire
29 They deal in futures
31 Samovar, e.g.
32 Special skill
33 Hotel lobby
34 Architects' reading
37 Big name in computers
40 Lon ___, former Cambodian premier
41 Sister of Calliope
42 Fails completely
47 Comic's writer
49 Bell-bottoms wearer
50 Spoon for eaters?
52 Val d'___, French ski resort
54 Traffic alert
55 Jim Davis' pup
56 Bodybuilder's concern
57 Bit in a bucket
58 ___ mater
59 ___-do-well
60 "Salome" solo
61 Patricia of "The Fountainhead"
62 Identical

139 Back and Forth

by Lynn Lempel
Edited by Timothy E. Parker
Answers in back

ACROSS

1 Continually finds fault
6 Fine spray
10 Falls away
14 Feature of many sci-fi films
15 Clued-in regarding
16 One of five great waterways
17 Palace brew?
19 "Show Boat" composer
20 One reason for an incomplete pass
21 Apprehension
23 Say further
24 Forceful
26 Film giant
28 Sandy behaved egregiously?
33 Cause of a hippie high
36 "Heavenly" songwriter Bacharach
37 Axis, to the Allies
38 Outback gem
40 Jobs to do
43 Peak
44 Doll babe
46 Whiskered maze runners
48 "The Spanish Tragedy" playwright
49 Cosmo comment?
53 Underneath
54 Protective envelope
58 Letters on a wanted poster
60 Absorb
63 Storied plantation
64 Angry venting
66 "I hate polo shirts!"
68 Little lad
69 Between jobs
70 Ghostly
71 1998 MVP slugger
72 Noshes
73 Mountain chain of South America

DOWN

1 Bingo needs
2 Attentive
3 Severity
4 Stir-fry veggie
5 Weekly TV satire, informally
6 Sound of suffering
7 Dramatist who wrote "Picnic"
8 Round and strip, e.g.
9 Some busts
10 Comics comment
11 Recklessly fast
12 Charlie Parker's sobriquet
13 Dispatch
18 Car wheel securer
22 ___ Adams, wife of Kovacs
25 Part of the La. Purchase
27 "The King and I" tutor
29 Anti-gun-control org.
30 Words upon removing a disguise
31 Primetime honor
32 Enhanced, color-wise
33 Canal feature
34 Cowboy boot feature
35 Stores of information
39 Green shade
41 "Batman" co-star Basinger
42 Little rascals
45 Snaky swimmers
47 ___ of Good Feelings
50 Greenhorn
51 Hotel hero Rusesabagina's homeland
52 Ball of yarn chaser
55 Nixon's defense secretary
56 Henson character
57 Tools with teeth
58 Liberal follower
59 End a bout early
61 Skirt with a safety pin
62 Beehive State tribe
65 Dorset drink
67 Kind of horse or monkey

by Ron Halverson
Edited by Timothy E. Parker
Answers in back

ACROSS

1 "The Wizard ____" (comic)
5 Muscle maladies
10 "... for children of all ____!"
14 Rice-A-____
15 Unit of light
16 Traditional knowledge
17 Risk it all
19 Period of penitence
20 Cheap cigars
21 Comes to mind
23 Raison d'____
24 Shooting sport
25 Attractive device?
28 "Master of the Game" author
30 Fugard's "A Lesson from ____"
31 LSD pioneer Timothy
32 The Boy King
34 Till the ____ come home

35 Styptic pencils' targets
36 Spelling on TV
37 "Come again?"
38 Like the typical dryer screen
39 Hold a stickup for water?
40 Gives to charity
42 Didn't suffer quietly
43 Beastly homes
44 ____ of Kachchh
45 Ersatz
47 Giving the slip to
51 Sounds coming from a doctor's office
52 Beat the rap
55 Plumlike fruit
56 Boy in a famous tug-of-war
57 Enthusiastic thumbs-up review
58 Sonic the Hedgehog creator

59 Half a cone, in geometry
60 Teller's pile

DOWN

1 E-mail address endings, sometimes
2 "My Left ____" (1989)
3 It comes in a scoop
4 He carried a lamp, looking for an honest man
5 "Fat" Cosby character
6 Turn the air blue
7 Med. care provider
8 "A mouse!"
9 Gym shoes
10 United, as nations
11 Works very well
12 Beach bird
13 Soap sites
18 Formal ceremonies
22 Bank on

24 Unstable or teetering
25 Speed of sound number
26 How storybooks are often read
27 Do thoroughly
28 Sunnis and Shiites, e.g.
29 Nightingale or Barton, e.g.
31 Actor's memorizations
33 Even-steven
35 Primary constituent of air
36 Back and forth
38 ____ an egg (bombed on stage)
39 Stereotypical snack for cops, briefly
41 Queasiness
42 "Cheers" bar owner
44 Show highlights

45 Free ticket
46 Word with "for" or "white"
48 Rafsanjani's home
49 "Scream" star Campbell
50 Turns right
53 Pay stretcher?
54 Drink daintily

141 Unspoken

by Matthew J. Koceich
Edited by Timothy E. Parker
Answers in back

ACROSS

1 Hindu prince
6 Las Vegas feature
11 Sine _____ non
14 Lobe at the middle of the soft palate
15 "Me, Myself & ___" (Carrey film)
16 Pedestaled vessel
17 Christmas carol
19 Bond's Fleming
20 ___ chi (martial art)
21 Type of dancer
22 Boxing trainer Dundee
24 Sound sleepers?
26 Kind of furnace
27 Something to be assayed
28 Jamaican liqueur
31 Moral beliefs of a group
34 Wind-___ (carried by the wind)
35 Suffix with "surreal"
36 Sullen expression
37 Parcel of land
38 Type of machete
39 Carders' requests
40 Not canned or frozen
41 Olympic race unit
42 Understandable
44 Prevarication
45 Skirt fold
46 Perceived through the senses
50 Artificial channels carrying streams of water
52 Chinese dynasty (traditionally 1122 to 256 B.C.) (Var.)
53 "For ___ a jolly good fellow!"
54 Once around the track
55 1994 movie with Alec Guinness
58 Band prop
59 Turkish covered wagon
60 Maternal
61 Lock partner
62 Connecting link
63 Automobile type

DOWN

1 Gives in to oxidation
2 For the birds
3 Crooner Iglesias
4 Fermented beverage
5 Closet staples
6 Warbles
7 The Andrews Sisters, e.g.
8 "Andy Capp" cartoonist Smythe, to friends
9 Nasal spray, for example
10 Sugar plum or sweetie pie, e.g.
11 '80s metal band
12 Mountain range between Europe and Asia
13 ___ Domini
18 Ruptured
23 Juliette Low's org., formerly
25 Tooth part
26 Canoe wood
28 Breakfast item
29 Minute land mass
30 Roman god of love
31 Long narrative
32 Kind of list
33 Deep-fried cornbread ball
34 Sportscaster Musburger
37 Buried chest, perhaps
38 Hairy-bodied insects
40 Miss Daisy's Morgan
41 Official record of a meeting
43 Nightmarish street of film
44 First in a string of 13 Popes
46 Neutral middle vowels (Var.)
47 One way to plan
48 Outer coat on a seed
49 German metropolis
50 Excessive criticism
51 Hobbling
52 Domesticated ox
56 What Matthew collected
57 Florida-to-Maine dir.

by Gregory Pace
Edited by Timothy E. Parker
Answers in back

ACROSS

1 Lectern platform
5 Revealing dress feature
9 "De profundis," for one
14 Masha and Irina's sister, in a Chekhov work
15 It makes charges in Madrid
16 Personal, invisible emanations
17 Grammy-winning song by Ray Charles
20 Mezuzah, e.g.
21 Keanu Reeves character, in "The Matrix"
22 Dog-eared item
23 Cost of belonging
25 "Up Where We Belong," for one
27 Kettle's critic?
30 Emulate Albrecht Durer
32 Gives way to rage

36 Partner of amo and amat
38 Art colony in New Mexico
40 Bridge authority Charles
41 1978 star-studded movie directed by Herbert Ross
44 Nat King Cole's "___ Things Money Can't Buy"
45 Kind of swoop
46 Like Mercury's surface
47 A Japanese immigrant's grandchild
49 One who is not very bright
51 ___ es Salaam, Tanzania
52 It comes between money and everything
54 Bar from the locker room
56 A new one may be turned over

59 One way to swing
61 Dover scenery
65 Jazz tenor saxophonist famous for "Flying Home"
68 Approach midnight
69 Reached terra firma
70 Golden rule preposition
71 Positively charged terminal electrons flow toward
72 One is anterior, in the brain
73 Catchall Latin citation

DOWN

1 Pursues relentlessly
2 Meg's "Prelude to a Kiss"co-star
3 Helicopter pioneer Sikorsky
4 Many-stringed lute of India that is played with a bow
5 Small dagger with a tapered blade
6 Mauna follower, in a volcanic name

7 Hemoglobin component
8 Improved muscle definition
9 Suffer the consequences
10 Rich and superior in quality
11 "Che gelida manina," e.g.
12 "Shadowland" singer k.d.
13 Native of Media
18 Viscous substance
19 Disdainful grimace
24 Boa or babushka
26 Units of work or energy
27 Kellogg-Briand and Warsaw
28 6/6/44 beachhead
29 It may connect a limb to a branch
31 Improved an edge
33 Minded someone else's business
34 One more than tri-
35 Look of disdain

37 Cowardly
39 Some military installations
42 Lawyers' income
43 Intentionally set aside
48 The 411
50 It's lowest on the Mohs scale
53 Due process process
55 Arouse, as interest
56 Wallace of Reader's Digest
57 Distinctive and stylish elegance
58 Second highest, in a family of instruments
60 City renamed in 1624 by Christian IV
62 Legendary "Candid Camera" name
63 Greek salad ingredient that could come from ewe's milk
64 Convertiplane acronym
66 About 22.5 degrees
67 Triangular foresail

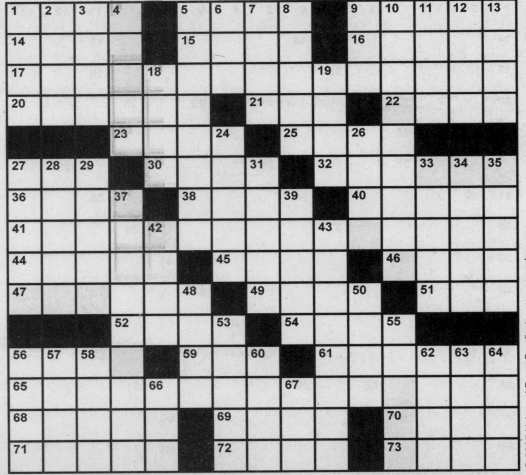

by Fran & Lou Sabin
Edited by Timothy E. Parker
Answers in back

ACROSS
1 "___ goes!"
5 Blizzard aftermath
10 Greek p's
14 Store sign
15 Ziti or penne
16 First name in architecture
17 Engine sound
18 Sluggish by nature
19 Birmingham buggy
20 Query at a diner
23 You may build on it
24 Lovely lass of Persian myth
25 Santa's landing sites
30 Cause failure
34 First person in Vienna
35 "Free Willy" animal
37 Vice ___
38 Query for 007
42 "To ___ human ..."
43 ___ de foie gras
44 Take up space
45 Trump's line
47 Quagmires
50 Don't ditch
52 Wish otherwise
53 Query for a supermarket customer
60 1976 horror hit (with "The")
61 Soother of the savage beast
62 "Aeneid" city
64 On the bright side
65 Absinthe flavor
66 Tribal history
67 Award presented by Chris Berman
68 Arboreal array
69 Termini

DOWN
1 Bygone school event
2 Tale on a grand scale
3 Silver State city
4 Surround
5 Tobacco chewer's target
6 "Penny ___" Beatles hit
7 Software purchaser
8 Barber belt
9 Loathing
10 Mr. Fixit, e.g.
11 Food flavorer
12 Like speeches
13 Uncertain number
21 "___ to mention ..."
22 Famous film fountain
25 Stairstep face
26 Artist's pigment
27 Name on Tara's deed
28 Knife or gun, in a play
29 "Beat it!"
31 Rich tapestry
32 River to the Rhone
33 Puts in the hold
36 "Now, about ..."
39 County in SE Ireland
40 Ethyl acetate, e.g.
41 Apartment balconies
46 Petty officer
48 Salzburg's nation, briefly
49 Legal advice, sometimes
51 Wrinkly fruit
53 Give the finger to?
54 Iowa city
55 Tiniest protest
56 Trident-shaped letters
57 Shopping guide
58 "The ___ Giant" (animated film)
59 Bungee, for one
63 "___! We Have No Bananas"

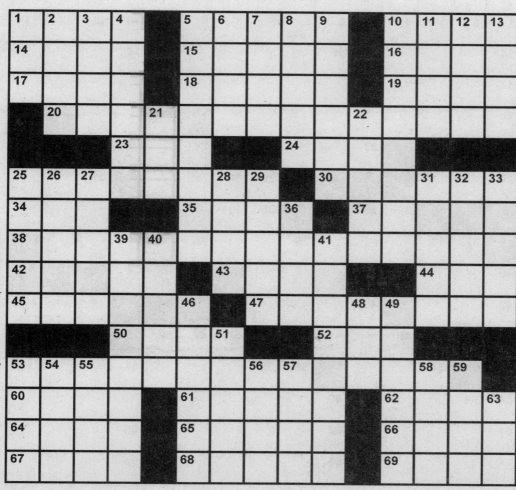

by Tracey Snyder
Edited by Timothy E. Parker
Answers in back

ACROSS
1 Ponderosa boy
5 In confusion
10 Made payments
14 Greek letter
15 Word with the starts of 17-Across, 37-Across and 58-Across
16 Chinese dynasty
17 Activity for couples
20 Places of prayer
21 Not safe
22 "__the season .."
23 Asian ox
24 Anxiety cause
27 Unit in tennis
28 Savory jelly
31 Sound of awe
32 Computer key
35 Rooster's ideal location
37 Mozart opus
40 Down Under animal
41 Approx.
42 Unit of energy
43 Greg Norman's turf
45 Yankees uniform item
48 Orderly displays
50 "Wheel of Fortune" purchase?
53 Argentina's Peron
54 Tool for shaping wood
55 Every now and then
58 Robert Young show
61 Word form for "Mars"
62 Pre- and neo-ending
63 Division word
64 CD word
65 Muscle weakness
66 Galactic bit

DOWN
1 Monastery superiors
2 Honeybunch
3 "Finally!"
4 Soda shop offering
5 The heart of ancient Athens
6 Russian carriage
7 Identical
8 NFL positions
9 Toothpaste approvers, for short
10 Take place
11 Desk drawer item
12 Indefinable time period
13 Burrowed
18 Siegfried's partner
19 Record-keeping cuts
24 Inasmuch as
25 Not that great
26 Boat pronoun
29 Nudged awake
30 Bic item
32 Present attachment
33 Scan thoroughly
34 Natasha's mate
36 Food scrap
37 Henry VIII's last wife
38 Unappreciative ones
39 Swindle
40 New Zealand parrot
44 From Pago Pago
45 Sidewalk material
46 Prayer book of Zoroastrianism
47 Church figure
49 Committee type
51 Word with "wed" or "married"
52 "___ a girl!"
55 Game with 32 cards
56 Fully aware
57 Wading bird
58 Mood rings or the Macarena, once
59 Onassis, to friends
60 Cell component

145 What's the Scoop?

by Lynn Lempel
Edited by Timothy E. Parker
Answers in back

ACROSS

1 Sugary topper
6 Work week-ending utterance
10 West Coast gas tank filler
14 Drug buster
15 Florence's river
16 Clout
17 Versatile aircraft
19 Beseeched
20 Italian hot spot
21 Bench press unit
22 Trojan War epic
23 Olds' car company
24 Device providing good reception
27 Notorious skinflint
29 "Scram!" oater-style
30 "My ___" (Mary Wells classic)
31 Buffalo bunch
32 Verbal groaner
33 Venomous vipers
34 Dan Aykroyd film about aliens
38 The middle-sized bear
41 Terminus
42 Bridge seat
45 It comes before a holiday
46 Yield, as a dividend
47 First American in space
50 Soup accompaniment, often
53 Bobby of '60s rock
54 Sings like Ella
55 Mount in Edom
56 "Gorillas in the Mist" subject Fossey
57 Looking down on one's peers
58 One way to seal a deal
61 Cause of an "aha" moment
62 Bus starter?
63 What a protractor measures
64 Gives a signal
65 Handy carryall
66 Cop's stunner

DOWN

1 Uses deductive reasoning
2 Science institution near L.A.
3 Raw material for steel
4 Final Four org.
5 Caught
6 "Unto the Sons" writer Gay
7 Economics textbook feature
8 Travelers' stop
9 Opponent
10 Brown betty ingredient
11 Court pronouncements
12 Rake it in
13 Nostalgic time
18 Stuffed shirt
22 Electronics giant
24 Extinct, flightless bird
25 Tropical malady
26 1492 ship
28 SeaWorld attraction
32 Prof's credential
33 Memo shortcut
35 Almost there
36 One-named Irish singer
37 Highway crosser on signs
38 Soldier's cookware
39 Guacamole base
40 Came in first, second or third, in the Olympics
43 Nest egg
44 Sewing machine pedal
46 Windows boxes?
47 It's just north of Chicago
48 Roll call response
49 More concentrated
51 Hit-the-road guide
52 Intone
56 Funny man Carvey
58 Barfly
59 Med. group
60 Magician's prop

by Fran & Lou Sabin
Edited by Timothy E. Parker
Answers in back

ACROSS

1 Duffer's dread
5 Barber's device
10 Cartoon dog
14 Shakespearean baddie
15 Diminish
16 Mob soldier
17 Henley racers
18 Picnic staple
20 Play to the balcony?
22 Culex's kin
23 The Gipper, to Reagan
24 Something to check
26 Masterfully competent
29 Some pitchers
35 Moves through a crowd, in a way
37 Once upon a time
38 Republic on the Caspian
39 Senate cover-up, once
40 "____ Paradiso" (1966 film)
42 Great-great grandson of Augustus
43 Worry-free locale
44 It may be added to impress
45 Hannibal "the Cannibal"
47 Antique specialists
50 Pointer's word
51 The "M" of "MIB"
52 O.K. Corral combatant
54 /, to a kegler
58 Showed to movie critics
62 Pickled peppers picker
65 "Nick at ____"
66 Nutritive mineral
67 Semisoft cheese from Holland
68 March Madness org.
69 Sprinter's concern
70 Queen ____ lace
71 Vocal outburst

DOWN

1 Jerky moves
2 Most uncommon
3 "Teen" ending
4 Energy source
5 Flower part
6 Interleague activities?
7 Hawser
8 Keats creation
9 "As ____ your instructions"
10 Act the letch
11 Disney's "The Adventures of Ichabod and Mr. ____"
12 "Bag" or "board" beginner
13 Wallet fatteners
19 Cyclist's route
21 Item passed in class
24 Epic
25 Bikini, among others
26 Rayed bloom
27 Semiconductor, perhaps
28 Advances gradually
30 Roy Rogers flick, e.g.
31 Tightwad
32 Glacial ridge
33 Peddler's goods
34 Nocturnal sound
36 "Rocky" actress
41 Tandoor, for one
46 French 101 verb
48 One-tenth ephah
49 Pull out
53 Fabric with pictorial designs
54 Barbecue bar
55 Prefix with "scope" or "meter"
56 Tiny particle
57 Philosopher Descartes
58 Whirled
59 Heading on Santa's list
60 List ender
61 It may follow a shuffle
63 Woods' org.
64 Charged particle

by Thomas Kandy
Edited by Timothy E. Parker
Answers in back

ACROSS

1 Lessen the density of
7 It gets one's dander up
10 The third degree?
13 Inauspicious
15 Comparatively cuckoo
17 Anonymous trio of well-known guys
19 Sound of water hitting a hot frying pan
20 Cicatrix
21 More than just ask
22 Senator's U.S. constituency
23 Knot again
24 Example for example, for example
27 They run only when broken
30 First word in a "fighting machine" phrase
31 Like many business cars
34 Monadic
36 King's domain?
37 Lone wolf
39 Word of exception
42 Photographic pigment
43 Mother of Sean Preston and Sutton Pierce
45 John Irving's title hero T.S.
48 Result of a hair-splitting experience?
50 First name among the cast of "The Graduate"
51 Cantilevered window
53 Perform in a knightly tournament
56 Abrogate legally
58 Remove unceremoniously
59 Zugspitze, for one
62 Name given for any fun-loving fellow
65 Difficult to grasp
66 Person paid to drop hints
67 What both Miss Muffet and Humpty Dumpty did
68 Like F.D.R.'s Deal
69 Temporary holding

DOWN

1 Putrefies
2 It follows Joel
3 What swish shots miss
4 Participant in some receptions
5 Insert surreptitiously
6 State flower of New Mexico
7 The Crossed Harpoons, in "Moby-Dick"
8 European freshwater fish
9 Old sleep inducer
10 Software copyright ignorer
11 Abdominal protrusion
12 "Fool that I was" poet John
14 It lays a mermaid's purse
16 In a docile manner
18 What the common guy is?
22 Mayday relative
24 Group that featured T-Boz
25 Kobe cash
26 Forty-niner's tool
28 Fresh antelope?
29 Answer back in an impudent manner
32 Palindromic preposition
33 "A Nightmare on Elm Street" actor
35 Agent, colloquially
38 Org. whose seal contains a bald eagle and a compass
39 Officially bar from entry
40 Subject for Keats
41 Prufrock creator's monogram
42 100 and 400, to a photographer
44 Absorb, as a loss
45 Overeats to the max
46 Ring of color, as around the human nipple
47 Extract forcibly, as a magazine page
49 Affect emotionally
52 Language for the masses?
54 "Confessions" singer
55 Like jokes you've heard before
57 Like early television
59 Reached terra firma
60 The King's daughter
61 Avenger Emma
63 Sound from a Siamese
64 Opie, really

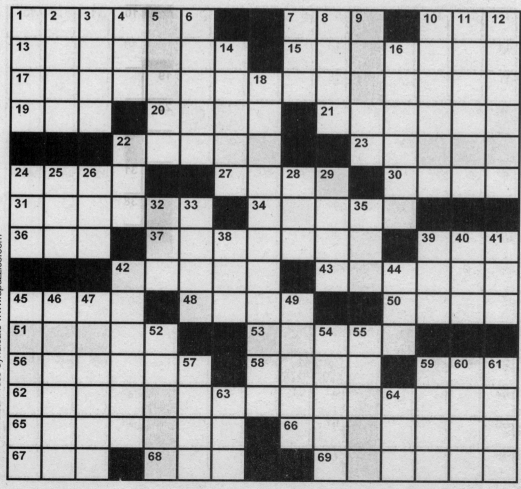

148 The Damage Is Done

ACROSS

1 Four musical Swedes
5 Strapped for cash
10 They may be overhead, on a car
14 Flying maneuver
15 It's the reel thing
16 Arabian Peninsula nation
17 Deck on the stern superstructure of a ship
18 Some major tournaments
19 Tribal wisdom
20 Telling a joke at a party, e.g.
23 Part of a schooner's cargo, often
24 "I've Seen All Good People" band
25 Accompanying music
28 Tatami, for one
31 More than ask
35 Toreador's trophy
36 Place for nonresident patients
39 Words with "cost to you" or "time"
40 Demanding obedience
43 Folkestone farewell
44 You might give one the slip?
45 Oxford-to-London direction, briefly
46 Choreographer's specialty
48 Seat of a religious office
49 Runs in place?
51 Phalanx locale
53 Jamaican pop music
54 Making petty distinctions
62 Hodgepodge
63 Virgin of Quranic paradise
64 Nucha
66 Resident of the funny farm
67 Punjab's friend
68 In boxing shape
69 Has made the last payment on
70 Puts one within another
71 Strong inclinations

DOWN

1 Piz Bernina, for one
2 Nitwit
3 An uncultivated person
4 Materialize
5 Mirrors companion, in deception
6 Kachina carvers
7 It's within your range
8 Symbol of troth
9 Irritable and impatient
10 Alternative to tossed salad
11 Mine, in Marseilles
12 He eulogized Julius
13 Blade of yore
21 Smart ___ (wisenheimer)
22 With it, '40s-style
25 Breakaway groups
26 Jeweler's weight
27 Deliver from a dais
28 Where gold diggers can be found
29 Secret motive
30 What cover letters spell out?
32 Waters of jazz
33 Liqueur enhancer
34 Birdbrains
37 On, as a kerosene lamp
38 Bearded revolutionary
41 Explanations for some shots
42 Eleniak of "Baywatch"
47 Winebibber
50 Gracefully delicate
52 Wharton's Frome
53 Starts from fright
54 Flight school final
55 Furrow former
56 Friend of Androcles
57 "Gas Food Lodging" actress Skye
58 Wimple wearers
59 Sandpaper surface
60 Far from everyday
61 Self-serving slant
65 German spa, Bad ___

149 Idle Thoughts

by Fran & Lou Sabin
Edited by Timothy E. Parker
Answers in back

ACROSS

1 Member of the walking dead (Var.)
6 Workout center
9 Butch and Sundance chasers
14 Vidalia product
15 Roof application
16 Swinging singer O'Day
17 Idle
19 Pompous walk
20 June '03 Smithsonian acquisition
21 Downspout sites
22 In those days
23 Pipe wood
24 "There you ___!"
25 OKs
28 Fifteenth anniversary gift
32 Right-hand pages
33 Copier problem
34 Lounge group, perhaps
35 Wrinkled facial features
36 Cook's measure
37 Net's preceder
38 Shrek, e.g.
39 Harbor craft
40 Ring of color (Var.)
41 Goofed at the bridge table
43 More costly
44 Anti-Depression agency
45 Strikers' commotion
46 Indian royal
48 Capital on the Nile
49 Ness or Hoover, e.g.
52 Signs of divinity
53 Idle
55 Classy equines
56 Stage light coating
57 Sierra ___
58 Complicated
59 Sounds of uncertainty
60 "Pomp and Circumstance" composer

DOWN

1 Crazy places
2 The heavens, to Atlas
3 Pitcher's target
4 "You stink!"
5 Places of pain and turmoil
6 Some are pot-bellied
7 Kitchen utensil
8 Capacious crafts
9 Bear claw, e.g.
10 Idle
11 Foal's father
12 Phaser setting
13 Break bread
18 Shows patience
23 Idle
24 Vest's lack
25 Ann ___, Michigan
26 Twilled fabric
27 It may be heaped on one
28 Salary limit
29 Cavalry unit
30 Bridal path
31 Typical Las Vegas gambler
33 "Little Brown __"
36 Twice-chewed food
37 Site of the 1968 Winter Olympics
39 Blackpool break
40 Name in games people play
42 Covered with fescue
43 Con artists' decoys
45 Provide food, service, etc.
46 "Still mooing," at a steakhouse
47 "Tsk! Tsk!"
48 Lovebirds' place
49 Potential prince?
50 Sicilian bubbler
51 Beautician, now and then
52 Strutter and fretter
54 Unagi, at a sushi restaurant

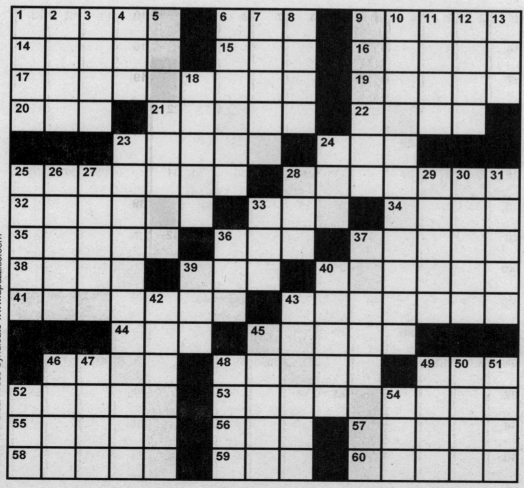

150 Long Number

by Jerry Hart
Edited by Timothy E. Parker
Answers in back

ACROSS

1 Walked back and forth
6 Workplace watchdog org.
10 Ritzy
14 Winged ant
15 Flying stunt
16 Mae West's "___ Angel"
17 Jolly Roger flier
19 Simon or Newman
20 Classification system for blood
21 Slangy switch addition
22 The E in Einstein's formula
24 Homer or Marge
26 He eulogized Julius
27 "___ alive!"
28 "As You Like It" character
32 Small excavators
35 Submarine captain's command
36 Hairy one of the Bible
37 Jai follower
38 Like wartime messages
39 Objectives
40 Advertising sign element, perhaps
41 Prepares for planting, in a way
42 Atlas detail, perhaps
43 Questionable remedies
45 Top card
46 Red-___ (franks)
47 Saddle attachment
51 Lyricist Hart
54 In vogue
55 "___ as directed"
56 Father of Fear and Panic
57 Gas stove feature
60 Mild partner
61 Shakespeare's river
62 Glowing coal
63 Good wine quality
64 Half of an infamous dual personality
65 "Heidi" author Johanna

DOWN

1 Pontiffs, in Roma
2 "___ Ike"
3 Strike and rebound
4 Greek letter
5 Can't stand
6 "Maximus to Gloucester" poet Charles
7 Manhattan locale
8 ___ polloi
9 Placated
10 Meerschaum user's need
11 Tent tycoon
12 Comfortable and cozy
13 Sacred
18 Greek god of love
23 Gun owner's org.
25 Impractical prospect
26 Has a change of address
28 Hitches successfully
29 Horned goddess
30 Implicate
31 Composition of some clouds
32 "Buddenbrooks" novelist
33 A toast topper
34 Vietnam neighbor
35 Destines to a tragic fate
38 Audacity
42 Frozen spikes hanging from eaves
44 Wood of the Stones
45 Busily working
47 Exhibited brilliance
48 Football's British relative
49 One at the wedding, perhaps
50 ___ dish (lab item)
51 Mary's pet
52 Nabisco goodie
53 Marsh growth
54 Earth clump
58 Wrigley Field feature
59 Young rascal

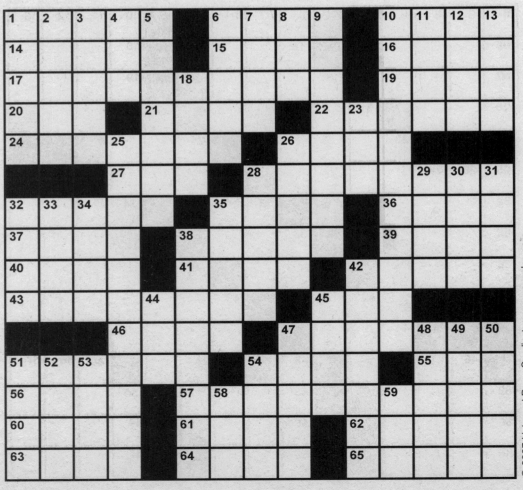

151 Am I Blue?

by Cate Cove
Edited by Timothy E. Parker
Answers in back

ACROSS

1 Anderson and Grier
5 Associate with
10 Egyptian symbols of royalty
14 Oscar-nominated Peter Fonda role
15 Pyromaniac's crime
16 Nickname for a baseball manager
17 Potentially explosive situations
19 Tricyclist, typically
20 Starbucks phrase
21 With "The," Jodie Foster film
23 "My Three Sons" dog
26 Campus org. for Colin Powell
27 One responsible for keeping wackos off the air
30 He's known for shouting "Bam!"
33 Nickname of baseball's $252 million man
34 Part of an LP
36 "The Phantom Menace" boy
37 "The Defense of Fort McHenry" author
38 Annual foursome
40 "Don't be fuelish," for one
41 Classic TV mom Morgenstern
42 "The Goodbye Girl" girl
43 Bach's "____ , Joy of Man's Desiring"
44 It connects circuits to a circuit board
46 Takes under one's wing
49 Dirt used on a new homesite
50 Brownstone feature
51 "Anna Karenina" author
54 Type of salon for him and her
58 Styptic substance
59 First job, for many teenagers
62 Mona that just hangs around
63 Demagnetize, as a tape
64 "First Lady of Song" Fitzgerald
65 German leader Helmut
66 Harp and elephant
67 Promising, as one's future

DOWN

1 Cocoon inhabitant
2 Matty, Felipe, Jesus or Moises
3 Whimper like a baby
4 Under, in the OR
5 Kilt pattern
6 Raise one's hackles
7 Legal conclusion?
8 Garment for Gaius
9 Kind of personality
10 Shrewd or savvy
11 It offers many stories
12 Peak sighter Zebulon
13 Did 90 or 100, e.g.
18 Ireland, in Ireland
22 Sean John, P. Diddy, or just plain Diddy
24 Southwestern flattops
25 Places found up the river?
27 Small, arboreal, bushy-tailed monkeys
28 System of principles
29 Poker player's dream
31 "Ocupado"
32 The thumb-sucking Van Pelt
35 Stereotypical snack for cops, informally
38 Refine, as ore
39 Where studs hang
43 The largest of a heavenly eight
45 Bleak and cheerless
47 Wakes
48 "Breathe Again" singer Braxton
51 Radio format
52 Salmagundi, e.g.
53 Easily maneuvered, as a yacht
55 Capital of Manche
56 Snigglers' wrigglers
57 It can show you the breaks
60 Rambouillet cry
61 Fashionable initials

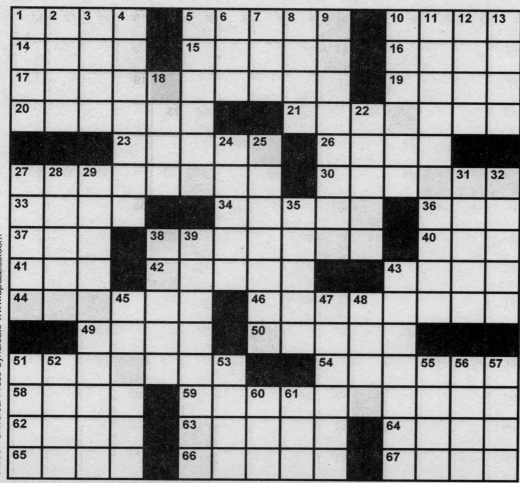

152 Duck for Cover

by George Keller
Edited by Timothy E. Parker
Answers in back

ACROSS

1 Classic song by the Kinks
5 Become swollen
10 Clever comment
14 Australia's national gemstone
15 66, famously
16 Official language of Pakistan
17 Surfer's tool
19 Ice and Iron, for two
20 Stat for a pitcher that's better low than high
21 Brooklyn Bridge's river
22 Feature of a bay window
24 Removed splinters, in a way
26 Pitcher's boo-boo
27 Ukrainian Black Sea port
30 "Burn the midnight oil," for one
34 Move from a frozen state?
37 He moonwalked before Michael
38 Hero who left his mark
39 Definitely overcooked
41 Coming-out-party honoree
42 Highest stages
43 Betraying disbelief
44 Enthralled
46 World Heritage pueblo site
47 Become less severe or strict
48 Close by
50 Barks incessantly
52 Achieve stardom
56 Radcliffe graduate
59 Like the "tough" of a Burt Reynolds film
61 Tony-winning director McAnuff
62 Abounding
63 He has a "Journal" on PBS
66 Shakespeare's river
67 Like some interpretations
68 Mansard overhang
69 How father knows
70 Lead-in for Mongolia or Hebrides
71 "Family Ties" character

DOWN

1 Big name in do-it-yourself supplies
2 Phantom's passion
3 With whom Jacob contracted to marry Rachel
4 Priestly vestment
5 Expand, as one's horizons
6 Cattle calls
7 Dispossess
8 Went to mess
9 It may be incognita
10 Medically unqualified physician
11 Hard-to-resist yen
12 Roman calendar notation
13 Word with "sour" or "glamour"
18 Famed army doctor Walter
23 Henry's fair lady
25 Partial outlay
26 The Italian Stallion
28 They have at least four seats
29 Steven Seagal film, "Under ___"
31 Miss La Douce
32 Cookie for 95 years
33 Plant that can grow on trees
34 Chairlift alternative
35 Bunyanesque
36 Shrinking Soviet sea
40 L.B.J., by birth
45 He played the same character for 20 years
49 Quartet with a defection
51 Poet Neruda
53 Consummate
54 Exuberance or brio
55 Thomas Cromwell, Earl of ___
56 Kasbah resident
57 Start of New Hampshire's motto
58 Abduction vehicles, supposedly
59 Opening for a mail carrier
60 Last word in an ultimatum
64 Chit used when you're out of chips
65 Proponent's vote

ACROSS

1 Last word in the title of a Lindsay Lohan film
5 It gives a barber an edge
10 Palindromic "Beetle Bailey" canine
14 Enemy of the Moor
15 Chip away, as support
16 Mob soldier
17 All hands on deck?
18 The least expensive "dish" you can serve?
20 Sing to a lover, or the song itself
22 Yellow-fever mosquito
23 Chris Gardner, to Will Smith
24 You may check it, although it's over your head
26 Masterfully competent
29 Randy Johnson, Paul McCartney and Ned Flanders
35 Moves in a crabby manner
37 It may come after many moons?
38 Persia, since 1935
39 Belushi's wrap, in "Animal House"
40 Paradiso, in a Gina Lollobrigida film
42 The emperor featured in "Quo Vadis"
43 Her belly button was famously censored
44 Common contraction hidden in "river"
45 Hannibal the Cannibal
47 Antique specialists or some museum employees
50 The "Eyes" in a hit song by The Guess Who
51 The "M" of "MIB"
52 Man who was a supporter of a Holliday in Tombstone
54 /, to a kegler
58 Showed to movie critics
62 Pretty popular pickled peppers picker
65 Nick's time, in TV lingo
66 Hemoglobin component
67 City in the Netherlands, or its semisoft export
68 It invites 65 teams to March Madness
69 This is something that every single convict does
70 Two wives of Henry VIII
71 One way to reach the hard-of-hearing?

DOWN

1 Involuntary twitches
2 Nearly extinct
3 "Golden" ending
4 Where to find Homer Simpson at sector 7-G
5 Part of the calyx of a flower
6 Industry publications
7 Hawser, for one
8 "Intimations of Immortality," e.g.
9 Word before "second," "hour" or "mile"
10 Take in cheesecake?
11 Disney's "The Adventures of Ichabod and Mr. ___"
12 Schlep
13 The ten in a sawbuck
19 Well-traveled place "of least resistance"
21 Hemi-demisemiquaver, for one
24 Elephantine
25 It consists of a circular coral reef surrounding a lagoon
26 Rayed autumn bloom
27 The "D" in LED
28 The outer limits
30 Shoot-'em-up
31 A miserly person, or when reversed, what he does
32 Narrow mountain ridge
33 Peddler's merchandise
34 In comics, it's represented by a string of Z's
36 Actress in the first five "Rocky" films
41 Appliance in "Hansel and Gretel"
46 French 101 verb which means "to be"
48 One-tenth of an ephah
49 Withdraw from a union
53 Elaborate hanging tapestry
54 Barbecue sticker
55 Roz Doyle portrayer Gilpin of "Frasier"
56 Ant who once teamed with Secret Squirrel
57 Surrealist painter Magritte
58 Created a web site?
59 Heading on Santa's list
60 List-ending Latin abbreviation
61 Word Howie Mandel often uses twice in the same sentence
63 Organization that features Woods, woods and woods
64 Cyclotron particle

154 Stuff It!

by Carol Lachance
Edited by Timothy E. Parker
Answers in back

ACROSS

1 Two of a kind
5 Where ___ (trendy place)
10 They can be hedged
14 Slight advantage
15 WWI soldier
16 "Put a lid ___!"
17 Monetary unit of North Korea
18 ___ and Gomorrah
19 "Strange" prefix
20 Percussion instrument
22 Sting operation
23 Crop up
24 Insect told to "fly away home"
26 Vietnamese New Year
27 Athletic supporter?
29 Constellation near Perseus
32 Some machetes
34 Passover bread
35 Water color
38 Pretty, to Burns
40 Hyena from Dogpatch
41 Thrill-seeker's cord
43 "I wanna!"
45 Cousin of FORTRAN
46 Letter that sounds like a question
47 Architect Maya ___
50 Attempts
54 Make amends
56 Lobster pincer
58 Air show stunt
60 Popular pasta
61 Exchange premiums
62 French part of U.S.A.?
63 "I'll say!"
64 Georgia city or county
65 Barcelona boy
66 Rip to bits
67 "Don't ___!" ("I haven't the foggiest!")
68 Peachy follower

DOWN

1 Nag, or eat like a bird
2 Stick like glue
3 Outfielder's cry
4 Monopoly payments
5 ___ dixit
6 Parting word
7 Gulf off Libya's coast
8 For all to hear
9 It may be tucked by a doctor
10 Shelled North American creature
11 Command from Captain Kirk
12 Fey, formerly of 33-Down
13 Do this in the name of love
21 Jared of "Panic Room"
25 Ruminant sound, perhaps
28 Dresden's river
30 Exceedingly long time
31 ___ Na Na
32 Blowhard
33 NBC weekend comedy show
34 "Goodness gracious!"
35 Network that wants us all to get "Lost"
36 Quid pro ___
37 With no defeats or like an egg still in the shell
39 Reporter's milieu
42 Santa's little helper
44 One square a day?
47 Canadian dollar coin
48 Kind of skates
49 Ozzie or Harriet
51 Clinton's competitor
52 Hindu hits
53 Fool
55 Babar's snout
56 Biz bigwig
57 Key ___ pie
59 Ancient serf

ACROSS

1 Israel's neighbor
6 Having ___ hair day
10 An itemized deduction
14 Craves
15 Andes country
16 Rombauer or "la Douce"
17 Pixies
18 Analgesic target
19 Trim with scissors
20 Start of a quip
23 Some math answers
24 Tease
28 Quip (Part 2)
32 Fleshy fruit
33 Propose a candidate
34 Cardinals great Brock
35 Copier
38 Greek letters
39 Bundle
40 Extensively
43 Group of girls, e.g.
44 Quip (Part 3)
48 Old port of Rome
49 Tally on a gun handle
50 End of the quip
56 Wine region
59 T-bone order
60 Implant
61 Swank
62 On the Indian
63 State of the union
64 Foot part
65 Visionary
66 German industrial city

DOWN

1 Knocked off a dragon
2 Time to drink eggnog
3 Invitation letters
4 Say over
5 Maintain
6 Seem
7 Words with "mind" (remembers)
8 Excessively dry
9 Sand pile
10 Contempt
11 Very large coffee holder
12 Beatles label
13 Easy mark
21 Membership cost
22 Upbeat, in music
25 Beaver, at times
26 Musical interval of eight tones
27 Destitute
28 Restaurant seating choices
29 Protective trinket
30 Billion-year stretch
31 Dallas sch.
32 Philosopher who wrote the "The Republic"
35 Lend ___ (pay close attention)
36 Grp. for Els
37 Airport info.
41 Imposing structure
42 Award recipient
43 Group of Atlantic islands
45 "Have ___!" (hero's reassurance)
46 Catchall abbr.
47 Conspire
51 Precambrian and Paleozoic
52 Relaxation
53 Stats for David Ortiz
54 Trait carrier
55 Adam's habitation
56 Rm. coolers
57 HBO alternative
58 Up to that time

ACROSS

1 Out of kilter
6 Settled up
10 Stable newcomer
14 Jay Silverheels role
15 Light brown
16 Plumb crazy
17 Late bloomer
18 Mall rat, most likely
19 Grand Ole ____
20 Goal that never gets off the ground
23 Distress signal
24 Blow it
25 Ben & Jerry's measures
29 Yachting maneuver
31 Historic beginning?
34 WASP part
35 Actress Ward
36 Skelton's Kadiddlehopper
37 "Don't clap until I'm done"
40 Brooklyn trailers?
41 Magazine contents
42 Flounder's frat brother in "Animal House"
43 Retirement place?
44 National rival
45 Stuck up
46 "___ you serious?"
47 Surveillance device
48 "Since you put it that way" follower
55 Something to fill out
56 Give a hoot
57 Caribbean island
59 Machu Picchu resident
60 Leave out
61 Type of terrier
62 Noodle
63 Direction recommended by Horace Greeley
64 "Goodbye Yellow Brick Road" singer John

DOWN

1 One day ____ time
2 Pit for crowd surfing
3 Keen on
4 Big event for a baby
5 Touchy subject
6 "___ Dragon"
7 Unreturnable serves
8 Angers
9 Symbol of bad behavior
10 It may come with a Gold Medal
11 "My bad!"
12 43,560 square feet
13 Myrna of the movies
21 ____ Gatos, California
22 Genesis vessel
25 Madras mister, formerly
26 100 smackers
27 Made goo-goo eyes at
28 Cutlass manufacturer
29 Lions and Tigers and Bears
30 Chow chow chow
31 Planet from 1930 to 2006
32 Bowling alley button
33 Manicurist's material
35 Quarterfinal follower, briefly
36 The Censor of Rome
38 Lose it
39 Loser's look
44 Javelin's path
45 Mystery novelist Grafton
46 "Gimme a break!"
47 Packers quarterback Favre
48 Sharpen
49 Penguin predator
50 April, May or June, e.g.
51 State flower of Tennessee
52 River through Kazakhstan
53 Corporate cheese?
54 River through Spain
55 White lie
58 Political commentator Coulter

by Mark Lintz
Edited by Timothy E. Parker
Answers in back

ACROSS

1 Deli pocket
5 Backbreaker, in proverb
10 Wilbur Post's pet
14 Press agent?
15 This might give you a flat in London
16 Top-drawer
17 Big Apple river
18 Georgia of "The Mary Tyler Moore Show"
19 Start of an explanation
20 Unyielding
22 Laugh like the Wicked Witch
24 Circus safety equipment
25 Recital performance
26 Pungent root
29 "Home Improvement" star
33 Stew or miscellany
34 Behind schedule
35 Aldon of "The Barefoot Contessa"
36 Distinctive clothing
37 Patron saint of the lame
38 Bog
39 Blues legend James
40 A disagreeable responsibility
41 "Peter Pan" beast, briefly
42 Debbie of film
44 Member of the violin family
46 Baby's favorite art movement?
47 Angelic aura
48 Splendid
51 Palindromes may be read this way
55 ____ off (switch choice)
56 Rob's wife of classic TV
58 One of five Great ones
59 Merrill of "True Colors"
60 Egged on
61 "I ____ Song Go Out of My Heart"
62 Phrygian deity (Var.)
63 Billiards stroke
64 Bakery item

DOWN

1 Berth place
2 "Dies ____" (Latin hymn)
3 Play horseshoes
4 Recent Zorro
5 Magnifying glass carrier
6 Woodstock '99 sites or sights
7 Over-the-top anger
8 Peer Gynt's mother
9 Invites in enthusiastically
10 "My Life So Far" star
11 Chess piece
12 Organic compound
13 Fake out, on the rink
21 "____ Miserables"
23 Chicken-King divider
25 Building locations
26 "Copy that"
27 Sporting wings
28 Ready to be washed
29 Anklebone
30 Nixon defense secretary
31 Flynn, the swashbuckling film hero
32 Extended family member
34 Blair or Lavin
37 "Holy Man" star
43 Boathouse item
44 False front
45 Sort
47 Hounds' prey
48 Dr. Pepper, for one
49 Platoon
50 Shetland, e.g.
51 Computer program errors
52 Martian prefix
53 Rudner or Hayworth
54 Like Helen Keller
57 Football coach Parseghian

158 Where?

by Fran & Lou Sabin
Edited by Timothy E. Parker
Answers in back

ACROSS
1 "Me oh my"
5 Defense grp. that includes the U.S.
9 Inflict a heavy blow on
14 Hollywood Blvd. crosser
15 Gossip topic
16 Office copier need
17 Mashie or niblick
18 Horror film feature
19 Management course subject?
20 Night application, for some
23 Be decisive
24 Suspect's demand (Abbr.)
25 Exhausting, hectic routines
30 Betty or Barney, of cartoons
34 A quarter of four
35 Let go from the job
37 Respiratory noises
38 Illusionist's feat
42 Kate's sitcom partner
43 Used a firehouse pole
44 Feminine subject
45 Close by
47 Woodworker's worry
50 Work as a barker
52 Brian of the original Roxy Music
53 Auction-ending statement
60 "Lemon Tree" singer Lopez
61 Ultimatum conclusion
62 Western writer Zane
63 Daniel follower, in the Bible
64 Deadly septet
65 "It's clear to me now"
66 Washstand containers
67 Barney fans
68 Silent bids

DOWN
1 Tel ____-Jaffa
2 Coin no longer minted
3 Prolific poet?
4 Year on campus
5 Romantic evening extender
6 "Yours," to the French
7 Gull relative
8 "The ____ Man" (Heston film)
9 Bravura performance
10 Wells Fargo pickup
11 Swenson of "Benson"
12 Rain, but good
13 Behave humanly?
21 Masseuse employer
22 Basketball pos.
25 1956 movie monster
26 Foolishly old-womanish
27 Electrical pioneer Nikola
28 They're no longer together
29 Navy elite
31 Criticize in no uncertain terms
32 Cafe con ____ (coffee with milk)
33 Acid-alcohol compound
36 Icicle starter
39 People can get quite high on it
40 Funnel-shaped flowers
41 Inaction
46 URL ending, sometimes
48 End for "end"
49 Bean or noodle
51 Cast off from the body
53 Mushroom
54 Seine feeder
55 Hodgepodge
56 Does not exist
57 Words of approximation
58 Can't live without
59 Head set?
60 Not just any

159 Grammar Class

by Ruma Collette
Edited by Timothy E. Parker
Answers in back

ACROSS

1 Go back to square one on
5 Maryland cake ingredient
9 German industrial city
14 Bunched in with
15 O'Grady of "Eight Is Enough"
16 Explosive liquid, briefly
17 Test of speed
20 Trucking rig
21 Appease, as a thirst
22 Night spot
25 Stock market pessimist
27 Lustrous material
31 Beatitudes verb
32 Feed the kitty
33 Wear down
34 Indicate shock
36 Ocean phenomenon
38 Stock holder of Roy Rogers?
39 "Gladiator," e.g.
42 "Take ___ out of crime!"
44 German "no"
45 King of Skull Island
48 The Guggenheim Bilbao, e.g.
50 Animals with antlers
52 Fish propeller
53 Heat source for backpackers
54 English poet laureate Nicholas
55 Winter malady
56 Fried chicken favorite
58 Moola
60 Obey an eight-sided sign
67 Nobelists Marie and Pierre
68 Walk unsteadily
69 Opera about an enslaved Ethiopian girl
70 Uses a swizzle stick
71 Porgy's beloved
72 Bassoon bit

DOWN

1 Cheerleader's sound
2 Relative of a rhea
3 Huge racket
4 Saratoga stats
5 Piano sonata composer Muzio
6 What a Geiger counter measures
7 "Pick a card, ___ card"
8 Prejudice
9 It may be near the sofa
10 Distract from the main subject
11 RR stop
12 Stalling-for-time sounds
13 Classic Japanese drama
18 Country music's McEntire
19 With tabula, it's a blank slate
22 "Paper or plastic" item
23 Historic time piece?
24 Loathe
26 Animal named for its coat color
28 Relent
29 Bradley and Sullivan
30 Classical prefix
35 "The Truman Show" director
37 Play enders, sometimes
40 Joins, as long-lost friends
41 Desk features of old
42 Forenoons
43 "… life is ___ a dream"
46 Nada
47 Serengeti beast
49 Like some old records
51 One way to move merchandise
57 Distinctive clothing
59 Bygone despot
60 Hypodermic needle amts.
61 Without without with?
62 CAT scan alternative
63 Cover charge, e.g.
64 Indecisive result
65 Poetic form
66 Mouse's milieu

160 Betting Man

by Tom Dirkshire
Edited by Timothy E. Parker
Answers in back

ACROSS

1 Hardly demanding
5 Burn slightly
9 MacKenzie of old beer ads
14 One doing a con job?
15 Word that rhymes with its opposite
16 Rabbit fur
17 German industrial region
18 Monumental
19 Elroy Jetson's dog
20 Toss the dice, e.g.
23 Use an ax
24 Individual beings
25 This and that
27 Dynamic opening
30 Executor's concern
33 Surmise
37 Matures
39 Camelot lady
40 Payment for a crossing
41 Shirley Temple trademark
42 Prep school since 1440
43 Charles Lamb
44 Pub potables
45 Rock concert venue
46 Predatory bird
48 What Sinbad sailed
50 Famous fabulist
52 Not just again
57 "Big" burger, at McDonald's
59 Bet a long shot
62 "Love"-ly word in a Stevie Wonder song
64 Sponge or face feature
65 They make waves
66 "Walk ___ in my shoes"
67 Related by blood
68 It may be about a foot?
69 Hall or Python
70 Baker's dozen of popes
71 ___ River, N.J.

DOWN

1 Trading centers
2 Make accustomed (Var.)
3 Word on old gas pumps
4 Nureyev's company, once
5 Kind of cake
6 The 36 of a famous measurement
7 Seed sheath
8 Divide the deck again
9 Satisfies thirst
10 Faux ___
11 Call one's bluff
12 Fraught with danger, as circumstances
13 It may be on the mountaintop
21 Proximal
22 Game that features mating
26 Rodeo attendee
28 Julia of "The Addams Family"
29 Mythical meanies
31 Suffix used to form abstract nouns
32 Poet St. Vincent Millay
33 Road for Nero
34 Vincent Lopez song
35 One way to make a decision
36 Tickle pink
38 Last word of an ultimatum
41 Yuletide song
45 New York City stadium name
47 Seabird
49 Greek capital
51 Like Vatican bulls
53 Chickens come home to do it
54 State known for potatoes
55 Kind of drive, in a computer
56 Letters that create hurdles for lispers
57 Polite palindromic address
58 Bullets and such
60 Pair up, as oxen
61 Group of three
63 Farthest or highest, briefly

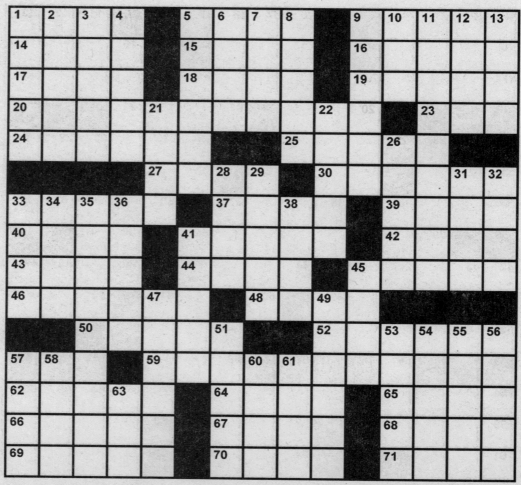

by Henry Quarters
Edited by Timothy E. Parker
Answers in back

ACROSS

1 It may be stared at for hours on end
6 What a con may assume
11 It may be pint-sized
14 Subject for Strunk and White
15 Incognito
17 Irish greeting for early birds
19 Increases, as the ante
20 Bird mentioned prominently in "Bringing Up Baby"
21 Emmy winner on "The Sopranos"
22 Group that may be marching around campus
23 Kind of statement an accountant may make?
26 Sheets, tablecloths, pillowcases, etc.
29 Gave some people in Vegas a hand?
30 Vitamin supplement
31 Partner of tranquility
32 One-word question from Miss Piggy
35 Place to find straddlers
39 Hollywood-to-Palm Springs dir.
40 Tijuana toodle-oo
41 Viscount's superior
42 Embarrassing public display
43 Fly near the equator?
45 Being born or emerging
48 Title word in the last song you'll sing this year
49 Treat for Cookie Monster
50 Recess at church
51 Chocolatier's vessel
54 Where some crooked deals originate?
59 Easily moved
60 If you play it, it could be grand
61 Acronym for linked computers
62 Smelling a rat
63 Monica familiar with the courts

DOWN

1 It was worn to dance with Rudolf Nureyev
2 Informative letters on a brandy bottle
3 Scam victims
4 "Super" topic for Sigmund Freud
5 Start of a slippery nickname for John Gotti
6 Type of committee
7 Lender's security
8 This can be the end to alcohol
9 Word before "in a galaxy far, far away"
10 "Big" part of California or of a Kerouac novel
11 Remark to an audience
12 Founder of the Bolsheviks
13 Trimmed along the walk, e.g.
16 Like krypton
18 Rugrats
22 Rip apart
23 "The Lake Isle of Innisfree" poet
24 When purchased alone
25 Downwind, at sea
26 Gimlet garnish
27 Diaphragm that controls the size of the pupil
28 Lymph gland
29 "Moll Flanders" penner, Daniel
31 Show the way, in a way
32 Water under the drawbridge
33 They make waves when used properly
34 Run without moving
36 Chantilly product
37 Hemingway's posthumous " garden"
38 Clarinet, or Rex the critic
42 Director of "Gladiator"
43 Keister or fanny
44 Visits the Land of Nod
45 Prize for Nelson Mandela
46 Subject for a wine connoisseur
47 America's first saint
48 How things may be "put" with competence
50 From whence some worship
51 Scaloppine, often
52 Teenage problem that breaks out
53 Letters that can officially stop fights
55 Black gold
56 He's a slap-happy stooge
57 1300 hours
58 Word in the title of four Bruce Willis films

162 A Dog's Life

by Craig Holman
Edited by Timothy E. Parker
Answers in back

ACROSS

1 "Give that ____ cigar!"
5 "That ____ no lady …'"
8 No longer novel
13 Samovar's cousin
14 Slithery Egyptian
15 Prefix meaning "sun"
16 Its head is tufted
20 Stable employee (Var.)
21 180 degrees from SSW
22 Monumental 151?
23 Eye shade?
26 Reanimate
28 Short-legged creatures
33 Titan, formerly
34 Diarist Frank
35 Ducky shade of blue
39 One authorized to act for another

40 Lead-in to "choo" or "plunk"
41 Wyeth's model
42 Gp. listening for signals from space
43 Item for a Mexican pot?
44 Citified
45 Lost skier's friend?
48 The Earps, e.g.
51 Lunar or leap, e.g.
52 Unforgettable time for historians
53 Lobster coral
55 Fictional Roger or Peter
60 Some police dogs
64 Motionless
65 Chop suey sauce
66 River in Arizona
67 Cafe au lait holder
68 Be beholden to
69 Crystal consulter

DOWN

1 Bulletin board notice
2 Creates wonderment
3 On deck
4 Litchi-nut feature
5 Pallid
6 Type of tray
7 Wing measurement
8 Astute
9 Aviv antecedent
10 Smart guy?
11 Strong cotton thread
12 Rose-red dye
17 Stalky veggie
18 Trapped like ____
19 Harebrained
24 How James Bond likes his martinis
25 It's the best policy
27 Rearward
28 Conks on the head

29 West Yorkshire river
30 It welcomes change
31 Gender discrimination
32 Strip
36 Island of a noted exile
37 Culture medium
38 Polaroid inventor Edwin
41 Triumphal shout
43 Attach a tail to a donkey
46 Make bubbly
47 Lawman Wyatt
48 Not phony
49 Sports venue
50 Peddler's merchandise
54 Rival of Phillips 66
56 Supplicates
57 Camembert cousin

58 Twiddling one's thumbs
59 Romanov, e.g.
61 "____ Doubtfire"
62 Questioning word
63 Word with "black," "red" or "pink"

by Alice Walker
Edited by Timothy E. Parker
Answers in back

ACROSS

1 Eye swatter?
5 You may test for it by saying "Hello!"
9 "The Fox and the Grapes," e.g.
14 Word with "each life" or "thin air"
15 Pouchong and gunpowder
16 The Jackson Five had them
17 Home of the Royal Swedish Ballet
19 Vegas game featuring shooters
20 Small earthen boiler
21 Supply mother's milk
23 It made Jed a millionaire
25 Mother of Ashley and Wynonna
26 Where a Biblical road led
31 Coat of arms features
34 The Beatles' "Eight Days ___"
35 Guisewite's girl
37 Blip on a polygraph
38 Ankle-length
39 Nevada/California lake
40 Acquire the old-fashioned way
41 Noted Verdi aria, "___ tu"
42 Jerry Lewis film, "___ to a Small Planet"
43 Chalet overhangs
44 Small, yellowish-brown variety of pear
46 City at the confluence of the Danube and Sava
48 Dawning
50 Excavated
51 Cutting type of kick?
53 Make invalid
58 One way to be wanted
59 Setting of "Black Hawk Down"
61 Best thing to put on Mediterranean Avenue
62 Voting coalition
63 A stone's throw away
64 Unfathomable chasm
65 Emulate Buffy
66 Brussels-based defense organization

DOWN

1 Thylvethster's thpeech problem
2 Prefix with "body" or "corrosion"
3 Word in an octagon
4 What a poor gambler may be in
5 Italian-American, Mexican-American, etc.
6 Steve Ballmer, at Microsoft
7 "Kiss on My List" partner of Oates
8 Founder of the Ottoman Empire
9 Type of "Girl" in a 2006 Sienna Miller film title
10 Inverted-V structure
11 Capital of Slovakia
12 Run in long, smooth, easy strides
13 Superman's logo
18 Stand in the mall?
22 Rhyme for "stash," appropriately
24 Skywalker Ranch owner
26 Agatha Christie and Judi Dench, e.g.
27 Well-apprised
28 Tenochtitlan, nowadays
29 Series of letters before "O"
30 Title of respect in colonial India
32 Tuckered out or ready to roll?
33 One of five faculties, six for some
36 Lugged, as a large shopping bag
39 Typical bath flooring
40 Van Gogh had one later in life
42 Blood carriers
43 Pelted with certain ovoid objects
45 Bowie's weapons
47 Obsolete term for legal insanity
49 What the pyramids are
51 Oscar Madison, famously
52 What either a hot person or dog is on
54 Ted, the Dolphins' first pick in the 2007 NFL draft
55 On open waters
56 Just one of those things?
57 It's worth about a dollar
58 "Eureka!"
60 __, Daman, and Diu

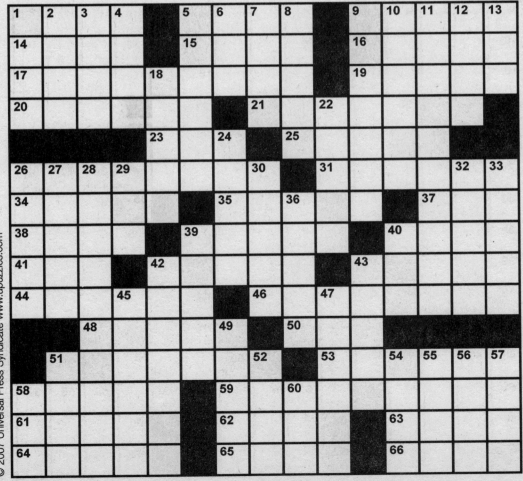

ACROSS

1 "Buona ___" (Italian greeting)
5 Grins from ear to ear
10 Internet letters
13 Landed
14 One of a knight's arms
15 "You've gotta be kidding!"
17 Ethereal
19 Some are prime
20 Fruit-bearing tree
21 Far-reaching views
23 Field of operation
26 Evening reception
28 Mounted the soapbox
29 It may be on a bulletin board
30 Swiss river into the Rhine
33 Causes ennui
34 Pigeon shelters
35 ___-cone (summer treat)
36 Goes no further
37 Wise folks
38 High-ranking NCO
39 Make-double connector
40 Madras wraps
41 "John Brown's Body" poet
42 How-___ (book genre)
43 Fly or worm, on occasion
44 Early release
45 Creaks and squeaks
47 "Star Wars" role
48 "The Last King of Scotland" setting
50 Outspoken
51 Hawaiian dishes
52 Absolutely reliable
58 Part of a ready trio
59 Dropped fly, e.g.
60 Mail delivery org.
61 Concorde, notably
62 Board game square
63 Far or Middle

DOWN

1 "Do the Right Thing" pizzeria owner
2 "Bingo ___ Yale" (Porter song)
3 18-wheeler, e.g.
4 They play in all the big games
5 Pointed a finger at
6 "___ on down the road"
7 Santa ___, Calif.
8 1,101 in old Rome
9 Duties performed
10 Successor to bad?
11 Like Mary's lamb's fleece
12 Swoopes' gp.
16 Covert WWII org.
18 Flags
22 Gets on the nerves of
23 Confirming phrase
24 "Right now!"
25 Tough
26 Humidor fill
27 Author Joyce Carol
31 Tina Turner portrayer Bassett
32 Morally despicable
34 "A Perfect Spy" novelist John le ___
37 Bangers of a Brit's breakfast
38 Pie topping
40 Displayed baserunning skills
41 They're in Toyland
44 Work from Lichtenstein
46 Early stages
48 "___ Lazy River"
49 Plenty
50 Wavy lines, in comics
53 Scrap for Odie
54 "... man ___ mouse?"
55 Mama bear, in Madrid
56 Ancestors of CDs
57 Time zone letters

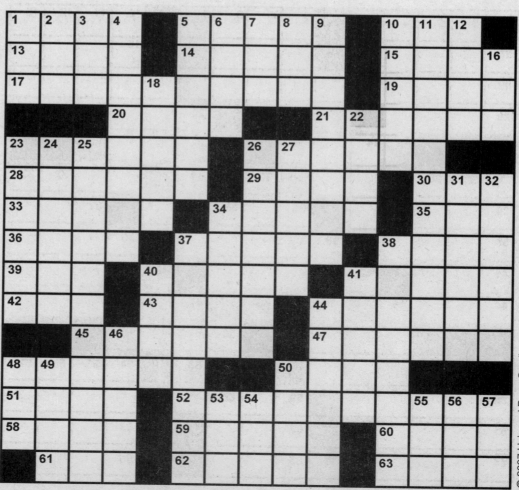

by Paul Litz
Edited by Timothy E. Parker
Answers in back

165 The Shadow Knows

ACROSS

1 "To your health!"
6 Person exchanged for Powers in 1962
10 They're for hackies
14 This can be right
15 Brand of toy blocks
16 Solo delivered at the Met
17 Emulating a private
20 Flock members
21 Type of meat or pepper
22 Works dough
23 At that time
25 The thing there
26 Biblical Promised Land
29 Bowl over
30 Did the butterfly
34 Bitter
35 Blazing
37 Mother of 6-Across
38 Getting nowhere
41 Nameless woman
42 Drops of sadness
43 Trunk with a chest
44 Old name at the pumps
46 You can dig it
47 Census unit
48 Monocle part
50 Come in behind the others
51 Borg and Edberg, e.g.
54 Aurora's counterpart
55 Capital on a fjord
59 In last place
62 Do high-tech surgery
63 Sandpaper surface
64 "Otello" composer
65 Makes a choice
66 Launching org.
67 Licorice-flavored seed

DOWN

1 Decision made at home?
2 Be familiar with
3 What some beach loungers do
4 Premier players
5 Tolstoy's first
6 Sci-fi character
7 Reach for your toes
8 Fabergé creation
9 Photographer's request
10 Military trainees
11 General vicinity
12 Boston Celtics legend, Larry
13 Backtalk
18 Meadowlark's warbling cousin
19 Stuff studied in genetics
24 Tough thing to kick
25 Mary-Kate and Ashley, e.g.
26 Secret storage spot
27 Aspirin targets
28 Closes in on
29 Prefix for "mentioned"
31 Deteriorates from use
32 Dispatch boat
33 Item in a patch
35 Seaweed extracts
36 Colorado park
39 Broadway attention-getter
40 Ripped into, as a bag of chips
45 They're golden
47 Swanky
49 Slim, slimy swimmer
50 "Whole ___ Shakin' Goin' On"
51 Town in Normandy
52 "That's a ___!" (director's shout)
53 Geographic area
54 Sponsorship (Var.)
56 Wrap for a rani
57 Digital displays
58 Depression-era migrant
60 Gun owners' gp.
61 One of the Gabors

by Lynn Lempel
Edited by Timothy E. Parker
Answers in back

ACROSS
1 Rocks
4 Builder's guidelines
9 Procedures
14 Cosmetics Factor
15 Bottom of the barrel
16 Foolish
17 Many a lawyer's office
20 Corby of "The Waltons"
21 Trojan War survivor
22 South Beach, for one
23 One of the Jacksons
25 Pile of wood for a final fire
28 Ultimately became
30 Rate indicator
32 Has permission
33 Takes a backseat

35 Able to vote, e.g.
37 Top-notch
40 Office recorder
42 Sing up high?
43 Pipe material
44 Seize
47 Indentations
51 Queens stadium name
53 Cat doctor?
55 Fellini film of 1972
56 Ducks
58 Fiance, post-wedding
59 Country club?
63 Like one of the flock
64 Veep elected in 1968
65 "To Kill a Mockingbird" author
66 Formal agreements
67 Develops compassion

68 Mickey Mouse's beginnings?

DOWN
1 Slow the progress
2 George, the first "SNL" guest host
3 Banned from the land
4 Tchaikovsky heroine's animal form
5 Crack or crock follower
6 Before, in verse
7 Spot for news junkies
8 "Adaptation" star
9 "An American Tail" critters
10 Ready to serve, as ale
11 Sadie Hawkins Day racer
12 SASE, e.g.
13 Notice
18 Pro

19 Player's payment
23 Pastime to throw you
24 Copycat
26 Gossip sheet
27 Hook's partner
29 French city for gastronomes
31 Noted wordsmith
34 Wily
36 Pivot
37 Clunker's savior
38 Eternities
39 Ruckuses
40 Healthful retreat
41 ABC outlets
45 Alaska's neighbor
46 Chaos
48 Walk unsteadily
49 Insignia
50 Give the go-ahead
52 Datebook entry
54 Writer's concern
57 Hidden treasures
58 Chops down
59 Bush league?

60 Juan Peron's first lady
61 D.C. spoofer
62 Harden

by Carl Cranby
Edited by Timothy E. Parker
Answers in back

ACROSS

1 Prepares for the holidays, in a way
6 Pants specification
10 Vent one's fury
14 Half the name of a Western city
15 Gulf near Yemen
16 Magma exposed
17 ALF, for one
18 Like the obvious type
20 Steal
22 Declares
23 Places to find steals
24 Milk snakes, e.g.
26 Sort of sailing race
31 Patron saint of young girls
32 O'Hare postings
33 Famed literary initials
36 Dart
37 Grier of football
39 WWII battle locale
40 Vietnamese holiday
41 Cartoon possum
42 Silenced
43 Caustic in speech
46 Not out
48 Actor Stephen
49 Time's partner
50 Some house adjuncts
55 Left hastily
58 Symbol of slowness
59 QED part
60 Financial predicament
61 Functional
62 Kind of media
63 Cast
64 Pushed a barge with a stick

DOWN

1 Stolen goods
2 Good ring to wear
3 Vaudeville shtick
4 Appealed
5 Footwear for the beach
6 Ohio feeder
7 Rocker Billy
8 Marina ___ Rey, California
9 Call it quits
10 Worked too hard
11 Indiana pro
12 Civil rights leader Medgar
13 Billfold stuffers
19 Drops out of contention
21 Dutch commune
24 Start the kitty
25 June 6, 1944
26 More than zany
27 Impolite look
28 College credit
29 Take the odds
30 Man of fables
33 Two of Caesar's last words
34 Medicinal plant
35 Polliwog home
37 Knock about
38 Fairy tale villain
39 Droop
41 Graph starter?
42 Acquires quickly
43 Changes gears
44 How some not-so-good ballplayers find themselves
45 "___ the fields we go ..."
46 Greek marketplace
47 Soho "so longs"
49 "Pardon me"
50 Pen part
51 "___ victory!"
52 Marsh bird
53 Bit of mosaic
54 Rosebud, e.g.
56 Bit of resistance
57 Besides

by Fran & Lou Sabin
Edited by Timothy E. Parker
Answers in back

ACROSS

1 Renaissance fiddle
6 "Like, yesterday!"
10 What Ian Thorpe did
14 Field of play
15 Cutting remark
16 Country name, 1937-49
17 Cartoon bird
19 Big wheel
20 Conduct an interview
21 Put up
22 Like old gossip
23 Far from 22-Down
24 Cupid by another name
25 Campfire remains
28 Compensated
32 ___ to be different
33 Pivot bar
34 Shout to the cuadrilla
35 Three-dimensional scene
38 Pop vocalist Gloria
40 "Can I take that as ___?"
41 Fake book contents
43 Yogi wore one
44 School time
46 Many have maids
48 Colorist's choices
49 Bit of ocean property
51 Dictator's dictum
53 Like a cheetah
54 Drum kit
57 Cash holder
58 Cartoon moose
60 "___ Love Her" (Beatles)
61 So it would ___
62 Shrieking, screeching, etc.
63 Fill, as bases
64 Alan of "The Aviator"
65 "As You Like It" forest

DOWN

1 ___ avis
2 Cupid's counterpart
3 Bird's-eye view?
4 Call off
5 Medicine or law, for many
6 "Citizen Kane" actress Moorehead
7 Straight-shooting
8 Help in a heist
9 "As ___ our agreement"
10 Distinct part
11 Cartoon spell-caster
12 Sea near the Caspian
13 Kind of bagatelle
18 Ash containers
22 Mentally blessed
23 Tick carrier
24 Wows
25 Collections of Icelandic myths
26 The chickadee is its state bird
27 Cartoon witch
29 You can't have big days without them
30 Give a lift, in a way
31 Significant impressions
33 Passers use it
36 Beauty or brains, e.g.
37 Clever remarks
39 Give off
42 Gave the third degree
45 Greek geometrician
46 Exploded, as a tire
47 Desired Scrabble sextet
50 Memorable march site
51 List conclusion
52 Cartoon dinosaur
53 Rocket requirement
54 Driving hazard
55 "Anyone ___?"
56 "___ Angel" (1959 song)
58 Camporee org.
59 Easter preceder

by Matthew J. Koceich
Edited by Timothy E. Parker
Answers in back

ACROSS

1 African antelope
6 Word with "ice" or "six"
10 "___ Magic Moment"
14 Do a tailor's job
15 Field measure
16 Magazine section
17 Head on straight
20 Seemed to go quickly
21 Shoe widths
22 Overseas money
23 Dark black, to Keats
25 "You Light Up My Life" star
27 1980 Neil Diamond hit
33 Challenger problem part
34 Certain photo order (Abbr.)
35 Snakelike fishes
37 Hardly Mr. Right
38 Horror ville?
40 First name among Batman portrayers
41 Seals the victory
43 Vegas opener?
44 Acid type
46 Where the deer and the antelope play
50 Domain
51 W. Texas university
52 Unrefined
55 Condor condo?
57 Yard sign
61 Not the least bit off
64 "Let Us Now Praise Famous Men" author James
65 Wind indicator
66 Don
67 Rolls of money
68 Collections of anecdotes
69 "JFK" director

DOWN

1 "Carmina Burana" composer Carl
2 Stagger
3 "Ah ... say no more"
4 In the middle of
5 ___ Jima
6 Inventor's legal document
7 Need liniment
8 Kind of roll
9 It may be tapped
10 Defeat soundly
11 Time piece
12 Pay ___ mind
13 Lays down the lawn
18 Gaseous element
19 Gambling town
24 Morass
26 Gateway to Paris
27 Set of points
28 Spinachlike plant
29 Visible part of a television transmission
30 Bank robber's job
31 "Home Alone" boy
32 Street talk
36 Blackthorn
38 ___ vera
39 Celtic god of the sea
42 Some tennis strokes
44 "__we there yet?"
45 Plans in detail
47 Once, formerly
48 Quiets
49 Bachelor's end
52 Bird pouch
53 Capital of Latvia
54 Ripened
56 Sicilian mount
58 Aware of
59 "Mila 18" author Uris
60 Force unit
62 Female gametes
63 They patrol the bases

170 Write It Down

by Tracey Snyder
Edited by Timothy E. Parker
Answers in back

ACROSS

1 Rap composer, in a way
5 Bird projection
9 Pinch pennies
14 Coffee makers
15 Chantilly product
16 Carreras or Domingo
17 An early visitor to our shores
18 White-tailed bird of prey
19 Be a pain in the neck
20 A debit or a credit, for example
23 Rope-a-dope inventor
24 Possessive pronoun
25 Swimmers' ailment
29 Attacked on all sides
31 "Last Action ___" (1993)
33 Harrison's "Star Wars" role
34 Wood pattern
36 Filling-station feature
39 It may be required for access
42 Complete disaster
43 Laugh provider
44 Vegas activity
45 Spreadsheet filler
47 Venomous snake
51 Reside
54 Genealogy word
56 M.D. alliance
57 It played Bing Crosby
60 Volume measure
63 Rhinoplasty site
64 Nuclear reactor part
65 Without company
66 Soothing lotion ingredient
67 Harbor boats
68 Part of a football shoe
69 Not as much
70 Margin mark

DOWN

1 Northwest Indian region
2 Cal Ripken, once
3 Feelings of boredom
4 Ivan the Terrible, for example
5 Feeble complaint
6 A royal status
7 Teen worry
8 More perceptive
9 Beatle Ringo
10 It's between Somalia and Tanzania
11 Night spot
12 Cow's response
13 Ask a few too many questions?
21 Corrosive acid
22 Lao Tzu find
26 Blacken
27 It's given after a performance
28 Complete
30 Breakfast choices
32 Put into law
35 Like a battery
37 Desk chair feature
38 Centers
39 Creditor's paper
40 Solemn promise
41 No-goodniks
42 Mob chasers
46 Out of key
48 Lottery winner's choice
49 Become evident
50 Most unique
52 Concert site
53 Brimless cap
55 Fencing needs
58 Play part
59 Play parts
60 Fond du ___, Wis.
61 Under the weather
62 Piggy, e.g.

Page 172

© 2007 Universal Press Syndicate www.upuzzles.com

by Paul Litz
Edited by Timothy E. Parker
Answers in back

ACROSS

1 ___an egg (failed)
5 "The Parent ___" (1961)
9 A colored warning flare
14 Hemingway's "The Sun ___ Rises"
15 Weevil found in cotton
16 Lagoon surrounder
17 Clever maneuver
18 Spumante source
19 Urban transports
20 Grease remover
23 Cow part
24 Banks or Kovacs
25 Type of code
28 "Enter the Dragon" star Bruce
29 Go bad, as fruit
31 Monk's haircut
33 Main bloodline
35 Ever's partner
36 Song in tribute to Marilyn
42 Three-toed bird
43 Semimonthly tides
44 Morning mush
48 It's after pi
49 It may follow a wash
52 "Antiques Roadshow" network
53 Big fissure
55 Escapade
57 Tempt fate
59 Roberts of Hollywood
62 Atom, e.g.
63 Valhalla presider
64 Subject of a Middle Eastern sultan
65 Half brother of Hermes
66 Bassoon bit
67 More courageous
68 Word with "love" or "empty"
69 Is mistaken

DOWN

1 Twins, maybe?
2 Imply, with "to"
3 Tristram's lover
4 Creator of Sherlock Holmes
5 Uphill conveyance
6 British poet Christina or Dante
7 Do a tailor's job
8 Easily swayed
9 Make plump
10 Donny and Marie's home state
11 Boston's Red or Chicago's White
12 Pharmaceutical founder Lilly
13 Trains over the street
21 Mr. Flynn of film
22 Brazilian hot spot
25 New Mexico native
26 Monopoly token or type of curtain
27 Await
30 Rich rock
32 Trims two-by-fours
33 Genesis man
34 Bay State cape
36 Trim a photo
37 "Moby-Dick" captain
38 Fish snares
39 Wood-eating building menaces
40 "That'll show 'em!"
41 Date of reference
45 Bakery treat
46 "Eureka!"
47 Professional's antithesis
49 Miss Muffet's interloper
50 Twice as weird
51 Passing fashions
54 Vowed
56 Prior to, old-style
57 Construction wood
58 Exam
59 Run for exercise
60 Thurman of Hollywood
61 Hasty flight

© 2007 Universal Press Syndicate www.upuzzles.com

by Gia Kilroy
Edited by Timothy E. Parker
Answers in back

ACROSS
1 Part of B.A.
5 Refuse to raise
9 Edible mushroom
14 Like an academic point
15 Domingo rendition
16 Plump and then some
17 Meditative exercise
18 Dearth
19 Form of fortification
20 Time after time
23 Parts of binary code
24 Senate approval
25 Embraces as one's own
28 Well-chosen
30 "Ed Wood" star
34 Where the bull may throw
35 One of the Titanesses
37 Gift from a wahine
38 Time after time
42 Bob Hope's WWII gp.
43 They're in galleys
44 Surrender
45 Ventnor Avenue payment
47 Hand-wringer's feeling
48 Biblical divisions
49 Sweet suffix
51 Foyer
52 Time after time
59 State-run game
60 Ethnic dance
61 Without much meat or fat
63 Cafe patron
64 Proficient in
65 Sport with a point-less point to it
66 Become weatherworn
67 Lasting impression
68 Slowly permeate

DOWN
1 '70s White House kid
2 Odor anagram
3 Ceremonial gown
4 Admit customers after hours
5 Film festival host
6 Locales
7 Claim against property
8 One of "Charlie's Angels"
9 Sharp-toothed eel
10 Did as told
11 Go over a second time
12 Birthright seller
13 Spring observance
21 Lock, stock and barrel
22 Librarian's gadget
25 Mr. Rubinstein
26 Search for water
27 Pope's "___ Solitude"
28 Came to light
29 Dien Bien ___, Vietnam
31 "The King"
32 Pet annoyance?
33 Cone droppers
36 Also
39 Went temporarily off course
40 Partner of to
41 Piercing places
46 Proclaimed
48 Without an occupant
50 Siesta sound
51 Great blue bird
52 Away from the wind, nautically
53 Deafening sound
54 Palindromic emperor
55 Sound of a dull drop
56 Crosby's road companion
57 Handle problems
58 Place to get a spanking
62 "Darn tootin'!"

ACROSS

1 Tucker's go-with
4 Dish's beloved, in rhyme
9 Scraps on the table
13 Glance
15 It has Civic pride
16 Moon landing, notably
17 Oklahoma tribesman (Var.)
18 ___ Mongolia
19 F.D.R.'s dog
20 The Great Bambino
22 In its entirety
24 Heartbeat indicator
25 Baltimore sweetie
26 Time unit
29 Most appreciative
34 Dale who rode Buttermilk
35 Like a valedictory
36 Compos mentis
37 Political cartoonist, Thomas
38 Swiftly
39 "What's your sine?" subj.
40 Aromatic river?
41 Repair roads, in a way
42 Mount Ida's island
43 Order more stock
45 More relaxed
46 British miler Sebastian
47 Game for little Little Leaguers
49 Uttered
52 Drove off
56 Word near "Off Duty"
57 Puts one's cards on the table
59 Joyce's land
60 "___ mouth, insert foot"
61 Author Zola
62 Brown alternative
63 Hungry feeling
64 Gobi formations
65 Bodybuilder's motion, briefly

DOWN

1 1958 chiller (with "The")
2 Wee bit
3 Nitwit
4 "Would" cousin
5 Is obviously sullen
6 Doing very well with little effort
7 Shelley lyric
8 Arctic marine mammal (Var.)
9 Loony tunes
10 Kind of estate
11 "Long ___ Sally"
12 Corset bone
14 "Don't stop now!"
21 Seeks office
23 In
26 Mexicali mister
27 Avoid, as capture
28 "Boston Legal" matters
30 Saratoga action
31 Travel expenses
32 Marry
33 "Machine art" painter
35 October stone
38 Tacked on
42 Composer Porter
44 Whom the Edgar honors
45 Minor memory failures
48 "Beauty and the Beast" beauty
49 Getting-off place
50 He was a rollin' stone
51 Team in the field
53 Pinocchio, memorably
54 Gardner, of mysteries
55 Like a basso profundo
58 Aussie with six toes

by Paul Litz
Edited by Timothy E. Parker
Answers in back

ACROSS

1 Cover completely
5 "Spartacus" novelist
9 States of unconsciousness
14 Angel's trademark
15 Hodgepodge
16 Muscat native
17 Word sometimes paired with "perched"
18 Little streamlet
19 Site for a set
20 Something done to death
23 Hit the campaign trail
24 Menu words
25 Ironfisted one
29 Sprightly
31 Tanner's tub
34 Fundamental truth
35 Kiln for drying hops
36 Resigned sound
37 Boring to the max
40 6/6/44
41 Inkling
42 Lacking any point
43 Willing word
44 Huff and puff
45 Sleekly suave
46 Flood refuge
47 Shoshone
48 Something not worth the effort
57 Divvy out
58 Gobi's location
59 Not well grounded
60 Publicity feat
61 Bumpkin
62 Schemer's conception
63 Comfortably informal
64 Crooner Bennett
65 Plies a needle

DOWN

1 Swap words on the Web
2 Colorful language
3 Shower gel ingredient
4 Best in the field
5 Prescribed layout
6 Green card holder
7 Missile housing
8 Driving expense
9 Exorbitant
10 Creighton University site
11 Sudanese Republic, today
12 Soon
13 Tell all
21 Tantalizing fragrance
22 Villainous Vader
25 "My Heart Belongs to ___"
26 Ooze from
27 Companion of Paul's
28 Roly-___
29 Francis or Augustine
30 Attention-getter
31 Of utmost importance
32 Star's broker
33 Scores in sixty
35 Valhalla VIP
36 All there
38 Plumed military hat
39 Some spouses
44 Way of sitting
45 Not jumpy at all
46 Make amends
47 Grant's command
48 Hamper contents
49 Kind of sax
50 Urban renewal target
51 Bit of truth
52 Capital by a fjord
53 Bugler's farewell
54 Greek getaway
55 Persian comment
56 Diner sign

175 On the Mark

by Tom Dirkshire
Edited by Timothy E. Parker
Answers in back

ACROSS

1 Massage palace
4 Marine biology subject
9 Kind of radioactive particle
14 It follows sunset, in poetry
15 Holiday tune
16 Disinterested
17 Well-sighted?
20 Blondie, to Dagwood
21 Molecule pieces
22 Bison's pride
23 Sought-after statuette
25 Sawbuck
28 "You ___dog, you!"
29 Idle chitchat
31 Spick-and-span
32 Main artery
33 Greek column
34 Precisely on the mark
38 Raise objections
39 Companion of Clark or Martin
40 Mane setting
41 Purloins
43 "The ___ Story" (1959)
46 Tizzy
47 Harbor floaters
48 Oil-rich country
49 Cohere
51 Warning sounds
53 Is dead-on
57 Zones
58 Twangy
59 Biological container
60 "___ and the Pirates"
61 Employs a stiletto
62 Metal-shell filling

DOWN

1 Earthshaking experiences
2 Foreign correspondent
3 Cleopatra's love
4 Go-to guys on the pitching staff
5 Debilitating spray
6 Slip up
7 Bronx cheer
8 French wine region
9 Detest
10 Topsoil
11 Uncorrupted
12 Possessive pronoun
13 Product pitches
18 Orange or lemon, e.g.
19 Luminary
23 Not taken by
24 Coveted cup some fight for?
26 Computer menu option
27 U.S. capital, 1785-90
29 Danish physicist
30 Monet's "Water Lilies," e.g.
31 Bib and tucker
32 Malarial condition
33 Part of the eye
34 Peruse
35 Charlatan
36 Afternoon gatherings
37 Piercing tool
38 Trial evidence
41 "No ___ luck!"
42 Game coins
43 Least confined
44 East Indian tree
45 Creepy-crawly
47 Tiny
48 Return letters
50 Figure in a Rimsky-Korsakov opera
51 Thick, flat slice
52 Troubles or woes
53 Bowler or porkpie
54 Umbrage
55 Club of diamonds?
56 1994 World Cup host

by Matthew J. Koceich
Edited by Timothy E. Parker
Answers in back

ACROSS

1 Hard to comprehend
5 Middle Eastern muck-a-muck
9 Public square
14 Cambodian monetary unit
15 Corn or beans
16 Perfected
17 Taj Mahal site
18 Prefix meaning "wine"
19 "Day the World ____" (1955)
20 Billy Idol hit
23 Exorbitant
24 Downright unpleasant
25 Barely get (with "out")
28 Hebrew patriarch
30 Slob
32 Hours before noon
35 A little garlic
38 Changed location
39 Salinger novel (with "The")
43 Holmes quest
44 Dodge model
45 Asphalt
46 Photocopied
49 Hoopla
51 Word with "collection" or "critic"
52 Panelist of sorts
55 Render harmless
59 Snowmen accessories
61 Odd
64 Cause of adolescent anxiety
65 Sheepskin holder
66 Make corrections to
67 Takes to court
68 Dog in "The Mask"
69 Bar diversion
70 Formerly, long ago
71 Something for the poor

DOWN

1 Reasons for overtimes
2 Sides in an octagon
3 Spooky
4 Typewriter component
5 "Don't have ____, man!" (Bart Simpson saying)
6 Tyro
7 Name on a motorcycle, sometimes
8 Footless amphibians, e.g.
9 Group derived from benzene
10 Word on some jacket labels
11 &
12 Last of 26
13 Calculate the sum
21 Date of reference
22 "___ Not Unusual"
25 Tennis legend Chris
26 Republic in eastern Africa
27 Word in a script
29 Fermented beverage
31 Be indebted to
32 Capital of Ghana
33 Pertaining to the cheekbone
34 Dangerous feat
36 Caesar's seven
37 Provides with power
40 Corp. bigwig
41 "____ To Remember"
42 What you might have to do to sit on a barstool
47 Narrow inlets
48 Lassie's coat
50 Riddle or puzzle
53 Catalyzing enzyme, briefly
54 Come to pass
56 Patriots' Day month
57 Kingdom
58 Early operating system developed for PCs
59 One penny
60 Kindest regards
61 Letters after a proof
62 Actress Thurman
63 Perpetually, poetically

ACROSS
1 Castle enclosure
5 Titles for Coptic bishops
10 Wing-shaped
14 "Alice's Restaurant Massacree" singer Guthrie
15 One way to hang
16 VCR alternative
17 Kennel sound
18 Raccoon cousin
19 More than desire
20 How I feel
23 Creeping colonists
24 Apple product
25 Caveat follower
28 What this puzzle is, really
33 Chou En-____
34 Catch with a long rope
36 Japanese prime minister, 1964-72
37 How I feel
41 ____ Ben Adhem, Sufi saint
42 "Gang" or "mob" attachments
43 "Gimme ____!" (Indiana cheerleaders' cry)
44 Trendy nightclubs
47 Morse code elements
49 What one might pick up in a bar
50 "Star Wars" princess
51 THE question I need to ask you
58 Actress Adams
59 Extremely mad
60 Harvard rival
62 Start of a diary entry
63 More clever
64 Relative of etc.
65 Houston and Peckinpah
66 Nicholas I and Nicholas II
67 What the Lusitania did

DOWN
1 "If I ____ be so bold …"
2 City near Provo
3 Great Britain, vis-a-vis the United States
4 1935 Astaire/Rogers film
5 Locale for 1996's "The Rock"
6 Unmannerly ones
7 Gravy dish
8 Italian wine city
9 Graph lead-in
10 Absolutely free
11 Stead
12 State absolutely
13 Partners of cones
21 ____ Gay (famous B-29)
22 Trap to shut?
25 Religious leader Muhammad (Var.)
26 Caribbean dance
27 Ornamental edging
28 Jr.'s college warm-up exams
29 After-bath wear
30 Doctor's request
31 Make amends
32 The Brown Bomber
35 Pt. of CBS
38 Stock takers of the Old West
39 Catalog customers or restaurant visitors
40 Successor to Allegheny Airlines, for short
45 "Crime doesn't __"
46 Member of a wind section
48 What I'd love for you to do after solving 51-Across
50 It's better than never
51 Takes as a bride
52 Brainstorm
53 He played Rob in "Rob Roy"
54 WWW addresses
55 "I Know Why The Caged Bird Sings" author Angelou
56 ____ Hari
57 Joie de vivre
61 Moose, in Europe

178 Table Discussion

by Alice Walker
Edited by Timothy E. Parker
Answers in back

ACROSS

1 Lumpish mass
5 Religious observances, at times
10 Perry's creator
14 Unstable star
15 Like the Las Vegas strip
16 Clark's love
17 "Rock of ___"
18 "A Bell for ___"
19 Short lengthy lunches?
20 Computer terminal
23 Influential lobby
24 Discommode (with "at")
25 Proprietor's dread
27 Nike slogan
32 Seek the heights
33 Uris hero Ben Canaan
34 Type of belly or barrel
36 Danish coin
39 Rolls of C-notes
41 Type of engine
43 Ski lift
44 Winter hazard
46 Hammett hound
47 Org. with many schedules
48 Times to live through
50 Life or death, e.g.
53 Repressed
56 Salt
57 Cat fancier from Melmac
58 Blackjack shark
64 Dam up
66 Shot by Willie Mosconi
67 Lake seen from the Rock and Roll Hall of Fame
68 Whale of an attraction
69 Cornhusker State city
70 Completely convinced
71 Gp. headquartered in Brussels
72 Train attachment, of old
73 Propped the pigskin

DOWN

1 Eat beaver-style
2 Recognizable symbol
3 "___ the Rainbow"
4 Picnic carryall
5 Some manly haircuts
6 Opera that opens in Memphis
7 Sports figure?
8 North African capital
9 Thread holders
10 Center of Dallas?
11 Tournament format
12 Many an October baby
13 Gore Vidal piece
21 Heavyhearted
22 Cranny companion
26 Witch feature, often
27 Hit film of 1975
28 Caspian Sea feeder
29 Unpleasant result
30 Scintilla
31 Lock of hair
35 Winslet of "Titanic"
37 Popeye Doyle, for one
38 Gaelic
40 Vassal
42 Poor defense for containing a hoops superstar
45 One-time baby duster
49 Manatee
51 Sigma follower
52 Famous Papa's first name
53 Member of a secret order
54 Conservative beginning?
55 Sophocles' forte
59 Race on a strip
60 Blue jack
61 Test response, about 50 percent of the time
62 Where the Shannon flows
63 Clarinet or bassoon
65 Chinese leader Zedong

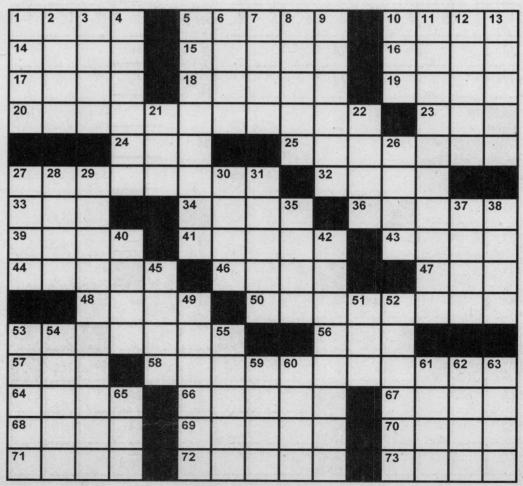

by Carl Cranby
Edited by Timothy E. Parker
Answers in back

ACROSS

1 "Old" British buddy
5 All het up
9 Arizona city
13 Look angry or sullen (Var.)
14 Do a cover-up job?
15 It's pulled occasionally
16 Storybook giant
17 Seaweed product
18 Cellar-dweller's victory
19 Oceanographer's measure
22 Intertwine
23 Methuselah's claim to fame
27 Kuwait noble (Var.)
30 "The Virginian" author, Owen
31 Kublai ___
34 Halos of light
36 Philosophical "way"
37 British sleuths' center
41 Ob-gyn's gp.
42 Out of bed
43 Highland tongue
44 Spoken
46 Great bargain
49 Salad plant
50 "It's about time!"
54 Municipal coin collector
58 Kindly
61 One on a pedestal
62 Ready to come off the stove
63 Stove covers
64 Fishtail
65 Queen before George I
66 Wistful desires
67 Caused a swoon
68 Hot or iced drinks

DOWN

1 T. rex in "Jurassic Park," e.g.
2 Golf great Ben
3 Caesar's gold
4 Years of innocence, perhaps
5 Western warrior
6 Bitten by the love bug
7 Face form
8 Bug's beginning?
9 Lightweight road vehicles
10 Bananas have two
11 "Told you so!"
12 Hanging display
15 Picked on
20 Attachment for "skeptic" or "cynic"
21 Sioux City Sue, e.g.
24 Floral essence
25 They may be stripped
26 Eat away
28 Digs in
29 Criterions
31 Jack in the deck
32 Macho guys
33 Blue ribbon, e.g.
35 Talk up a storm
38 Neckpieces
39 Houston athlete, once
40 Attacked vocally
45 Humans, e.g.
47 Aerie inhabitant
48 Modern money source
51 Set things square
52 1990-91 Formula One champion
53 Linden and litchi
55 Glancing contact, in billiards
56 Between assignments
57 Part of speech
58 Like Bashful
59 Agony
60 L-o-n-g time period

180 Guys Will Be Guys

by Lucas Whetstone
Edited by Timothy E. Parker
Answers in back

ACROSS

1 Acknowledge frankly
5 Crimson Tide, for short
9 "Way to go!"
14 Big partygoer?
15 Greek war god
16 "The Addams Family" character
17 Where Farsi is spoken
18 "The Greatest American Hero" star
19 Animated dog
20 Zephyr
23 Vague references, informally
24 "Coffee, Tea ___?"
25 Stats for QBs and receivers
28 Scottish cap
30 Mason's tool
32 Solos
38 El ___, weather phenomenon
39 Complete description
42 Bring on board
43 "Take It Easy" group
44 Pastors' assistants
47 ___ Ramon, California
48 Foxlike
49 Diminishes
52 Paternity test site
57 Permanent place?
59 Veronica of "Hill Street Blues"
62 Civil rights activist Parks
63 "Doctor Zhivago" heroine
64 Excuse
65 Big name in faucets
66 Tolkien's tree creatures
67 Weighed down
68 Financing abbrs.
69 One famous for saving couples

DOWN

1 A way to set
2 Insectivorous bird
3 Qaboos bin Said, e.g.
4 Habitual ways
5 Fund-raiser, of a sort
6 Stately steed
7 Paris' subway
8 Fall bloomer
9 Trail end?
10 Subterfuge
11 High school course
12 TV adjunct
13 Expression of surprise
21 "___, c'est moi"
22 CPR expert
25 Spin
26 Crowded
27 Tart fruits
29 Cartoonist Walker
31 Single NASA acceleration unit
32 Sore spots
33 "The Big ___" (1983)
34 Behind time
35 Admiral Graf von ___
36 Slangy refusal
37 Chemical suffixes
40 Delivers the joke with a straight face
41 She appears on TV for a spell?
45 Land, as a fish
46 Federal loan agcy.
50 Rangoon is its capital, to the U.S.
51 Front porch
53 "Let's Fall in Love" composer
54 South American plain
55 Main line from the heart
56 Offensively bold
57 Actress Neuwirth
58 River through Belgium
59 Computer in "2001: A Space Odyssey"
60 In the manner of
61 Word with "day" or "night"

181 Headed for the Shower

by Casey Rumblach
Edited by Timothy E. Parker
Answers in back

ACROSS

1 Splashy party
5 Dressing type
10 Current choice?
14 Cause for cramming
15 Warm welcome
16 Gunk
17 Follow a Japanese custom
20 Friends in Firenze
21 14-Across takers
22 Poetry's "rare and radiant maiden"
24 The Mad Hatter's beverage
25 Joint for health?
28 Gene's makeup?
29 Types
32 Asimov topic, often
34 Where leks are spent
37 Make public
38 Be a poor gambler?
41 Mimicking bird
42 Strongly built
43 Take the honey and run?
45 Lounge lizard's look
46 Saxony, for one
49 Pin number?
50 Some batteries
53 Charitable Mother
55 Strong revulsion
59 Was under the weather
60 Defeat soundly (with "of")
63 Inner drive
64 "Penny wise, pound foolish," e.g.
65 Take by truck
66 Light weight
67 Horse end
68 In a purposeless manner

DOWN

1 Noted Ford
2 Guys who do hatchet jobs?
3 Thin layer
4 Big name in petroleum
5 "Norma ____"
6 Zillions
7 Word before "the worse"
8 Nut head?
9 Waste maker
10 Need liniment
11 Kicker's practice target
12 Past follower
13 Modern records
18 Macho
19 Blacken on the grill
23 Macaroni shape
26 Left at sea
27 Pigged out
30 Batman cartoonist
31 Tackle box item, perhaps
33 Short final notice?
34 Memo directive
35 Man, e.g.
36 Cash on hand, e.g.
38 Lovett's first or Sparky's last
39 New York salt lake
40 Because of this, in contracts
41 Chanced upon
44 It may be Far or Near
46 Put in more film
47 Beneficial
48 Troublemaker
51 Muslim officials (Var.)
52 Napped leather
54 Hindu sage
56 Couple, to tabloids
57 Reach across
58 Makes it?
60 Wiretap
61 Muff
62 Bridal bio word

by Gia Kilroy
Edited by Timothy E. Parker
Answers in back

ACROSS

1 "The Ten Commandments," for one
5 Pursue wild geese?
10 End-of-week letters
14 Carpentry groove
15 An animated dwarf
16 Eat, as a meal
17 Reginald of "Mrs. Miniver"
18 Time unit?
19 Indy 500 winner Luyendyk
20 Waves, once
23 Tout's forte
24 "___ Before Dying"
25 Female prophet
28 Like Niagara Falls
31 Commotion
32 African antelope
35 Send packing
39 Waves

42 Certain singing voice
43 Traveler's bane on choppy waves
44 Word with "bed" or "board"
45 Blackflies
47 Legendary quarterback Bart
49 Irish actor Milo
52 One way of learning by
54 Waves
60 Desired Rogaine result
61 Looking glass girl
62 Computer input
64 Ocean-fish feeder
65 Saturn's largest satellite
66 Musical composition
67 Accomplishment
68 It's okay to dribble in this
69 Bills on birds

DOWN

1 Tokyo, formerly
2 Minor chess piece
3 Inventor's forte
4 Accumulation
5 Family member
6 Metal fasteners
7 Church recess
8 Goad
9 "___ of Laura Mars"
10 Response to "What do you say?"
11 "Enhanced," on some menus
12 Outdoor climbers
13 Isn't insensitive
21 Off-the-cuff
22 Kind of bran
25 Lengthy narrative
26 Matinee follower?
27 Bad thing to get on the job
28 One of the Three Wise Men

29 Seine sights
30 Business letter enc.
33 Talkative pet
34 Decayed matter used as fuel
36 Bear that's looked up to
37 Crystal gazer
38 Russian leader before 1917
40 Like a used paperback, perhaps
41 One of the five senses
46 Palindromic fictional twin
48 Muscle-to-bone connector
49 Exclaimed in pleasure
50 Alarm
51 "Book of Songs" writer Heinrich
52 Summarize

53 Portents
55 Short HS course
56 Mishmash
57 One of the Corleones
58 Finish line feature
59 Pencl remnant
63 Beast of burden

183 Teensy Beginnings

by Paul Litz
Edited by Timothy E. Parker
Answers in back

ACROSS

1 ___ YOUR DOG
5 Tarzan's friends
9 Less desirable berth, perhaps
14 Popular cookie
15 Harmless prank
16 Born yesterday
17 Nightgown wearer of rhyme
20 Pretentious syllables
21 Chicken recipe
22 Benevolent one
23 "Electric" creatures
25 It can be pressing
27 Kind of burglar
30 Skywalker cohort
32 Fodder for a shrink
35 Diva's delivery
37 Canonical hour
39 "Hit the road!"
41 Film about a boy inheriting the Twins
44 Gal's guy
45 Touchy
46 Zero, in a sport
47 Lists
49 Fit inside
51 After taxes
52 Flat-bottomed boat
54 Erstwhile despot
56 Short whistle-blower
59 Mark's replacement
61 Catch phrase
65 Jenner contribution of 1796
68 VCR part
69 Famous Diamond
70 Have no doubts
71 Cloth fold
72 Flying nuisance
73 Without

DOWN

1 Monk's hood
2 Compound used in fertilizers
3 Hoops great Willis
4 Jim at the Alamo
5 Completely deserted
6 Good buddy
7 "CHiPs" star Estrada
8 Yarn coil
9 Cosmologist's concern
10 Prospector's need
11 Peak discoverer Zebulon
12 Like Edmund in "King Lear"
13 Stench
18 One day in March
19 Unvalued growth
24 Ones guilty of disorderly conduct?
26 Window sticker
27 Shin's back
28 "The Little Mermaid"
29 Lord or Lady, e.g.
31 Frank option
33 Inert gas
34 Purplish hue
36 He bore a heavy load
38 Source of ornamental plumes
40 Track tourney
42 Lover of Guinevere
43 Health food ad claim, perhaps
48 Beginning course, perhaps
50 Powder type
53 Misguided
55 Ice, to a mixologist
56 Invitation letters
57 Famed runner Zatopek
58 Dim
60 Yoke pair
62 Ms. Lollobrigida
63 Shakespearean "soon"
64 Latest buzz
66 Pastoral expanse
67 By way of

Page 185

ACROSS

1 Zoroastrian
6 Knock about
10 Gets off the fence
14 Companion of Artemis
15 Upper hand
16 Moan and groan
17 Pitch
19 Side product?
20 Mr., abroad
21 Took in
23 Paver's supply
24 Half of a carefree phrase
27 Oil field sight
29 Pitch
32 Lively Latin dance
33 Certain Coyote
34 British rule in colonial India
37 Kyoto fast food
40 Belarus, once (Abbr.)
41 Historic mission
44 Hastened
47 Pitch
52 National park allure
53 Frankness
55 Actor Linden
56 Bogart film
59 One is dynamic
60 Monty Python's Idle
62 Pitch
65 Site of the fabled forges of the Cyclopes
66 Give a nudge
67 1996 Best Picture nominee
68 Try out
69 Indeterminate quantity
70 Place or show horse

DOWN

1 Western chasers
2 Noah's landfall
3 Gusto
4 Ed.'s request
5 Driver's lic. and others
6 Short collection?
7 Valhalla honcho
8 Business at hand
9 Donnybrooks
10 "L'___ del Cairo" (Mozart opera)
11 Overtones or harmonics, in music
12 Excessively sentimental expressions
13 Quiet firework
18 Shows displeasure
22 Attracted
25 Jr. and sr., e.g.
26 Tibetan gazelle
28 Bonds stat
30 Pac-10 member
31 Port in southeast Iraq
34 Felon's file
35 Dining option
36 Track and field projectiles
38 It may be cocked
39 Polar feature
42 Hour div.
43 ATM's lack
45 Stat that is better when lower
46 Racket
48 Understands
49 Rescued damsel's cry
50 Some serpents
51 Waiting room
54 Copter component
57 Quarky item?
58 Definitely not polite
61 Grimalkin
63 Samuel Gompers' org.
64 Eastern philosophical principle

185 Eyes on the Clock

by Henry Quarters
Edited by Timothy E. Parker
Answers in back

ACROSS

1 Group that votes alike
5 Lamb or veal items
10 Waist band?
14 Nickname among Yankee greats
15 Condor's digs
16 Piedmont wine center
17 Vase-shaped pitcher
18 Lariat in the Southwest (Var.)
19 Fiction enthusiast?
20 English, to some
23 IV x XIII
24 Sean Connery, among many
25 Put aside
29 "Bragh" preceder
33 Radical '70s org.
34 Sitting on
36 Prepare for knighthood
37 Voluptuous physique
41 Kuwait biggie (Var.)
42 It jumps through hoops
43 Apt. grouping
44 South England county
46 Places of "action"
49 "Fame" singer Irene
51 Brew holder
52 1979 Doobie Brothers hit
59 Tommie of Mets history
60 It's projected
61 Off course
63 Show fury
64 "Awake and Sing!" playwright
65 Mudville group
66 Misses the mark
67 Action after an alarm
68 Freshly

DOWN

1 Luck of the draw?
2 Down times
3 Architectural curve
4 Geometric shape
5 Traveling amusement show
6 Take, as advice
7 Kind of contract
8 Pocket breads
9 Meeting with a medium
10 Greeting an officer
11 It covers plenty of ground
12 Type of beetle or party
13 Take on
21 Black gold
22 Russian novelist Maxim
25 Replay effect, briefly
26 Rutger of "Blade Runner"
27 Frat letters
28 Prescription data
30 Kind of surgeon
31 Lysol targets
32 Matador boosters
33 Food fish
35 HS junior test
38 Nick-of-time types
39 "___ Caesar's ghost!"
40 Most subject to chance
45 Earth mover
47 Cub Scout group
48 Spiny lizard
50 Living quarters
52 Colt's kin
53 Operatic prince
54 Kind of miss
55 Part of YSL
56 Wee pest
57 Half a matched set
58 Shore prospector
62 Bow wood

by Carl Cranby
Edited by Timothy E. Parker
Answers in back

ACROSS
1 Deceived
6 Battle mettle
11 Dr. Seuss character
14 Branch of wickerwork
15 City on the Penobscot
16 "Nod" or "mod" attachment
17 Boys with badges
19 Org. in "Patriot Games"
20 "Rich Man, Poor Man" author
21 Film editor's units
23 Sunblock?
27 Polish remover
29 Removed from memory
30 Start for Vallarta or Rico
31 Biblical king
32 Bernstein and Lewis
33 Twist-off, e.g.
36 Atlas statistic
37 Flower component
38 Toast-topper, sometimes
39 Novelist Deighton
40 Military assistants
41 Nose-offending stimuli
42 He may swing from the heels
44 Mint product
45 Got going
47 Moved quickly and nimbly
48 Crop up
49 Equine check
50 Feathers partner
51 Rat
58 Opening-day pitcher
59 Gabardine or serge, e.g.
60 "The Barber of Seville," e.g.
61 "The Simpsons" neighbor, Flanders
62 They're rung up
63 Drew, of fiction

DOWN
1 Female hare
2 Inits. on a rocket
3 Kind of iron
4 Sushi offering
5 Attired
6 Outspoken
7 "... pretty maids all in ___"
8 Bodybuilder Ferrigno
9 Can. province
10 Personnel lists
11 Noisy timekeeper
12 Immigrant
13 Kid a kid
18 Equipped with footwear
22 Telecom co.
23 Piano feature
24 "What ___ mood I'm in ..."
25 Black-tressed
26 It's east of the Urals
27 Saintly radiances
28 Spreadsheet unit
30 Writing material
32 Gave up, as land
34 Condor's nest
35 Did some modeling
37 Locale
38 Keats' creations
40 Bears witness
41 Your view or mine
43 April 15 addressee
44 Transport commercially
45 Underworld figure
46 Kind of element
47 Water holes
49 Proper function
52 One-time Delta competitor
53 Black gold
54 3.75, e.g.
55 Poe's evening
56 Mythical monster
57 Thumbs down

187 Cool It!

by Alice Walker
Edited by Timothy E. Parker
Answers in back

ACROSS
1 Embarrass
6 Renal artery feeder
11 Needle-holding tree
14 Athletically slender
15 Milk byproduct
16 Cell letters
17 North or south line of latitude
19 Town sign abbr.
20 Tuesday of note
21 Basketball basket height
23 Rickman of "Die Hard"
26 Sugary cookie snacks
28 Pound of poems
29 Knowledge
30 Adds pitch to a roof?
31 Ekland of films
32 Come to grips with impending bankruptcy, e.g.
34 Ex-Senator Sam of Georgia
35 Hill dweller
36 Coffee holder
37 Degenerate
38 General Motors brand
41 ___ fixe
43 Notified, in a way
45 Heston film
47 Frosh follower
48 New Year's word
49 Many popes
50 Class
51 Brooklyn followers?
52 Large, heavy knife
54 Sea that's a lake
56 Adlai lost to him
57 Little consolation
62 Stephen of "Michael Collins"
63 Kukla and Fran's pal
64 Use a blender
65 Prince Valiant's son
66 Bounds partner
67 Incline

DOWN
1 High spot
2 Brief outline of life and work
3 Much of N.J.'s coast
4 Algonquin nation
5 "___ You Come Again" (Parton hit)
6 Ecological danger
7 Ex-Bruin Bobby
8 Right-hand pages
9 Stories
10 Prayer ending
11 Excluding, in a stony way
12 Computer key
13 Drum sounds
18 Debate-limiting method
22 Plant with fronds
23 Romeo's leader?
24 Savings partner
25 North Pole surrounder
27 European sea eagle
31 Target, as of a prank
33 Was sorry
34 Not the courageous type
37 Puts back
39 Kenton or Gardner
40 Bookie's numbers
42 Real looker
43 Protein source
44 Lamenting
45 New York city
46 Source for the press
47 Stevens of "In Cold Blood"
50 Went quietly
53 EPA's concern, briefly
55 Band boosters
58 Go down momentarily
59 Target of a conquistador's quest
60 Public image, for short
61 Little elevator

ACROSS

1 Diaper woe
5 Word on terrycloth, sometimes
8 King and queen, e.g.
14 Canyon bounceback
15 Giants great
16 Highway access
17 Word with "movie" or "party"
18 Opening for a maid?
19 One-named folk singer
20 Mechanic, in slang
23 Key's went national
24 Dole (out)
25 Brave moguls
28 Test-track curve?
29 Break fast or breakfast
31 Mimic
33 Half an audio cassette
35 Hearing aids
36 Burdensome possession
41 Long, long time (Var.)
42 Regions
43 Super saver?
47 Pt. of USDA
48 Public transport
51 Mork's planet
52 They sometimes clash
54 A-flat, enharmonically
56 Result of a rough workout, perhaps
58 Pancake comparative
61 Olive, for one
62 Elisabeth of "Leaving Las Vegas"
63 Sound at an opened floodgate
64 "Just the Way You ___"
65 Informed
66 Noted Kitt
67 Born
68 Fix, at the vet's

DOWN

1 Ska relative
2 Squirrel's horde
3 Linen closet collection
4 Israeli round dance (Var.)
5 Like Mom's apple pie
6 List unit
7 Senator Thurmond
8 Grew fond of
9 Financially strapped
10 Deuce beater
11 Relative of long.
12 CPR giver
13 Relaxing resort
21 "Now you ___, now ..."
22 Compaq rival
25 Sweep with binoculars
26 Small racer that makes kids "go"
27 "___ Now or Never"
30 Driver's aid
32 Pro votes
33 Trap topper
34 Chicken ___ King
36 Tear partner
37 Pawn
38 Big Band ___
39 "Fever" singer
40 Like some criticism
41 GI's address
44 Go over and over and ...
45 Mystery writer Christie
46 Craggy height
48 Cruise the pubs
49 Actress Andress
50 Rapid
53 "Wake of the Ferry" painter
55 Party givers
56 Coagulate
57 Land of the leprechaun
58 Wonderment
59 ___ Na Na
60 "___ he's a jolly ..."

by *Matthew J. Koceich*
Edited by Timothy E. Parker
Answers in back

ACROSS

1 A ruler before the revolution
5 ___ Raton, Florida
9 Quixote and Marquis
13 4,840 square yards
14 Stratford-on-___
15 Pie contents, often
16 Aquatic plant
18 Print type, briefly
19 Conformed to a particular format
20 Sudden collapse
21 One of Jacob's sons
22 With anticipation
23 Family planning
28 Beginning
29 "The one that got away," e.g.
30 Short trip
33 Unstable star
34 Call to arms
36 Tumbler of rhyme
37 One-time econ. measure
38 Powerful shark
39 Bulgarian capital
40 Swimmer's bane
43 Bibulous
46 Egg cells
47 One paying a flat fee
48 Member of a North American Plains people (Var.)
53 Vary
54 Air movement on one regular course
55 Skating competition
56 Salary
57 III x XIX
58 Larry King has a few
59 On the mattress
60 Rectangular paving stone

DOWN

1 Shooter marbles
2 Shout to a stray
3 Pretentious
4 Roll of film
5 French novelist (1799-1850)
6 Spanish metropolis
7 Absence of heat
8 One or some
9 Twaddle
10 Like some garments
11 It meant nothing to Nero
12 Unfeeling
15 Large metal vessel with a handle and spout
17 Field position
20 Keep in stock
22 And others, briefly
23 Reverberate
24 Knows the plan of attack
25 Invitation letters
26 New York's Russian ___Room
27 Synthetic fabric
30 Characterized by minimal distortion
31 Collection of miscellaneous pieces
32 Prepare for the future
34 Harder to find
35 Related by blood
36 Write briefly
38 Creators
39 "Dream" or "sea" ender
40 Uses the front door
41 Search for food
42 Circumvented
43 Curtain
44 Frankie Goes To Hollywood debut single
45 Loosen, in a way
48 Bedouin or Omani
49 Pointed tools for punching small holes
50 Bee habitation
51 "I'll get right ___!"
52 Change a manuscript
54 Airline whose last flight was Dec. 1, 2001

ACROSS

1 Rhetorical device
6 Initials on Sputnik
10 Holds the deed on
14 Threaten to surpass
15 Workplace oversight agcy.
16 Reporter's query
17 1967 Robert Knight song
20 One end of the political spectrum
21 Opposes
22 Blown up, as a neg.
23 Soccer star Mia
24 Word with "tiger" or "water"
27 Hiroshima's river
29 Sackcloth companion
33 Vladimir Nabokov character
34 "Who's the Boss?" star
36 Carnegie and Radio City Music
38 Mechanical impossibility
41 Multivolume tales
42 Blink of an eye
43 Lead-in for "light" or "night"
44 Like a rock
46 Bit of Morse code
47 Medical advice, often
48 Deteriorates
50 Dined in or out
52 Man from Acre
56 Put into office
60 What go-getters seem to have
62 Satie or Estrada
63 Kind of rug
64 Traditional truism
65 Lawless role
66 Alphabetical run
67 Some interoffice mail

DOWN

1 Nonkosher
2 Kentucky Derby winner ___ Ridge
3 "Message complete"
4 Informal truce talk
5 1942 Pulitzer novelist Glasgow
6 Part of a profit calculation
7 K.C. time zone
8 Fancy dinnerware
9 1903 independence declarer
10 Birds that may be spotted
11 "Stop, Silver!"
12 Sailor's employer, perhaps
13 Canonized femmes, for short
18 Waterborne
19 Sneaker
23 Golfers' obstacles
24 Drinks like a cat
25 "Don't get any funny ___!"
26 "Key ___" (Bogart film)
28 Fastening item
30 Tip from a gentleman?
31 Oligarchy
32 Taps on the brakes
34 Prayed for
35 Inter ___ (among other things)
37 Irritated condition
39 Crony
40 Sitcom role for Borgnine
45 Word with "sand" or "bottom"
47 Go back, as a hairline
49 Layers
51 Time for a coffee break, maybe
52 Surefooted goat
53 Like some losers
54 Wrack partner
55 Singer/songwriter Paul
56 Genesis twin
57 Rail transport
58 Waffle brand
59 Turns red, maybe
61 It may follow a wash

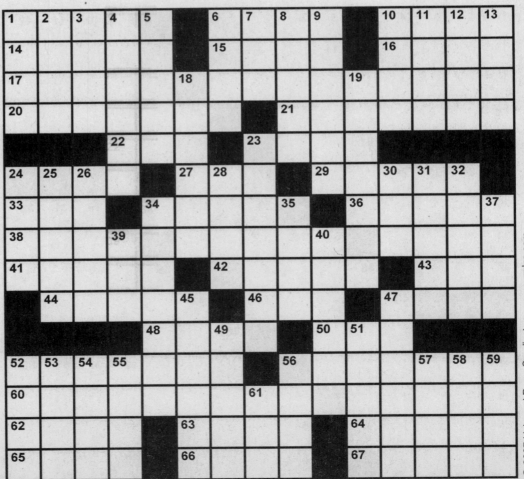

by Fran & Lou Sabin
Edited by Timothy E. Parker
Answers in back

ACROSS

1 Computer or chess group
5 Pool-player's powder
9 They can cause tears or laughter
14 Yuri Zhivago's love
15 Israeli carrier
16 Bloodhound's forte
17 Impetuosity
18 Allot
19 Eighth Greek letter
20 Storable seat
23 Endeavor
24 D.D.E.'s campaign handle
25 Boosts octane, e.g.
27 Swap-shop deals
31 Acapulco address
32 Change an estimate
34 Silly sort
37 Jackie's last hubby
38 Considers
41 Poison Ivy portrayer
42 Cicely of "Fried Green Tomatoes"
45 Lakeside house renter
48 Carlo Levi's "stopping" town
51 Branches and twigs, to a bird
52 Florida tribesman
55 It's hard to bear
56 "Ab ____" (from day one)
57 Phone-owner's convenience
62 Slowly, to Muti
64 Kuwait biggie
65 Albania's Ramiz
66 Late-night time
67 Button pressed after a closing
68 Jamboree unit
69 Optical annoyances
70 "____ chic!"
71 Mates no more

DOWN

1 Sheet music symbol
2 "Symphonie Espagnole" composer
3 Caspian Sea feeder
4 Highwaymen
5 Hardened by heat and cold
6 Baldwin of "Cats & Dogs"
7 Woodworker's machine
8 Antisepticizes
9 Guitarist's purchase
10 Cologne cry
11 Transparent, as some veils
12 ____ nous (just between you and me)
13 Doesn't say "hit me"
21 Hawaiian guitars, for short
22 Cause of a red face
26 Bill partner
27 Someone else's kid compared to yours?
28 Condor's pad (Var.)
29 Foundations do it
30 Kazakhstan-to-Nepal dir.
33 Wink of an eye
35 "Peter Pan" nasty
36 They're big on Clark Gable
39 GI party item
40 Flight attendants
43 Japanese wedding band?
44 Sgts. Bilko, York, etc.
46 "Star Trek: TNG" counselor
47 Old phonograph record material
49 Mauna ____
50 Least well
52 Thrills for choristers
53 Wedding or commencement, e.g.
54 Bugs' animated nemesis
58 "Sideways" subject
59 Holm oak
60 "A stitch in time saves ____"
61 Roscoes
63 ____ kwon do (Korean karate)

by Lynn Lempel
Edited by Timothy E. Parker
Answers in back

ACROSS

1 Course of action
5 "Gosh!"
9 Split-off groups
14 Angelic feature
15 Dove known for poetry
16 Actress Barkin
17 Bandleader
19 In solitary
20 Pago Pago's American locale
21 Zee's counterpart
23 Robt. E. Lee's cause
24 Theme park lure
26 Called a pen pal?
28 Essayist with Addison
31 Noisy napper
33 Common dot follower
34 Blissful
36 Soft powder
39 Tow
40 Cartoon series about the Pickles kids
42 The Smothers Brothers, e.g.
43 Lion lairs
45 Close tightly
46 Feverish
47 Being displayed
49 Expired, as a subscription
51 Rapper with the album "Gangsta's Paradise"
53 In the past
54 From the past
55 Buffaloes
58 Large pitchers
62 Ration out
64 Weather benchmark
66 Tuscany town
67 Russian, for one
68 Home to most humans
69 No Child Left Behind mandates
70 Gumbo pod
71 Puppy's cry

DOWN

1 Coveted degrees
2 Pasternak heroine
3 Many a fan at homecoming
4 "Never again!"
5 Christian, for one
6 Boy toy
7 Chemical building block
8 Throw caution to the wind
9 Sailor's lungful
10 Kay's follower?
11 Item on a bedside table
12 Stressed out
13 Sam in the World Golf Hall of Fame
18 Cardboard tube, say
22 Altruistic act
25 False belief
27 Ping-Pong accessory
28 Happy realtor's sign
29 On the up and up
30 Casserole staples
31 Fountain freebie
32 "Breakfast at Tiffany's" actress Patricia
35 "The African Queen" scriptwriter
37 Humdinger
38 Kentucky Derby racer
41 Device to keep things apart
44 Weekend TV hit
48 Scenes from overlooks
50 Time for a fresh start
51 Sail along effortlessly
52 Dragon puppet
53 Director's dream
56 Thereabouts
57 "Wunnerful, Wunnerful" autobiographer
59 "If all ___ fails ..."
60 Stir up sediment
61 Give and take
63 Ottawa's prov.
65 Future embryos

193 United We Stand

by Gia Kilroy
Edited by Timothy E. Parker
Answers in back

ACROSS
1 Cook one's goose?
6 "Hey, Mac!"
10 Nonpoisonous
14 Wiser companion
15 The Hippocratic ___
16 Restaurant bill
17 Crowning touch?
18 They were spendable in Rome, once
19 They lay around the farm
20 Family financial figure
23 U.N. working-conditions agency
24 About 2.2 pounds
25 Memorable writer Bombeck
28 The life of Riley
31 Words with "stop" or "give"
35 Sundial numeral
36 Toll unit
37 "Bam!" chef
38 Largest American news agency
41 Withhold
42 That alternative
43 Jeanne d'Arc's abbreviated title
44 F neighbor
45 Fence part
46 Pt. of the NAACP
47 "Snicker" attachment
49 Bass attachment
51 Place for some frequent fliers
58 Give a nudge
59 Speak gratingly
60 Word with "spitting" or "mirror"
61 Leer lasciviously
62 Types
63 Kind of trail or lock
64 Letter opener
65 Old station identification
66 "Maria ___" (Dorsey hit)

DOWN
1 Academic mil. unit
2 Mixture
3 First of all?
4 Side in a 1990s war
5 Oregon or Chisholm
6 Either end of a magnet
7 The Shirelles' "Mama ___"
8 1/3 of an out, perhaps
9 "___ Kissed Her" (The Beach Boys)
10 Sailing vessel
11 Interjection to express doubt
12 Exquisite
13 Martians and such
21 Jean-Paul Sartre play
22 Workshop devices
25 Dodge, as the press
26 Resurrected
27 Perform incorrectly
29 ___ mode
30 Brief fight
32 Treat a wound
33 Main points
34 Mary-Kate or Ashley
36 Immigrant's giveaway
37 Crossword VIP
39 New kid in town
40 Sounds of hesitation
45 Uses a two-wheeler
46 "20 Questions" category
48 Hair-raising
50 It could be stuffed
51 Goad
52 Vincent Lopez' theme song
53 Seeks a favor
54 ___ facto
55 Scruff of the neck
56 Harold's "Ghostbusters" role
57 Part of Doris Day's theme song
58 Pea coat?

© 2007 Universal Press Syndicate www.upuzzles.com

Page 195

by Alice Walker
Edited by Timothy E. Parker
Answers in back

ACROSS

1 Faith that arose in Persia
6 One way to pose
10 Formal dance
14 Tennis scores after deuce
15 They may be boosted
16 Fonda role of '97
17 Whopper juniors?
20 "How was ___ know?"
21 Word with "fine" or "liberal"
22 Incenses
23 Shakespearean character
25 Hamilton commemoratives
26 "The Secret of ___" (1982 film)
28 All broken up
32 Life
34 Black and white predator
35 Words before "Z"
38 Arachnid of song
42 "Angeles" or "Lobos" starter
43 Arthurian days, e.g.
44 Becomes bitter
45 Begin, e.g.
48 Mish-mash
49 Soccer great Mia
51 Circuit
53 Surpass at the dinner table
55 Corset stiffener
56 Some sounds from Santa
59 Petty thieves, e.g.
62 Ship's storage area
63 Some are Horatian
64 They may be Dutch or French
65 It could be restricted
66 One concerned with rhythm and feet
67 Some are kept behind bars

DOWN

1 "Road" picture destination
2 Entrance for a collier
3 Random
4 Formicary inhabitant
5 One of the world's religions
6 Sir Isaac of science
7 Cries of aversion
8 "___ have to?"
9 Spanish 101 word
10 Sudden increases
11 Completely unfamiliar
12 Stares at lasciviously
13 More, in a phrase
18 "... ___ saw Elba"
19 Gets in a sting
24 "For goodness' sake!"
26 Carpenter's item
27 Involved with, as a hobby
29 "... off ___ the Wizard"
30 Ending for "mock" or "cook"
31 Summer coolers, for short
33 Unfathomable
35 When to stop growing
36 Garr with a "Tootsie" role
37 "... ___ I'm told"
39 Comparative ending
40 Start of a musical refrain
41 "___ Arabian Nights"
45 Mrs. Marcos
46 Hottest, as news
47 Apple offering
49 Sitcom material
50 "___ of Two Cities"
52 Richard E. and Robert C.
53 Workplace safety grp.
54 Roof with removable panels
55 Hook's assistant
57 Soup pods
58 Kettle sound
60 Words of commitment
61 Reset setting, perhaps

by Louis Lahey
Edited by Timothy E. Parker
Answers in back

ACROSS

1 Musical score notations
6 Largemouth or smallmouth
10 Great multitude
14 Flower of the primrose family
15 Words after "thanks"
16 Like cuttlefish defenses
17 Perfectly suited
19 Tide designation
20 Unit of electrical current
21 Bad-weather contingency plan
23 Without, in Paris
25 Sounded like a mad dog
26 Full house indicator
29 Morning lawn coverings
31 DDT banner
32 Italian resort island
34 It was once thought to be indivisible
36 Thumbs-down votes
40 Montezuma, notably
41 "The Running ___" (1987)
42 2006 Scarlett Johansson film
43 Southwest tableland
44 Analyze, as evidence
45 Swahili-speaking nation
46 "Norma ___" (1979)
48 Come to grips with
50 Long, long time
51 Honored with
55 Kramden and Norton, e.g.
57 Epitome of slowness
59 Meal
63 Spinach nutrient
64 Lingering sensation
66 Full of oneself
67 Blanket choice
68 Cousteau milieu
69 Mr. of fiction
70 Keeps folks in stitches?
71 Gets warmer

DOWN

1 "The Godfather" composer Nino
2 Midterm, e.g.
3 Rejection carrier
4 Pagoda roofing materials
5 Occurring irregularly
6 "Batman" sound effect
7 Sporting wings
8 Boston pops?
9 Ms. magazine co-founder
10 Obstacle
11 "Love Story" star
12 Get by on thin ice?
13 Banged out
18 "In the Line of Fire" actress Russo
22 Toddler's break
24 Hindu religious teacher
26 Swindle
27 Bring down the house?
28 Stops wavering
30 Rod of Moses
33 Set up differently
35 Like some beer
37 Top-of-the-line
38 It has its ups and downs
39 Distance between pillars
42 Bare bones model?
44 They also have their ups and downs
47 Consumer bait
49 Singer Vikki
51 Folks featured in Harrison Ford's "Witness"
52 Like a bad apple
53 Audibly
54 "Robinson Crusoe" author
56 The final frontier
58 Tuck away
60 Far from land
61 General decoration
62 Teller's stack
65 Golfer from Johannesburg

ACROSS

1 Baker's buy
6 Game catcher
10 Somewhat open
14 Cold comfort?
15 Bollywood tune
16 By oneself
17 Kiss
20 Inactive craft
21 Map legends
22 Has one's say
23 Collection of memorable remarks
24 Hearty quaffs
25 Kiss
31 Gridder's ground grabbers
32 Chaps
33 H.S.T.'s successor
34 Boston pro, familiarly
35 Travel method
36 Ransom, the auto maven
37 Would-be sgt.
38 Chilling effect
40 Pitchman's pitches
42 Kiss
44 "The lights are on but no ___ home"
45 TV E.T.'s planet
46 "Gunsmoke" actress Blake
49 Throws for a loop
51 Ref's decision
54 Kiss
57 Raison d'___
58 "Listen up!" in court
59 Paranormal, to some
60 Dump
61 Artist Magritte
62 Poet whose name is an anagram of 1-Across

DOWN

1 Sharp barks
2 They sometimes clash
3 "You're ___ of help!"
4 Ancient Roman sun god
5 Hair ball?
6 Busboy's burden
7 Tanning agents
8 "___ before beauty"
9 Conditionally freed
10 Pitch in
11 Name of XXIII popes?
12 Soap enhancer
13 Goes bad, in a way
18 Casually thumbs through, as a book
19 Visual aid, informally
23 Rat chaser?
24 Hardly close
25 First Hebrew letter
26 String quartet member
27 Coquet
28 Lounged
29 In a weird way
30 Monster's loch
31 400, on prescriptions
35 Some batteries
36 Wilbur's "whee!"
38 "Mister Roberts" star
39 Beatles' Rigby
40 Grouch's look
41 Popular food garnish
43 Bopped on the bean
46 War-minded deity
47 Butterfly relative
48 Spread section
49 Small songbird
50 Drain slowly
51 Chez O'Hara
52 Do needle work?
53 Lyrical lines
55 Salon request
56 Quilters' get-together

by Fran & Lou Sabin
Edited by Timothy E. Parker
Answers in back

ACROSS
1 On sick leave
4 Slow learner
10 "Alfie" actor Omar
14 "The Matrix" hero
15 Tighten a corset, perhaps
16 Sixth Greek letter
17 Babble on
20 Filled with passion
21 Porterhouse or strip
22 Hull's part
23 Cherry red
26 Pinochle card
29 Icelandic literary collections
31 Home retreat
32 Bargain hunters' site
33 Certain Pueblo Indians
35 Stand for
37 Long-loved Irving Berlin tune
39 Middle Eastern capital since 1788
41 Sawyer of "Good Morning America"
42 Wellsian race
43 Bookie's business
44 Shade in "America the Beautiful"
48 A small drink of liquor
49 U.S. Open winner, 1994 and 1997
52 Cape-wearing Lugosi
53 DNA may provide it
55 Antipasto morsel
57 "Look who just showed up!"
61 Snootiness
62 Rossini character
63 Before, poetically
64 Engage, as gears
65 "Passenger 57" star
66 X-ray dose

DOWN
1 Air, to a jet engine
2 Riffled, as book pages
3 Hung out
4 Stuff
5 Pear-shaped fiddle
6 Building extension
7 Frat letter
8 Strands, as by a winter storm
9 They're for the birds
10 Book before Nehemiah
11 "Surprise!"
12 School org.
13 Attached to "Steel," it's a Hefty trash bag
18 Botswana desert region
19 Booter's aid
24 Abridge, e.g.
25 Occupies
27 Kind of burglar
28 Storm center
30 Tofu source
32 Group of musicians
34 Jesse Ventura victory, once
35 Case-breaker, at times
36 Sicily's Mongibello
37 Patrons
38 Strikes a pose
39 Balance beam perfection
40 Bulldog
43 English Northwest Passage seeker
45 Jerry Mathers' role
46 New York state pen city
47 Scolded
49 Houston approval
50 Screws up
51 Grenoble is its capital
54 Allergy indication
56 Commotions
57 Classic TV's "Mayday" Malone
58 Symbol of easiness
59 ___ Friday's (restaurant chain)
60 Incident

198 Held in Place

by Oscar Klum
Edited by Timothy E. Parker
Answers in back

ACROSS

1 Chancel wear
5 Entreat
9 Like some children's books
14 Cleopatra's love Antony
15 Space attachment
16 Ouzo flavoring
17 Building support
18 Bandleader with the City Slickers
20 Computer menu option
22 Singer Horne
23 Tokyo, once
24 Con
26 Gentle, innocent type
28 Frontier craft
30 New Zealand natives
34 One way to send a document
37 Algonquian speakers
39 Carson successor
40 Vault
41 Bones partner
42 Arty town in New Mexico
43 Somewhat wet
44 Cooking amts.
45 Toyota model
46 Site of the first Olympics
48 Traffic jam, e.g.
50 Campus quarters
52 Mortgage accounts
56 Jamaican music
59 Singles
61 Bladed tool
62 Cosmetics purchase
65 Karmann ____ (old Volkswagen)
66 Warbucks' charge
67 "NYPD ____"
68 Trumpeter Alpert
69 Fictional rabbit
70 "There ought to be ____"
71 Wee ones

DOWN

1 Out of kilter
2 Father of Leah and Rachel
3 "Well done!"
4 Like some pop bottles
5 Bequeath
6 Bodybuilder's motion, for short
7 Seed coat
8 Rube
9 Kind of party
10 Lennon's Yoko
11 Yearn
12 Not brand-new
13 100 centavos
19 Wall or tooth covering
21 "The Iliad" character
25 Dark beers
27 Definitely not slouching
29 Blow one's top
31 Round up crops
32 "____ out?" (poker query)
33 Name in the '98 homerun derby
34 Super's concern (Abbr.)
35 Calendar unit
36 1980 Irene Cara film
38 Madison Avenue cow
41 Canned heat
45 It may precede or follow "as"
47 Rocker Alice
49 Avoid
51 Peachy dessert
53 Milo in "The Dream Team"
54 Quite strange
55 Rib servings
56 Lose it
57 Role for Welles
58 "____ that the truth!"
60 Framework timber
63 It isn't true
64 Latin possessive

199 Failed to Take the Stand

by Carl Cranby
Edited by Timothy E. Parker
Answers in back

ACROSS

1 The highest point
5 Radius neighbor
9 A tributary of the Missouri
14 "___ and Clark"
15 It's shaped like a bell
16 Inventor Nikola
17 Problems, problems
18 Paragon of meekness
19 Kingston and Nairobi, for two
20 Sit!
23 W.C. Fields persona
24 Like sashimi
25 "The Practice" practice
28 Blacken on a grill
31 Empty
36 WWII sub
38 Fiddler of legend
40 Stew or miscellany
41 Sit!
44 "Bonanza" role
45 Hurricanes' hearts
46 Great adventures
47 Madrid Mrs.
49 Genuine
51 Keanu's role in "The Matrix"
52 H-shaped letter
54 Soon-Yi's mom
56 Sit!
65 Ring-shaped reef
66 Enter
67 St. Paul's architect
68 It's between lather and repeat
69 Fully aware of
70 Made cheddar better
71 Chelmsford is its county seat
72 Warm, in a search
73 Cincinnati nine

DOWN

1 De-bused, e.g.
2 Burger and fries go-with
3 "Got ___?"
4 More than a third of Mississippi
5 Awake into the wee hours
6 Shakespearean character
7 Identify
8 Shady spot
9 Canada's capital
10 Kosovar's foe
11 Home to billions
12 Rounded lump
13 How some things come and go?
21 "Rica" or "Brava" front
22 Prefer
25 "Star Wars" director
26 Where you live
27 John Lennon hit
29 Raggedy doll
30 Give someone the business?
32 Place for a chicken
33 Cohort of Simon and Theodore
34 Caroline, to Ted
35 Body section
37 Peas, for a shooter
39 Second-hand gal of song
42 "Groovy!"
43 Museum artifact
48 Automatic, as a reaction
50 Key with no sharps or flats
53 Inert gas
55 Not just feuding
56 Remove, as an outer coating
57 Elevator innovator
58 Offspring
59 Ultimatum word
60 Top-flight
61 Pocket bread
62 Spontaneous motivation
63 Clarinet need
64 Drops the curtain on

200 The Thing in the Middle

by Alice Walker
Edited by Timothy E. Parker
Answers in back

ACROSS

1 White poker chips, often
6 Allen or Martin
11 Chest muscle, in gym lingo
14 Western "necktie"
15 Mayhem
16 ___ rule
17 Fumble
19 10th, 20th and 30th in NYC
20 Stocking stuffers?
21 Kickoff
23 One ankle-deep in shoes?
27 Official emissaries
29 Comes to terms
30 Lake Superior port
31 Like some nail polish
32 "___ and Sensibility"
33 Pt. of a flight plan
36 Furniture wood
37 Spaghetti accompaniment
38 Black, in some poems
39 Annoy
40 Bungle
41 Say without thinking
42 Colorful T-shirt
44 Responds to stimuli
45 Well-educated one
47 Certain prison guard
48 Concert venue
49 Kiss
50 Island chain?
51 Be victorious
58 Champagne word
59 Best of the best
60 Take downtown
61 J. Fred Muggs, for one
62 Thick as a brick
63 Ode fellow

DOWN

1 "___ away we go!"
2 Easter preceder
3 "Not a moment ___ soon!"
4 Uncommon sense
5 Homesteader
6 Like chiffon
7 Filing aids
8 Zsa Zsa's sister
9 Remote letters
10 Pastoral poem
11 Avoid responsibility
12 Lauder of cosmetics
13 Acting ensembles
18 Breaks new ground?
22 Holman or Turner
23 Desert sights
24 Impolite looker
25 Crack a little joke
26 Woodpecker's pride
27 Burroughs' was naked
28 "What," "who," "how," and "where"
30 It's often wild
32 Half-man, half-goat
34 Rich cake
35 On edge
37 Counter offer?
38 Joie de vivre
40 Tardy
41 Frenzied
43 It carries a small charge
44 Gain ground yardage
45 Nacho enhancer, for many
46 Dirty rotten scoundrel
47 He's in a class by himself
49 What some pools consist of
52 Stout relative?
53 Flesh and blood
54 Theatrical signal
55 Santa ___
56 Hobbyist's package
57 Northern borders?

201 First Names

by Maurice Rice
Edited by Timothy E. Parker
Answers in back

ACROSS

1 ____ quam videri
5 Renovated
10 Diamond decision
14 "Shane" star Ladd
15 Coliseum
16 The one thing about an amoeba
17 African grassland
18 Free-for-all
20 Japanese delicacy
21 Presidential runs
22 Activities
23 Pilot's favorite color?
25 Lacking in liveliness
26 Them, to us
27 Gilbert and Sullivan genre
31 Sign of a sellout?
33 Turkish officials (Var.)
34 "My ____ Private Idaho" (1991)
35 ____ d'oeuvre
36 Theater backdrop
37 Give off, as light
38 Cousin of Gomez
39 Hebrew letter
40 Clumps of hair
41 Mythical hero with a bum heel?
43 Old casino game
44 Opposition votes
45 Over-the-hill pug
48 Galileo's planetary oval
51 History test answer
52 Small boy
53 Manly towel material?
55 Prison sentence
56 Canal with a mule, in song
57 Like "The Shining"
58 "My Friend" at the movies
59 Daddies' soft drinks?
60 Kind of mill
61 Greenish blue

DOWN

1 Chalet features
2 Aerodynamically designed
3 Set out suddenly
4 Type of table or zone
5 Ulna's neighbor
6 Fall off, as popularity
7 Book-lined rooms, perhaps
8 Weekend getaway site
9 Class distraction
10 Torah copyist
11 Long, long time (Var.)
12 Horsewhip
13 Moose relatives
19 Wild pigs
21 Drained financially
24 Shows respect, in a way
25 Oxford doctorate, briefly
27 They're monstrous
28 Horseplay
29 Pinhead
30 Household invaders
31 Pet that grows on you?
32 Campus marching grp.
33 Pinnacles
36 Gun attachment
37 New currency on the Continent
39 Denzel Washington film
40 Fairy milieu
42 Accustoms
43 Word with "Time" or "figure"
45 Cookout spot
46 It was instant, according to Lennon
47 Space seller
48 Choreography bit
49 Prefix with "drome" or "space"
50 Take a header
51 You can find students here at night
54 Romanian currency
55 Involuntary muscular contraction

202 On the Down Low

by Horace Dampiere
Edited by Timothy E. Parker
Answers in back

ACROSS

1 Envelope closer
5 Sits down heavily
10 Float's base, maybe
14 Remarkable person, object or idea
15 Adjust an ascot
16 Privy to
17 "Beverly Hills Cop" character Foley
18 Chilling
19 Kimono cousin
20 "Mum's the word"
23 "Ich bin ___ Berliner"
24 Simile center
25 Sacred beetle
29 Traps or yaps
31 Govt. inspectors
34 Word with "Star" or "Ranger"
35 Curvy-horned goat
37 Fielder's flub
39 "Mum's the word"
42 Giver-upper
43 It can be pressing
44 "I" in "The King and I"
45 Before of yore
46 Exude
48 Graffiti writer, e.g.
50 Solomon, to David
51 Pot head?
52 "Mum's the word"
61 Consider
62 One-time pupa
63 Pull up stakes
64 "Othello" villain
65 Postpone, as enrollment
66 Tandoor, e.g.
67 Club in a bag
68 Contest mail-in
69 Strongest man on The Planet?

DOWN

1 Criticism, so to speak
2 Elegant and sumptuous
3 Out of the wind, on windjammers
4 Like some fiction
5 Ban
6 Stalin's predecessor
7 Elevator innovator
8 One-sixth of an inch
9 Majorie Daw's conveyance
10 Around
11 ___ about (roughly)
12 Place for a ring
13 Work without ___
21 Afternoon event in Chelsea
22 Ruhr Valley city
25 Piece of the pie
26 Shrink in fear
27 Battery terminal
28 Actress Russo
29 Free-for-all
30 Car bar
31 Fern leaf
32 Singer Summer
33 "He's ___ nowhere man" (The Beatles)
36 German auto pioneer Karl
38 Pitcher Nolan
40 Boy Scout group
41 Warning
47 Kind of kick
49 Citrus cooler ending
50 Brother of Theodore and Alvin
51 French cubist painter Fernand
52 Twice DCCLI
53 Four seasons
54 Building blocks brand
55 The final word, to theologists
56 Huck Finn's transport
57 Crazy way to run
58 Zero, to Sampras
59 "___ I know that!"
60 Fender flaw

by Henry Quarters
Edited by Timothy E. Parker
Answers in back

ACROSS

1 "___ from the Vienna Woods" (Strauss)
6 Girl rescued by Don Juan
11 Sylvester, to Tweety
14 In reserve, as money
15 For the birds?
16 Shade
17 Source of a digital coat?
19 Caterer's server
20 Participate in a British tradition
21 Greek letters
23 Uncommon eye color
26 Couch potato's lifeline
27 Shrivel
31 Call it quits forever
33 Emollient-yielding plants
34 "If" group
35 First follower
38 Word in a Forster title
39 Worn-down
40 International document
41 Go on a fast break?
42 Trite, joke-wise
43 Come from behind
44 Like triceratops
46 Uses a washer cycle
47 Sports complex
49 Jellied garnish
51 Soft, blue-gray mineral
53 Symbol of might
58 Mr. Onassis, to friends
59 Inept individual
62 Its tip may be felt
63 Come next
64 Sing "nyah-nyah" to
65 Before of yore
66 Loved ones
67 Site of ancient Sheba, possibly

DOWN

1 1920s chief justice
2 Laos, Tibet, etc.
3 "You are the weakest ___!"
4 Advantage
5 Gets really mad
6 South American capital
7 Stowe character
8 Jr.'s son
9 "M" director Fritz
10 Heartburn remedy
11 Small versions of larger images
12 Ear-related
13 High-strung
18 Be a mother to
22 Wheel type
24 Some to-do list items
25 Suspicious
27 Swell, at sea
28 Pelvic bones
29 Get ready to sprint?
30 Use an axe
32 Two cents worth
34 City near Cleveland
36 Wight or Avalon
37 Boxes of calendars?
39 Outran everybody
40 It may move you
42 Started an engine
43 Unsteady, as a house
45 Half and half?
46 Iranian monetary unit
47 In awe
48 Closer to extinction, perhaps
50 Jabs
52 Diarist Frank
54 You, in the Bible
55 Set of sheets
56 Lessen the load
57 Adam's apple location?
60 Dos Passos trilogy
61 Mongrel mutt

by Fran & Lou Sabin
Edited by Timothy E. Parker
Answers in back

ACROSS

1 Give an edge
5 Vegas attractions
10 Long sentence?
14 Exit gradually, very gradually
15 Buttonholer's target, perhaps
16 Superstar
17 "A Doll's House" housewife
18 Central Florida city
19 Plum role
20 Hemingway opus (with "A")
23 Diamond expert?
24 Albanian's neighbor
25 Lends a hand
30 Singers Shore and Washington
34 Cause of star wars?
35 Pants part
37 Dizzy music?
38 "Seven Hills of Rome" tune
42 Change unit
43 Noted tentmaker
44 Ruptured duck wearer
45 TV interference
47 Dieter's ultimate goal, perhaps
50 Sir Geraint's wife
52 "The Matrix" man
53 Auction closing
60 Alex Rodriguez, to fans
61 Parisian's year
62 Extinct "Wonderland" bird
64 NBA great Archibald
65 Indy entrant
66 Hop, skip or jump
67 Tickled
68 Marquee listings
69 Some shade givers

DOWN

1 Took first
2 Dance, slangily
3 Bible book before Nehemiah
4 Start to cry
5 Dawdler
6 Curtain fabric, perhaps
7 October stone
8 Blows the whistle on
9 On the schedule
10 Capp's rube
11 "Happy Birthday!" writer
12 Pub head?
13 Closes down
21 German spa, Bad ____
22 African antelope
25 Dilapidated cars
26 Plumed wader
27 "____ Doone"
28 Erase
29 Abounds
31 Superior to
32 Great Lakes mnemonic
33 Minor to-dos
36 "Fed" attachment
39 Had in mind
40 Competing
41 They obviously show fear
46 Expectant father's supplies
48 Tom's "You've Got Mail" co-star
49 Bean
51 Robert of "Goodbye, Mr. Chips"
53 "The Apple Dumpling ____" (1975)
54 Like word of mouth
55 Scintilla
56 Quechuan
57 At no time, poetically
58 Caroler's air
59 Cheese with a red wax coat
63 Word with "special" or "photo"

ACROSS

1 "Get ___ on yourself!"
6 Secret stock
11 ___ Mahal
14 Prove innocent
15 Blender setting
16 Biographical datum
17 Crossworder's bird afloat?
19 Actor's prompt
20 California location, with "San Luis"
21 Cigarette ad claim, perhaps
23 Gas-pump abbr.
24 Outline permanently
27 Kabuki kin
28 Crossworder's section of a solo?
33 ___-garde
36 Ring or music type
37 Kitty cries
38 Old photo
40 February 29th
42 Travelers to Bethlehem
43 Historic periods
45 Lethal loop
46 Crossworder's butter cookie substitute?
49 M quarter
50 Muslim leader
51 Ranting or raving
54 Flannel wear
58 Wankel engine type
60 Evil Amin
61 Leers at an S-curve, crossword-style?
64 McCourt memoir
65 Call
66 Glue mascot
67 Author's rep
68 Murrow's "See ___"
69 Crofts' partner

DOWN

1 Man with many parts
2 Piece of church land
3 Equip anew
4 Fleming and Rankin
5 Real estate
6 Jacuzzi
7 Ancient Egyptian boy king
8 Sea bordering Kazakhstan
9 Court by concert
10 Muppet creator Jim
11 Diplomat's forte
12 Rio contents
13 Give a raspberry
18 Staff symbol
22 Hair care step
25 Feature of some cell phones
26 Bally follower
28 Early center of Christianity
29 Prison in a Johnny Cash tune
30 Renovate
31 "Tennessee Waltz" opening
32 "___ sow, so shall .."
33 Sphere opening
34 Perfume container
35 French halo wearer
39 Keychain illuminator
41 Tentacled sea creatures
44 Singer DiFranco
47 More tentacled sea creatures
48 ___ avis
51 Volcanic stuff
52 Dizzy
53 Rit users
54 Naldi of the Ziegfeld Follies
55 "Understood," hippie-wise
56 General idea
57 North Carolina school
59 Painted metalware
62 Rock's Brian
63 Put in stitches

by Timothy E. Parker
Edited by Timothy E. Parker
Answers in back

ACROSS

1 "Antony and Cleopatra" creatures
5 Public relations concern
10 Did the breaststroke, e.g.
14 90-0, e.g.
15 Fable point
16 Sound and healthy
17 An inflorescence
18 Eleve, over here
19 Escape route
20 In paradise
23 Type of tray
24 Sponsorship
28 "Swan Lake," e.g.
32 It's between two aglets
35 Cantilevered window
36 Chance ____ (meet accidentally)
37 It's little when white
38 Highly pleased with oneself
42 Word with "ten" or "duck"
43 "No ___ allowed"
44 Fulcrum for an oar
45 Quality of uniformity
48 Scribe
49 Revered remnant
50 Island garland
51 Bonkers
59 Small job to do
62 Intended
63 Primal impulse
64 Away from wind, for a ship
65 ____ Island, Fla.
66 Zebra's mom
67 Certain gem
68 Of yore
69 Argued for

DOWN

1 Gloria's pop, to Meathead
2 Kind of bean, to Brits
3 Heart, for one
4 "____ right up!"
5 Collision
6 Modern clicker
7 Angelic Italian instrument
8 Borden of condensed milk
9 First lady of scat
10 Haifa currency
11 Mustache application
12 Foreman foe
13 Intersected
21 Road sign
22 Arctic explorer John
25 Awkward bloke
26 It used to be a drip
27 Player in a kids' game
28 Teeny finish
29 Make it
30 Toy train maker
31 Monetary unit of Romania
32 Old ankle covers
33 Beer ingredient
34 Next to nothing?
36 Applications
39 Wild way to go
40 Sunlit courts
41 X, in ancient Greece
46 Metal in meteorites
47 Cash register co.
48 "I'm Henery the Eighth, I Am" composer R.P.
50 Jouster's weapon
52 Peas, for a shooter
53 Gung-ho feeling
54 Swing place
55 Clay or coal unit
56 Like some history
57 No Mr. Nice Guy
58 Essential item
59 Eastern belief
60 Mont Blanc is one
61 Mermaid's milieu

207 Not So Common Critters

by Mark Gould
Edited by Timothy E. Parker
Answers in back

ACROSS

1 Derisive laughs
5 Unit of capacitance
10 ___ Hashana
14 Press agent?
15 Old-womanish
16 Choir part
17 Desperate, as a warning
18 Tropical water predator
20 ___ up (relented)
22 "There's no 'I' in team," for one
23 "QB ___" (Uris novel)
24 "All My Children" vixen
26 A grammatical case
28 "They're ___!" (racetrack cry)
30 English dog breed
33 Most hearty
35 Vital heart vessel
36 Cameo stone
37 Hog's place
38 You're looking at it
42 Relating to gold
45 Hauling around, as a shopping bag
47 Farmer's bane
51 Tic-tac-toe winning line
52 Members of a Jamaican religious sect
53 Navigational system
55 Man-mouse link
56 Daytime TV fare
59 "What's it all about?" guy
62 Long-legged crustacean
65 Add a little color to
66 Burn
67 One way to lay it on
68 Italian noble family
69 Old English letters
70 Sometimes they battle
71 Some Greek letters

DOWN

1 ___ and seek
2 Opera solo
3 Winged insect
4 Smile, in an evil way
5 Sort of chance?
6 "Twenty Questions" category
7 Latvia's capital
8 Host Trebek
9 Put-down artist
10 College cheer
11 King of Norway
12 Endeavor
13 More corny
19 Agent 86
21 "I call it!"
25 Abridge
27 Stretch of land
28 Expression of surprise
29 Sports buff
31 Gate fastener
32 "___ Story" (1995)
34 Compel payment
37 Pride, lust or envy
39 Aquarium attraction
40 One card game?
41 Id companion
43 Order from a czar
44 Vacation milieus
45 It's company, it's said
46 Creole veggie
47 Stick with a pocket
48 Talked nonstop on one subject
49 Hebrew prophet
50 Region of France
54 Change, as a hemline
57 Sore spot
58 Grand ___ (auto race)
60 Interested in
61 Somme summers
63 No and J
64 Library vols.

ACROSS
1 Bullets and shells, for short
5 Georgia of "The Mary Tyler Moore Show"
10 Very small amounts
14 Come down hard
15 African river or Italian physicist
16 Tennis great Lendl
17 Begin traveling
19 Film "sleeper" of 1978
20 Fury
21 Slippery trees?
22 Making a team, as from oxen
24 Catch sight of
26 Like river beds
28 Period of penitence
30 Test the strength of, chemically
33 Bean used in making chocolate
36 Rube
38 Constrictor
39 Scram
43 Extension
44 Inescapable outcome
45 Anoint, old-style
46 Keyboard experts
49 It gives support in the home
51 First name in whodunits
53 Single-masted vessels
57 Spirit of Muslim legend (Var.)
59 ___ fixe
61 What "My Bonnie lies over," in a song
62 Cartoon bear
63 Leave quickly
66 Superman's cover
67 Half the integers
68 Where kip changes hands
69 Unnamed alternative
70 Have a hunch
71 Predator's dinner

DOWN
1 Food for a ladybug
2 Wave-patterned fabric
3 Does a muffler's job
4 Bit for the dog bowl
5 Olympic track star Ashford
6 Vera's husband on "Cheers"
7 Lip cosmetic
8 Flight info
9 Demure, by some standards
10 Heart, in slang
11 Like careless mistakes
12 Controversial word for Rhett Butler
13 Fly in the ointment
18 Concerning this, in legalese
23 Giant Hall-of-Famer
25 Hardly nude
27 Hankerings
29 Beat the seeds out of grain
31 Type of bridge
32 Cushiness
33 Fireside event
34 High nest (Var.)
35 Presses the flesh
37 Cousin on "The Addams Family"
40 Frequently
41 Semi professional?
42 Prefix with "European"
47 Kindle
48 Start for "Marcos" or "Mateo"
50 Safari hazard
52 Pulitzer poet Conrad
54 Prestigious award
55 Black tea grade
56 Smart-mouthed
57 Dick Van ___
58 Grey of "Cabaret"
60 Lairs
64 Caesarean salute
65 Finsteraarhorn, for one

209 What's the Spread?

by Fran & Lou Sabin
Edited by Timothy E. Parker
Answers in back

ACROSS

1 Islamic pilgrimage (Var.)
5 Information booth visitor
10 "You're a ____, Alice"
14 Length X width
15 Result of a union success
16 Jason's carrier
17 Unread e-mail, often
18 Diet candidate
20 Pequod's missiles
22 Reacted to a pun
23 The Taj Mahal was built here
24 Cutworm, e.g.
25 Just a bit
28 "I didn't mean it!"
30 "Left turn, dobbin!"
33 Arranged in regular order
35 Harley, fondly
36 Bastille Day month
37 "Rule, Britannia" composer
38 Avoid
40 Jannings of "The Blue Angel"
41 Tournament position
42 Deface
43 Put together
45 Witch's work
46 Penalized, monetarily
48 Tribal chief
49 Detest
50 Fear-inducing (Var.)
52 Las Palmas lady
55 Like some art
59 Pop requests?
61 Musical medley
62 Seaweed product
63 Hotel accommodation
64 Building sites
65 Parliament member
66 Shoreline swoopers
67 Wine waste

DOWN

1 Breakfast side dish
2 A Marx Brother instrument, to a Mario Brother
3 ____ Abby
4 Stuffed to the limit
5 Day in spring
6 Post-exercise baths
7 Drum sets
8 Tough ending
9 Shows up again
10 Morocco's capital
11 Republic on the Caspian
12 Flirty look
13 Snitched
19 Promising
21 Curved molding
24 Range implement
25 Computer-screen depository
26 Street amusement (with "show")
27 Building addition
29 Chicago landing site
30 Damp, climate-wise
31 Rocker Cooper
32 William who directed "Funny Girl"
34 Small cup of black coffee
36 Piano man Morton
39 Windmill arm
44 Smart-mouthed
46 Kind of team or system
47 Forensic activity
49 Ancient
51 Sassafras quartet
52 "Shove off!"
53 For that reason
54 Get warm, in a way
55 Deuce follower, in tennis
56 Succulent, spiny-leafed, medicinal plant
57 Offer as an example
58 Get rid of
60 "____ Mutual Friend" (Dickens)

by George Keller
Edited by Timothy E. Parker
Answers in back

ACROSS

1 1942 Disney classic
6 Awe-struck expression
10 Kept one's head above water?
14 Oak, in a nutshell
15 Cut words
16 Scale down
17 Densely woven fabric
19 First name in soul
20 Affirmative votes
21 Emulates Delilah
23 "The Return of the Native" setting
26 With undue haste
27 Afflicted with ennui
30 Owned at one time
32 Vietnamese holiday
33 Make out of focus
34 Neglect
36 Last qtr. start
39 Ad-____
40 Archie's pal
41 Sardonic
42 Weep and wail
43 Having to wait
44 Journalist's source, perhaps
45 Yalie
47 Haul into court
48 Beetle Bailey's reprimander
49 Emphasize
52 Jogging gaits
54 They really take a beating
56 Partial
60 Poems of praise
61 It comes after the shower
64 Tour de France, for one
65 Kuwaiti ruler
66 Rogue
67 Antlered animals
68 Slot insert, sometimes
69 "____ alive!"

DOWN

1 "____, It's Cold Outside"
2 "God's Little ____"
3 Barnyard noises
4 Comparatively headstrong
5 "Oh, really?"
6 Cream alternative
7 Hubbub
8 Quarries
9 Once-popular anesthetic
10 Helpmate
11 Lookout post
12 Tempestuous spirit?
13 In disarray
18 U.S. foe of old
22 Obsolete
24 Chicken parts
25 Discuss fully
27 OPEC amounts, briefly
28 A little of this, a little of that
29 Stare
31 Aaron Burr, for one
34 Demand payment
35 Bummed out
37 Steep rock
38 Little guy
40 Floor support
44 Spaghetti cousin
46 Rents out
48 Is really lousy
49 Seed
50 Type of wave
51 Made two-by-fours, e.g.
53 ____-Wan Kenobi
55 Conductor's starter?
57 Neighbor of Neb.
58 Water drainer
59 Batik supplies
62 Poorly lit
63 Rapping Dr.

by Carol Lachance
Edited by Timothy E. Parker
Answers in back

ACROSS

1 Blotto
4 Close shave
9 Like cakes and some bricks
14 It sometimes needs a massage
15 Having spent less time in the sun
16 Gladiator's place
17 Kids put coins in them
20 Turn red or green, as fruit
21 "Paradise Lost" character
22 Nephew of Cain
23 Observant people
26 Female with a wool coat
29 "Platoon" setting, briefly
30 Hold in high regard
31 Sacked out
32 Mindless
33 Clay pigeon sport
34 Clarinet, slangily
38 Georgia pie nut
39 Light-flow measure
40 All square
41 Lindbergh's The ___ of St. Louis
43 Prefix for content
46 MOMA's locale
47 More profound
48 Hindu god of ruin
49 Mythical winged monster
51 Tight collar?
53 Best of everything
57 Lazy turner?
58 Princess Fiona's prison
59 On account of (with "to")
60 Prefix with "dollars"
61 Jagged, as a leaf's edge
62 "... ___ the fields we go"

DOWN

1 Fans of Betty Grable?
2 Tree-climbing lizard
3 Jungle drum
4 Box without harmful intentions
5 It's filled with numbers in boxes
6 The whole shebang
7 "Losing My Religion" rock group
8 '96 Arnold Schwarzenegger film
9 Thai coins
10 Song for Carmen
11 Maine river
12 Hydrocarbon suffix
13 "___ Boot" (German film)
18 Greyhound
19 Kind of package
24 Bygone science magazine
25 Man's fashion accessory
27 Half a fortnight
28 Summer hrs. in Albany
30 In a jiffy
31 Blood-related
32 "___ hardly wait!"
33 Galley mark
34 Eugene of "Best in Show"
35 Insulated cooler
36 Chartres river
37 Backbites
38 It's mightier than the sword
41 Calendar abbr.
42 Narc's find, maybe
43 Nanki-Poo's dad
44 Park or Pennsylvania
45 Pantry
47 Liquid-Plumr competitor
48 The sun, in Spain
50 From quite a distance
52 "Catch!"
53 Medicinal amt.
54 Shade of color
55 Part of FWIW
56 Double standard?

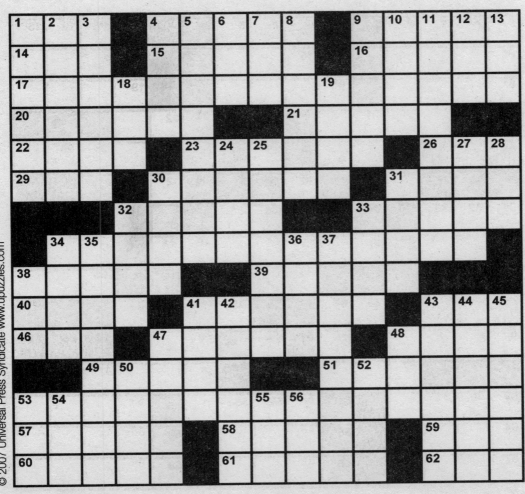

212 Clothes Make the...

by Lucille Evanstone
Edited by Timothy E. Parker
Answers in back

ACROSS

1 Jim Anderson, Cliff Huxtable, etc.
5 Flightless bird
9 Backup strategy
14 "En garde" weapon
15 Sandwich notable?
16 Country singer Tucker
17 Baby forest creature
18 Plumbing problem
19 Sat tight
20 University bad guy?
23 Mother of Calcutta
24 Partied down
28 TV for jocks
30 Shea and Arthur Ashe
31 The Buckeyes, for short
34 Disney's middle name
37 "Let's get crackin'!"
38 Storage of trawling gear?
42 "Dedicated to the ___ Love"
43 Remove the stubble
44 Half an African fly
45 More puffed up
48 Eliot's "Adam ___"
50 Cloths by the sink
53 Supplies with more munitions
57 Case against a firm?
59 Censoring sound
62 Clueless
63 Sting operation
64 Get a bead on
65 The skinny
66 Priest of the East
67 Grads
68 Per
69 Came down and settled

DOWN

1 Skim, as milk
2 Chop-chop
3 Kind of flask used by a chemist
4 Letter getter
5 Rhode Island's state tree
6 Mata ___
7 Segal or Fromm
8 Omega's opposite
9 J.F.K.'s vessel
10 Easygoing
11 In addition
12 "Bill ___, the Science Guy"
13 Michael Jackson hit
21 Ruhr valley city
22 "___ bodkins!"
25 Word on a ticket
26 Pride members
27 Jessica of "Tootsie"
29 Louse eggs
31 From way back
32 Moses' mountain
33 Internet surfers
35 Flame proof?
36 Wild try
39 Nighttime driver's selection
40 Go beyond
41 Hands over
46 Spews lava
47 ___ Tafari (Haile Selassie)
49 California section
51 Comedian Radner
52 Do detective work
54 Part of RFD
55 Home of the Heat
56 March 17 honoree, briefly
58 The NHL's Phil, familiarly
59 Ewe said it
60 Like Abner
61 Flightless bird

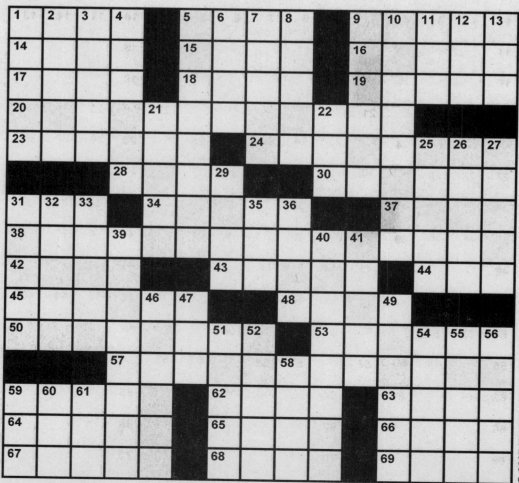

by Louis Lahey
Edited by Timothy E. Parker
Answers in back

ACROSS

1 Back talk
5 Moderate yellow-orange
10 Door frame upright
14 Handle of a sword
15 Arledge of sports broadcasting
16 Lamb by another name
17 Sixth month of the Jewish calendar
18 Massey of vintage Hollywood
19 Pinball goof
20 In the cast
23 Word from Scrooge
24 They're split for soup?
25 Item in some medicine cabinets
27 Type of wood
30 Hope or Jessica
32 Boxcar cargo, perhaps
33 Emulating Yankee Doodle
38 Shakespearean king
40 Suffix with "great"
41 Fare-well link
42 Obeying doctor's orders, perhaps
47 Chess pieces
48 The agony of de feet
49 Shoot-'em-ups
51 On liberty
54 Fairy tale villain
55 Menagerie
56 Risking a slap across the face
62 Tabloid subjects, often
64 Edgy
65 Word with "eye" or "final"
66 It's useful in October
67 Computer command
68 First name in architecture
69 Latin I verb
70 Haley novel
71 Steel mill refuse

DOWN

1 Iranian ruler ousted in 1979
2 Opera set in Eqypt
3 Croat or Bulgar, e.g.
4 Bacon portions
5 Japanese paper art
6 Soft drinks
7 Lion tamer's accessory
8 City of central Sicily
9 Bringing up
10 Word with "lag" or "stream"
11 Suspect's out
12 Lombardy's capital
13 Come clean?
21 A stone's throw away
22 Forum wear
26 Govt. branch, e.g.
27 It may come from the blue
28 Length times width
29 Reporter's source
30 Speech impediments
31 Nonconformist
34 College bigwig
35 Expression of weariness
36 ___-do-well
37 Cravings
39 Puerto ___
43 Standard
44 Antilles part
45 Lumberjacks
46 Yuri Zhivago's beloved
50 Plains dwellings
51 Blue color
52 Chesterfields
53 Some boxing blows
54 Start
57 Reno attraction
58 Division word
59 Skater's jump
60 Teasdale of poetry
61 Unwelcome cloud
63 Get the point

© 2007 Universal Press Syndicate www.upuzzles.com

214 Blowin' in the...

by Kelly Wilmark
Edited by Timothy E. Parker
Answers in back

ACROSS
1 Calcutta queen
5 Oxidizes, in a way
10 Cyber junk mail
14 "Couldn't have said it better myself"
15 Toughen up
16 Sweet spot?
17 Barroom projectile
18 Not so nasty
19 "Is that all right?"
20 Chats
23 Deuce topper
24 Birch kin
25 "Ditto"
28 Kind of ray
31 Collection of anecdotes
32 Manuscript gap
35 Zodiac delicacy
39 Unresolved
42 Word with "panty" or "fire"
43 So far
44 Keydets' coll.
45 Ones over there
47 Intentional nuclear blast
49 Slacken
52 St. Louis landmark
54 Film in AFI's top ten
61 Grandpa Munster's pet
62 Like many old fireplaces
63 Natural emollient
64 Longest river in the world
65 Muslim's faith
66 Disencumbers
67 Turned right
68 "Over ___"
69 Item on a to-do list

DOWN
1 CAT scan units
2 "The Joy Luck Club" nanny
3 Seneca the Younger's student
4 Altogether
5 Washer cycle
6 Kwanzaa principle
7 "___ is life!"
8 Genealogist's chart
9 One kind of Bosnian
10 Loafer's lack
11 Elbowed, perhaps
12 Knock the socks off
13 "California, Here I Come"co-writer Joseph
21 Feature of bird song
22 Meadow male
25 Window frame
26 Fully aware of
27 Speaker's spot
28 Word with "tour" or "TV"
29 Jodie in a 1999 romance film
30 Cartoonist Groening
33 It can get into a jam
34 Some Navy noncoms
36 Four-star review
37 Goals
38 Elton John or John Lennon, briefly
40 Received a varsity award
41 Therefore
46 Use a scythe
48 Oppose successfully
49 Winemaking process
50 Bacall mate, familiarly
51 Tropical lizard
52 Rose extract
53 What limericks do
55 "___ soup yet?"
56 Peter of reggae
57 Place for an ace
58 Hipbones
59 Some auction bids
60 Cubicle fixture

by Henry Quarters
Edited by Timothy E. Parker
Answers in back

ACROSS

1 Abolish (with "out")
6 Purcell specialties
10 Pound the poet
14 Word with "society" or "roll"
15 Cruiser's stop
16 Wading bird
17 Loosen, as a knot
18 Dubai ruler
19 Trygve Lie's birthplace, now
20 Astronaut's quarters
23 Motley
26 Harmonized melody
27 It may follow the dot
28 Speck
31 Dunce
36 Parts of a shower
39 Kofi Annan's country
40 Gawk at
41 More than enough
43 WWII power
44 Londoner's petrol purchase unit
46 Goliath's undoing
48 Where the Jesuits founder hails from
50 Etc. cousin
51 Architectural addition
52 Dine
54 "In Living Color" regular
56 Birthplace of many a doll
62 Clearly not locked
63 River to the Caspian
64 Certain state denizen
68 Big celebration
69 Short parody
70 Pueblo material
71 Escape route
72 Beginner
73 Armstrong with a bike

DOWN

1 ___ mai (dim sum dish)
2 Unit of nautical displacement
3 "A Bug's Life" bug
4 Highly humid
5 Gave money in advance
6 Big NYSE influence
7 St. Peter's Basilica feature
8 "All My Children" role
9 Overexertion
10 Cupid, to the Greeks
11 Pitts of "Life With Father"
12 Small brook
13 Medicinal plant
21 Venue for Socrates
22 Irritating snob
23 Proceed after getting doubles in Monopoly
24 Slowly, to John Williams
25 Caught red-handed
29 Alley skulkers
30 Kind of butter
32 As a result
33 Plumber's item
34 Shoe cushion
35 With a sharp tongue
37 Piano-playing Peter
38 Gash
42 Pass, as a law
45 Schiaparelli of fashion
47 Icy
49 Summer month
53 Full of zip
55 Seventies sitcom
56 Confine
57 Trojan War hero
58 One of the Lesser Sundas
59 Enfant terrible
60 Two of a kind
61 Violist's clef
65 Carried the day
66 Soup ingredients?
67 Word before a maiden name, often

ACROSS

1 Snakes in hieroglyphics
5 "Well-Tempered Clavier" composer
9 Segment
13 Troopers' head?
14 Simmering
16 Once more
17 "Johnny B. Goode" singer
19 Latvia's capital
20 Lowdown joint?
21 "The Star-Spangled Banner" preposition
22 "I ___ Rock"
23 Begin a revolt
24 Shopper's lineup
27 Flowed
28 Psychic sense
30 "Gangsta's Paradise" Grammy winner
31 "Bus Stop" playwright
33 "Uh-oh!"
36 "Dead Man Walking" actress Sarandon
37 Lexington and Concord fighters
40 Lofty space?
43 Rink star Lipinski
44 One of Taylor's husbands
48 Churchill Downs features
50 Watch chain
52 Kind of shooter
53 Popular locale for skiers
56 Change, as the Constitution
58 Luau garb
59 Audience insult
60 Double-edged literary device
61 Princess who founded Carthage
62 Tournament rotation
65 Privy to
66 Head roaster
67 Road hog's territory
68 Signing ceremony souvenirs
69 Mets' stadium
70 Jason's fleece-finding ship

DOWN

1 GI's cure-all
2 Awfully dry
3 Garden chore
4 Losses involving getting to the quarterback
5 Paul Bunyan's sidekick
6 Teddy's neighbor on Mount Rushmore
7 19th-c. French landscapist
8 Job offerer
9 Most important, or noted film studio
10 Characters in fables, often
11 Royal insignia
12 Former airline
15 Hammerstein's contribution
18 Inventive Swiss painter
23 Aristotle, to Jackie
24 Rainwater pipe
25 Stance
26 Colleague of Bela and Boris
29 Junior
32 Exhaust pipe discharges
34 School's booster org.
35 Feudal workers
38 Gets frosty
39 Red Guard promoter
40 Patients' utterances
41 Hauler's rope
42 Didn't just buy off the rack
45 Where the liquor flows freely?
46 Exercising a veto
47 Pop
49 Cavalry sword (Var.)
51 TV's Roseanne
54 Hovers menacingly
55 Joey's refuge
57 Greenbacks
60 Think tank nugget
61 Salsa, e.g.
63 Name-change indicator
64 Prefix with "phyte"

ACROSS

1 Hole that can be the source of pain
7 Mrs. Cantor
10 Fingerprint, perhaps
14 Eavesdropper
15 Call, as a game
16 Squeeze through
17 Indo-Europeans
18 Parting words
20 Cheerful
21 The '90s, for one
22 Like Chablis
23 Medical plan gp.
25 Valued gemstone
29 Winter beginnings
32 Course for a gourmand
33 Kournikova of the courts
35 Understands the humor
37 He sings to the man
38 Word with "bug" or "finger"
39 Parting word
41 Catch on (with "up")
42 Follower of Richard
43 Cooking fat
44 At any time
45 Frank admission
49 Until now
51 Bread seeds
53 Employ
54 Spanish couple?
57 Barked like a dog
59 Close or Ford
61 Parting word
64 City on the Illinois River
65 Biblical "you"
66 Bottom line
67 Spite
68 Breathe like a dog
69 First half of an Iowa city
70 Gas guzzler

DOWN

1 Blackens
2 Avian penthouse
3 Parting words
4 Today's Persia
5 Tithers' offerings
6 '01, '02, etc.
7 Dies ___
8 It may be wild
9 Peaked house
10 Kind of action
11 English lavatory
12 Submachine gun
13 Poetic contraction
19 Temptation location
21 "Is that a fact?"
24 Big start for bucks
26 Parting words
27 Sublet
28 Discourage
30 Thumbs-down vote
31 Ermine in brown
33 Nom de guerre
34 Dewy-eyed
36 Hide from view
40 Contributes
41 A type of blanket
46 Off-the-wall
47 "I second that!"
48 Stanford name
50 Sea west of Turkey
52 Mall fling
55 Spanish or Bermuda, e.g.
56 Forest trap
58 Erodes
60 Least popular kind of speech
61 Motor oil additive brand
62 "NOW I get it!"
63 Partner of hither
64 "Fix" or "game" beginning

218 Belly to the Ground

by Mark Gould
Edited by Timothy E. Parker
Answers in back

ACROSS

1 Beany's serpent buddy
6 "GWTW" plantation
10 Picket line crosser
14 American frontiersman
15 Served a winner
16 Verdi's "Caro nome," e.g.
17 Hidden enemy
20 Graceful aquatic bird
21 Available for retail (Var.)
22 Enmities
25 Tennis period
26 It's made daily
27 Collection of stories
28 Kind of treat
30 Simon's verb
32 Cut
34 Bud's old pal
35 Pull, as ropes
36 Avocado
41 It's better than none
42 Big bird
43 Instruction at many a corner
45 Small amphibian
47 Formal affairs, usually
49 Sigma follower
50 Word with "overboard"
51 "So that's it!"
53 On easy street
55 Vex
58 Black, poetically
59 Paul Hogan's 63-Across
63 Part
64 Oscar winner Crawford
65 Walks like a tosspot
66 Birds of prey
67 Hostelries
68 NW French port

DOWN

1 "Gunsmoke" network
2 Many, many millennia
3 Part of a formal suit
4 Press mechanism
5 Emulated Groucho Marx
6 "The Hundred Secret Senses" author
7 Deeds
8 Go over again
9 Fred Astaire's sister
10 Warshawski creator Paretsky
11 Testy
12 Nuptial paths
13 Headquartered
18 Enjoy to excess
19 Arises
22 Possesses
23 Role for Jodie
24 Greek portico
29 More baby-faced
31 "... for children of all ___!"
33 Farm implement
35 Took the trick
37 Completely
38 Melville novel
39 Participant
40 Horse color
44 Place
45 Tightly defined
46 Register formally
47 Philter
48 Residential locale
50 Prefix with "manage"
52 Muslim pilgrim (Var.)
54 Individualist
56 Chills
57 Vivacity
60 Print distances
61 Hollow center?
62 Time zone

by Henry Quarters
Edited by Timothy E. Parker
Answers in back

219 Do Not Toss It Here

ACROSS

1 Shut the door rudely
5 2007 erupter
9 Last alternative?
14 In good order
15 MGM sound effect
16 An ice place to live?
17 Narcissists' problems
18 Sour or bitter in taste
20 Disparages
22 Prefix meaning "solid"
23 Blue Triangle grp.
24 Start of a kindergarten song
27 "So what ___ is new?"
30 Like a famous dodger
32 Realize
35 "... Rich and Famous" host
38 Word with "high pressure"
39 Disparages
43 Part of NASCAR
44 It may connect a limb to a branch
45 Trunk contents, perhaps
46 Batter or battered
49 Pod pieces
51 Cunning
52 Chesterfield, e.g.
55 Beverage since 1898
59 Disparages
62 Range of skills in a particular occupation
65 Inveigh
66 Mindful
67 Scent
68 A lot, for many?
69 Dissuade
70 Rive
71 Examination

DOWN

1 Lets stand
2 End of a tunnel, proverbially
3 Dote upon
4 City of India
5 Significant periods
6 Eighty-six
7 Well-groomed
8 Directional sign
9 Kind of equation
10 ___ Benedict
11 Steak partner
12 Trinity member
13 Nursery moppet
19 Andean of old
21 Partner of Fargo
24 Big hairstyles
25 Vista or Park
26 Brooch part
28 Red or Black waterway
29 Manhattan border river
31 "Chi" lead-in
32 Remnants of healing
33 Artist's stand
34 "How I Spent My Summer Vacation," maybe
36 Figure head?
37 Household staff
40 Blowup source, perhaps
41 Caviar
42 Loses one's cool
47 Hardhearted lender
48 Larboard
50 Pointillist painter Georges
53 Elevator stop
54 Stage whisper
56 Locale
57 Mixes
58 Key
59 In this case
60 Golf club
61 Overly bookish type, stereotypically
62 Swell, '90s-style
63 Certain bleater
64 Frisk (with "down")

220 In the Grass

by Alice Walker
Edited by Timothy E. Parker
Answers in back

ACROSS

1 Stress result, perhaps
6 Immediately
10 Places for prayers?
14 "A Fistful of Dollars" director Sergio
15 Serve drinks
16 Have a yen for
17 Backs of necks
18 Trivial bit
19 Gumption
20 Certain Dadaist
21 Morning aftertaste?
24 Dodge
26 Requiring three hankies, say
27 Blended fine
29 Genially
33 Catchall column
34 Log house
36 Lobster eggs
37 Things that set pants ablaze?
38 Question
39 Miniature sci-fi vehicles
40 Part of a chef's jargon
41 Door hardware
42 "Home on the ___"
43 Make amends for
45 Takes hold of
46 Pitcher's stat
47 Hue
48 Obviously very scared
53 Ewe said it
56 Mata ___
57 Singer Falana
58 Spiral-horned antelope
60 Bakery mainstay
61 Was indebted to
62 Verso's counterpart
63 Flat-topped formation
64 Walk in water
65 Japanese wines (Var.)

DOWN

1 Bone in forearm
2 "All in the Family" producer Norman
3 Lincoln cent
4 Ending for Benz, not Mercedes
5 Firefighter, at times
6 Resentfulness
7 Tugboat signal
8 "Graph" or "pilot" starter
9 Send a message by wire
10 Oriental temple
11 Color of unbleached linen
12 Smidgen
13 One of Eve's brood
22 "The ___ Couple"
23 Common street name
25 Sediment
27 Type of bear
28 Of some benefit
29 French friar
30 Part of a suntanner's goal, perhaps
31 File, as a complaint
32 Sycophant's answers
34 Big house residents
35 Dog days mo.
38 Prohibit
39 Settled up
41 This location
42 People who correct printers' proofs
44 Eyeball tissue
45 That boat
47 Suit symbol
48 "For ___ the Bell Tolls"
49 Moneyed one
50 Angers
51 "Field of Dreams" setting
52 Offered an excuse
54 Lock opener?
55 Hubbubs
59 Grazing place

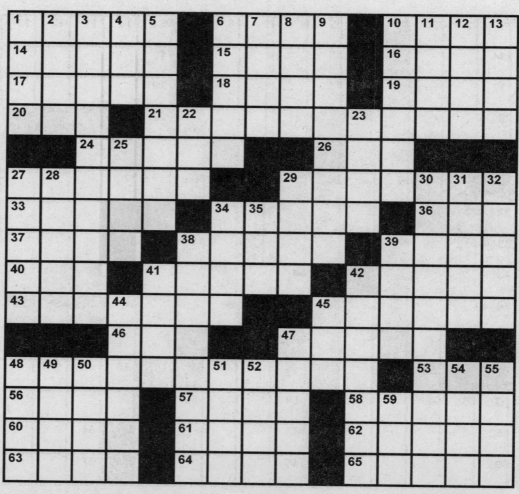

ACROSS

1 "... many a year ___" (Poe)
4 Man of great wealth
9 Morocco's capital
14 Whole bunch
15 Rolling live
16 Calliope's kin
17 She was long in a Beatles song
19 Mocked
20 Hipbone sections
21 Author Kesey
22 Mr. Rogers
23 Mercury ore
26 Engages, as gears
29 Providers of startup money
30 Paint a nick, e.g.
31 Envision
32 Goal on the green
33 Elizabethan or Gaslight
34 "Function" prefix
37 Car thief's door opener
40 "That looks tasty!"
41 Hubbub
42 Outs partners
43 Deranged
45 Tooth component (Var.)
48 Is a member
52 Gas guzzler
53 What a lake may do in winter
54 Bender
55 U.N. workers grp.
56 Latin 101 verb
57 Group of 20
59 Huge cannon in WWI
62 Routine responses?
63 Grow accustomed to
64 100 qintars
65 Young's partner in accounting
66 It's better than a bargain
67 Half a figure eight

DOWN

1 Basements' opposites
2 Hockey player for the defense
3 Connected
4 They may be pos. or neg.
5 Santa ___
6 European peninsula
7 Former Houston pro
8 ___ Mawr
9 Rue
10 Passage at the opera
11 Overgrown duck of comics
12 Downed
13 "Dracula" director Browning
18 Countries
24 Singing brothers' surname
25 Direct path
26 "Carmen" author Prosper
27 Sandy shade
28 Phony deal
30 Gandhi's woe
32 Thatcher and Blair (Abbr.)
34 Put together
35 Port in Yemen
36 Silver's beginning?
38 "Serpent" suffix
39 Y chromosome owner
44 "Bull" ending
46 Beauty pageant props
47 Swallow
48 Heavy shoe
49 Snuggle
50 Flows forth fiercely
51 Orates
53 Coburn film "Our Man ___"
55 Bird associated with the Nile River
57 "Thar ___ blows!"
58 It's driven to go far
60 Means of support?
61 Slim swimmer

© 2007 Universal Press Syndicate www.upuzzles.com

222 Starting Team

by Carl Cranby
Edited by Timothy E. Parker
Answers in back

ACROSS

1 Dextrous
5 Process a bite
9 Not quite summa
14 "I can't believe it's not butter"
15 Jungle sound
16 Time for showers
17 Belle of the ball
19 Brightest star in Virgo
20 Guy known for his honesty
21 Juice drink suffix
22 Rejected
24 "Hold on a ___!"
25 One thickness
26 Tuning fork's output
27 Where drives begin
28 Shot target
29 Variable star
33 Hemmed but didn't haw
36 Kind of school
37 Deer's scut, e.g.
38 Merit
39 Hibernation locales
40 Gossipy tidbit
41 Like diehard fans
42 Swing an Christian
43 Neutral middle vowel
44 Distribute
45 It can be for the course
46 "Murder, ___ Wrote"
47 React to an uppercut, perhaps
49 Actor activator
50 Gremlin's creator
53 Whoop-de-do
56 It may have a silver lining
57 Victor at Fredericksburg
58 Cookies with white fillings
59 Newbie
62 Apportion
63 Comes to the rescue
64 The "U" of BTU
65 Sheds feathers
66 Clueless
67 Understands, as a joke

DOWN

1 They're sometimes kept behind bars
2 Academy attendee
3 Medieval violin
4 "___ and Me Against the World"
5 Hold protectively
6 Ingredient in mead
7 Break bread
8 Some combatants
9 Street's boss
10 Trainee
11 It may be silly
12 Pleasantly pleasing
13 "When I Was ___" ("H.M.S. Pinafore" song)
18 Repaired a paper tear, perhaps
23 Brilliant feats
27 Novice Boy Scout
28 Tuck's title
30 "I do," e.g.
31 Panoramic sight
32 Diva Gluck
33 Coal stratum
34 Roof overhangs
35 Order in the court
36 Attorney's helper
39 Ostracized person
43 Glossiness
46 Most indisputable
48 Bridge positions
49 Sorority sisters
50 Peake novel "Titus ___"
51 Promotion basis
52 Word with 5, 10, 25 and 50
53 Type of rubber
54 Folk singer Guthrie
55 Title role for Jodie Foster
60 Maracana Stadium locale
61 Bear of a greeting?

223 Now Spit

by John Hanson
Edited by Timothy E. Parker
Answers in back

ACROSS

1 One of the Teletubbies
6 Thieves' undoer
10 You're tense on this
14 Way traveled
15 Hole-punchers
16 Atlas datum
17 Express verbally
18 "Gentlemen Prefer Blondes" author
19 Worked for Avon?
20 Diamond topper
23 Heartache
24 Go berserk
25 Metric unit of pressure
27 Make sport of
30 Taxing org.
32 Place to hibernate
33 Bone-dry
34 Made one's nose grow
36 Hipbone
39 Mrs., in Marseilles
40 Drillmaster?
42 High-tech ID
43 Above and beyond
45 Em, to Dorothy
46 Sponsorship (Var.)
47 Caspian Sea land
49 Tour for Woods
50 On deck
51 Sympathized with
54 Slack-jawed
56 Slim swimmer
57 Sport of kings rarity
62 Branch of math
64 Timbuktu's land
65 Asian capital
66 Grammarian's bane
67 ____ impasse
68 Meet segment
69 Brand for young builders
70 k.d. of country music
71 Ends one's case

DOWN

1 Thrash
2 Greek I
3 Some Wall Street bids
4 Turned the wheel
5 ____ mate (tealike beverage)
6 She's often on her toes
7 "Over the hill" in the military
8 City sector
9 Lay into
10 Pencil holder, at times
11 Castle feature, perhaps
12 Salami selection
13 Raring to go
21 Light on one's feet
22 Braid
26 Black gold
27 Part of a doorframe
28 Type of ant
29 Apples or cherries, sometimes
31 Arrange, as a blind date
35 Knucklehead
37 Windows alternative
38 Crow's-nest site
40 What dodgers dodged
41 "Coach" attachment
44 Gallery fare
46 Personalize a bracelet, e.g.
48 A body temperature of 98.6, e.g.
51 Kind of position
52 Creeps-inducing
53 Rodeo rope
55 Fall hue
58 Drawing-board product
59 They're white in Monopoly
60 Refusal word
61 Lousy deposits?
63 Muscle car ltrs.

by Henry Quarters
Edited by Timothy E. Parker
Answers in back

ACROSS

1 Allotted, with "out"
6 Pinza and Chaliapin, for two
11 Word with "lag" or "set"
14 ___ and beyond
15 Like most people
16 Canton at one end of St. Gotthard Pass
17 Former U.S. Open site
19 Bite from a chihuahua, maybe
20 More ridiculous
21 Area measures (with "square")
23 Nonsmoking area rarity
25 Traffic congestion
26 Penned, as a pig
28 Stow in a ship's hold
31 Cold and windy
34 Entangle
36 Have fun
37 Sikorsky or Stravinsky
39 Action movie highlight
41 Scrabble piece
42 Sound from the pond
44 Locations
46 Club or type of school
47 Mecca pilgrims (Var.)
49 Clear of vermin
51 "The House of the Seven Gables" locale
53 Medical problem
57 Systematic
60 Fortune-telling cards
61 U.N. workers' grp.
62 Where baseball stars get their start
64 C&W composer Davis
65 Become slippery, in winter
66 Three feet plus, to a Brit
67 Sort or type
68 Times in office
69 Infections

DOWN

1 Underworld family
2 Blacks, to a poet
3 Old Testament division
4 Social activities
5 Dry regions
6 "Humbug!" preceder
7 "Like that would happen!"
8 Farm storage structures
9 Where to get coiffures
10 Tuition classification
11 Alex Raymond's cartoon character
12 Canal that opened in 1825
13 Rewards good service
18 Gets ready for opening day
22 "___ they cute?"
24 Irish poet and Nobel Prize winner
27 Pre-Christian priest
29 Field mouse
30 Watched carefully
31 Abundantly endowed
32 Taj Mahal locale
33 1969 music festival
35 PC key
38 Indian ruler
40 Cylindrical and tapered
43 Computer information unit
45 Muslim greetings
48 Play the temptress
50 Archer's aim
52 Penny pincher
54 Sullen and looking unhappy
55 One cubic meter
56 Winding road features
57 "La Boheme" role
58 Israeli flyer
59 Pal or fisherman's lure
63 Forebears of CDs

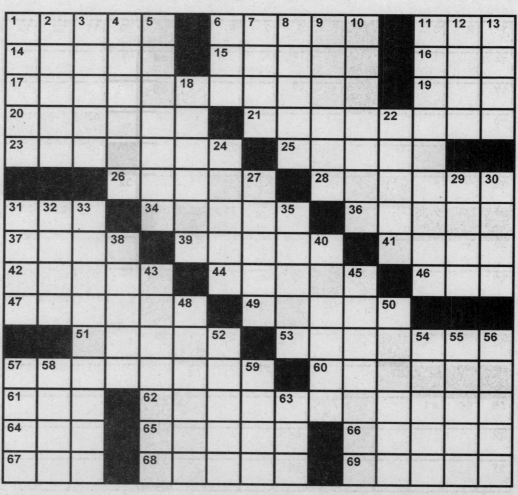

225 Sticking Point

by Oscar Luce
Edited by Timothy E. Parker
Answers in back

ACROSS

1 Wayne Newton song
5 Reason for a casino's edge
9 Famous uncle
14 Served perfectly?
15 Fairylike being
16 Dazzle
17 Ungentle-manly
18 Joie de vivre
19 Mischievous sprite
20 It's sold by the roll
23 Chocolate source
24 Pasta topping
25 Dollop
28 Be in a different form?
29 "Over There" conflict, briefly
31 For the most part
33 Burt Reynolds film
35 Tentmaker of yore
36 What a loyal follower does, perhaps
42 Skin-soothing ingredient
43 Gazpacho ingredient
44 Hornet's defense
48 Vichy, notably
49 "So, there you are!"
52 Load of bricks?
53 Santa Anna took it
55 Of interest to Peary
57 Certain NHL player
59 Red wine
62 Dino's master
63 Drug shipment, perhaps
64 Knute Rockne's Fighting ___
65 Sign of a hit show
66 Compound with doubly-linked carbon atom
67 Social event
68 Beanery sign
69 Bit of marginalia

DOWN

1 Musical gourd
2 Pertaining to the eyes
3 Cut the fat
4 Swelling, particularly in plants
5 Forthright
6 Mistaken opinion
7 Pulitzer Prize category
8 Wicked
9 Wit's weapon?
10 Track legend Zatopek
11 The Grinch's dog
12 Israeli weapon
13 Drop in on
21 Some Midwestern Indians
22 "L'___ del Cairo" (Mozart opera)
25 Salesman's vehicle
26 Apple spray, once
27 South Pole explorer
30 Subj. of a 1999 protest in Seattle
32 Oscar night attire
33 "Glengarry ___ Ross"
34 Pi's successor
36 Religious ritual
37 Like a certain sax
38 Kind of chop
39 Audacious
40 Sample tea
41 Some afternoon TV shows
45 Lacking social polish
46 Grimm shoemaker
47 Fundraising event
49 One lacking in pigment
50 Loose woman
51 Ring of color (Var.)
54 Song from "The Sound of Music"
56 "The Old ___ Bucket"
57 Seckel cousin
58 Keatsian output
59 Start for "day" or "term"
60 Don Larsen stat
61 Disturbance

Page 227

by Fran & Lou Sabin
Edited by Timothy E. Parker
Answers in back

ACROSS

1 High-ranking monk
5 Assessment quartet
10 Marquee listing
14 Seaweed product
15 "Funny Girl" composer Jule
16 "Hold ____ your hat!"
17 "The Big Chill" star
18 Tightened some strings?
19 Measured amount, in hospitals
20 Junk mail addressee
22 Deliberately not notice
24 Onward in time
25 Welcome sign?
26 Dig finds
29 Fire, air, water and earth
34 Heiden and Idle
35 Knock for a loop
36 Stir turbulently
37 Mongolian wasteland
38 Boxing ploy
39 Greek cheese
40 Sneaking suspicion
41 "Jaws" craft
42 Navel base?
43 Dumps, Wall Street style
45 Comes up in conversation
46 Platinum record, for sure
47 Like many a swinger
49 Nasty sorts
52 Offshoots of banks, libraries, etc.
56 Krakatoa output
57 "____ Bulba"
59 Slimy substance
60 Bakery worker
61 Pass over
62 About, in legalspeak
63 Irreverent
64 Walked the floor
65 Type of miss

DOWN

1 "The Wizard of Oz" star, Bert
2 Bone-shaking onset
3 Popular sci-fi site
4 Dr. Jarvik's medical invention
5 Organic compounds
6 Acrobatic feat
7 Nylon or rayon, e.g.
8 Weather vane dir.
9 Lees
10 Plugged nickel, e.g.
11 Part of A.D.
12 Make a move
13 Kind of bag
21 JAMA readers
23 Moll's leg
26 Kelly's morning co-host
27 Diminish naturally
28 Written smear
30 Type of moth
31 December airs
32 Sir or madam, as the case may be
33 Knocks 'em dead
35 Peasant of old Russia
38 Tread
42 Wise diet choice
44 Swill's opposite
45 Humbled
48 Kind of secret
49 Cut out, as coupons
50 10K, e.g.
51 Penultimate word of many fairy tales
53 Strop it!
54 Book after II Chronicles
55 Cassandra, e.g.
58 Cookbook phrase

ACROSS
1 Barbershop item
5 Gobi's location
9 Estrangements
14 Samson's pride
15 Puts on
16 Acclamation
17 Italian spouter
18 Perry Como player
19 Like lettuce
20 Uncertain notion
23 Present
24 Peke's bark
25 It gets pumped
28 Is irate
31 Cleopatra's undoing
34 In the offing
36 Mongrel
37 Up to the job
38 Scuttlebutt
42 Iraqi, perhaps
43 Hand holder
44 Singing group
45 Stallone, to friends
46 Refrigerant
49 Double agent
50 Lancelot du ____
51 Roman poet
53 Encourage-ment from the stands
60 Type of opera
61 Billion years (Var.)
62 Jacob's brother
63 Master of ceremonies
64 Adams and Malone
65 Faux pas
66 Hunger (for)
67 Ersatz butter
68 Flat fish

DOWN
1 Prepare to swallow
2 Salty retort
3 Sixties skirt
4 Cheeky
5 Hold fast
6 Evening event
7 Computer fodder
8 "Don't you wish!"
9 Put in a new supply
10 Collect frost
11 Blubber
12 U.S. president and chief justice
13 Porker's pad
21 Pasta topper
22 Makers of batik
25 Goggles
26 ____ of (in conflict with)
27 Heavyhearted
29 Jerk
30 Wish one hadn't
31 Drives the getaway car
32 Alarm's disruption
33 Small-minded
35 Out of the norm
37 Lob's trajectory
39 DEA agent
40 Give one's best shot
41 Elixir
46 Lurch and sway
47 Round third
48 Neverthe-less
50 Surgical beam
52 Woman's apparel
53 City on seven hills
54 Killer whale
55 Burkina ____, W. African nation
56 River duck
57 Largest city of Norway
58 Siren's sound
59 Patsy
60 Attention-getting shout

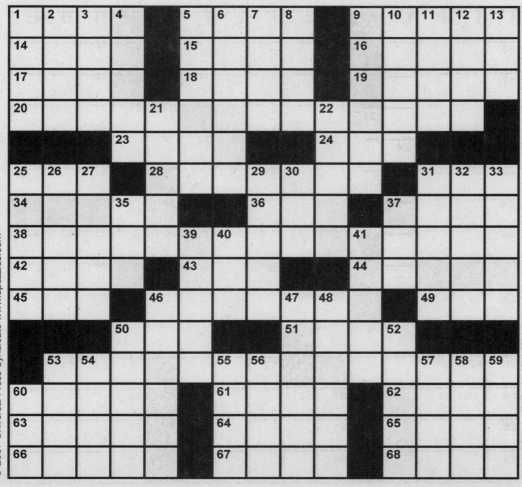

228 Light Treats

by Mose Lucie
Edited by Timothy E. Parker
Answers in back

ACROSS
1 "___ he grown!"
6 King's area
11 "___ My Party"
14 Foil giant
15 Sesame Street resident
16 Opposite of max.
17 Banquet figure
19 "Harper Valley ___"
20 Jabba the ___ of "Star Wars"
21 Cain's brother
22 Bathtub sealant
24 Deuces plus one
26 One leaving one country to settle in another
28 Kneading locale
31 Cincinnati team
32 "Star-Spangled Banner" preposition
33 Microbe
34 Le Havre-to-Paris dir.
36 Not docked
38 Weave's go-with
40 Wiesbaden, Germany is its capital
44 La-la preceder
46 One sort of miss
48 Galena, for one
49 Sans pizzazz
52 Street urchin
55 Make an old kitchen new, say
57 One, for one
58 Dispatch boat
59 Put oneself into a horizontal position
61 Make for shore
64 Shake a leg
65 "It's a snap!"
68 "___ in Black" (1997)
69 Competitive advantages
70 Hank, the former home run king
71 Alums-to-be
72 Performs, biblically
73 Produce a uniform mixture

DOWN
1 "What ___ God wrought?"
2 Moises of baseball
3 Disperses
4 Crime syndicate, with "Cosa"
5 Bit of body art, slangily
6 Use a sponge over and over again
7 Language spoken in Limerick
8 Buck's feature
9 Bald-faced bit
10 French "Thank you"
11 Unchaste
12 Having nobility
13 Creatures forming the hair of Medusa
18 Wishy-washy reply
23 Come to a consensus
25 Ventriloquist Bergen
27 Members of the AMA
28 Long, fluffy scarf
29 Dampen flax, e.g.
30 Honor ___ thieves
35 "Doesn't bother me" gesture
37 Cultural mores
39 Spangliest
41 Computer programs
42 ___ Lanka
43 Hallow ending?
45 Is for more than one?
47 Type of acid
49 Lullaby name
50 One imposing a tax
51 French cathedral city
53 Assert without proof
54 Kind of policy
56 ___-up (on strong medication)
60 They may be one or eleven
62 Sacred image (Var.)
63 Darn socks
66 Testifier's phrase
67 ___ Four (the Beatles)

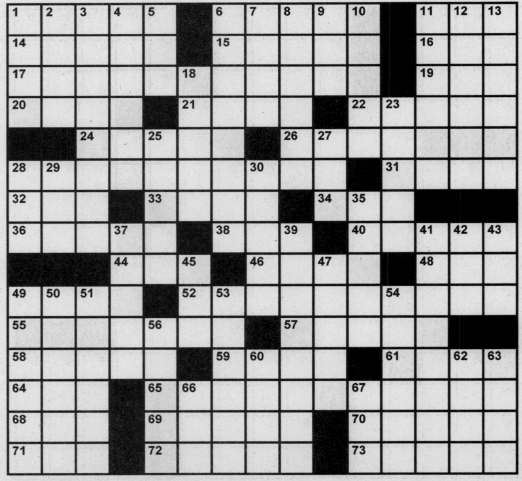

by Fran & Lou Sabin
Edited by Timothy E. Parker
Answers in back

ACROSS

1 Pride of St. Louis?
5 Whiffenpoof school
9 Shady place
14 Festive
15 Bypass
16 Slow, at the Philharmonic
17 Algerian seaport
18 Heart of the matter
19 Disconnected
20 Great guns
23 Low grade
24 Scull movers
25 "Satisfied?"
27 Full of life
30 Word-forming game
34 Red-faced
35 Piece for 30-Across
36 Brought action against
37 Actor Max ____ Sydow
38 "Halloween" sound effects
41 Humble horse
42 They justify the means
44 Sluggish from overeating
45 Opening line?
47 Put up with
49 Wahines' welcomes
50 Kuwait biggie
51 Pound hound, perhaps
52 Big Band ____
54 Pullers of 24-Across
60 Nose part
62 D-Day beach
63 Yearning
64 Range rover
65 Jules Verne sub captain
66 Songstress Brickell
67 Queen of Hearts' baked goods
68 Hoosegow
69 Tar's surface?

DOWN

1 Mightily impressed
2 ____ avis
3 Highlands kin
4 Place to loiter with pals
5 Cultured food
6 Out of kilter
7 Move to one side
8 Kitchen fixture?
9 The Last Frontier
10 Will Smith's genre
11 Family sitcom 1969-74 (with "The")
12 Tough boss
13 By the numbers
21 They're rounded on the way home
22 "Air Music" composer Ned
26 Workout target, often
27 Fasten firmly
28 University of Maine's town
29 Count Basie, notably
30 Longtime bother
31 Molder's medium
32 "You can ____ horse …"
33 Border lines
35 Easy pace
39 Santa in California
40 Like off-color humor
43 Sch. for ministers
46 Made a mess of
48 Lots of sweat
49 Name on a spine
51 Dolphin territory
52 Formerly, formerly
53 Actress Moreno
55 Box score entry
56 Dele's negator
57 Picked on
58 Sweeping story
59 Calendar division
61 "____ real!"

by Fran & Lou Sabin
Edited by Timothy E. Parker
Answers in back

ACROSS
1 Captain Kidd's haul, e.g.
5 Make ashamed
10 Jockey's equipment
14 Bestial hideaway
15 "Hey, you never know!" investment
16 Yodeler's feedback
17 Benjamin Franklin Pierce portrayer
18 Cavalry unit
19 Father of Fear
20 The purported prototype for Dracula
23 Tokyo, long ago
24 Dijon dad
25 Hold dear
30 Worker who may be found atop a house
34 Dorothy Parker, for one
35 Shift selection
37 Old-womanish
38 Russian czar with a bad rep
42 Dakota's digs
43 "Come here often?" say
44 Free (of)
45 Pub's mugs
47 Yenta's forte
50 "Mr. Smith ___ to Washington"
52 U.S. ranch bird, nowadays
53 Saint who denounced Herod Antipas
60 Lamp lighter
61 Kind of wave
62 "The Wind in the Willows" character
63 Free of knots
64 Like Bo-Peep's followers
65 McGregor of "Trainspotting"
66 45-Across filler, perhaps
67 Full, and then some
68 Shuts up

DOWN
1 Pole, for one
2 China's is Great
3 Turturro of "The Sopranos"
4 Egg carton designation
5 "However …"
6 What unexciting drillers do?
7 Much of the first half of the dictionary
8 Dance at the Savoy, in song
9 Equipment for 15-Across
10 "Spanglish" star
11 Farm segment
12 Cage's "Moonstruck" co-star
13 Bout enders, briefly
21 NFL stats
22 Bellowing
25 Silly sorts
26 Hold, as one's attention
27 Day's march
28 Rod companion
29 Cook at home
31 Whole grains, to a Brit
32 Island in New York Bay
33 Oboes, saxes et al.
36 City near Carson City
39 Girl next door, e.g.
40 Dovetail wedge
41 Closed after use
46 Brief arguments
48 Little devil
49 Applesauce topper, perhaps
51 Hinduism's destroyer
53 Calendar heading
54 Ye ___ malt shoppe
55 Make readable
56 ___ of one's existence
57 Illinois border sharer
58 Coal furnace waste
59 Gymnast's dream-come-true
60 "Mac" alternative

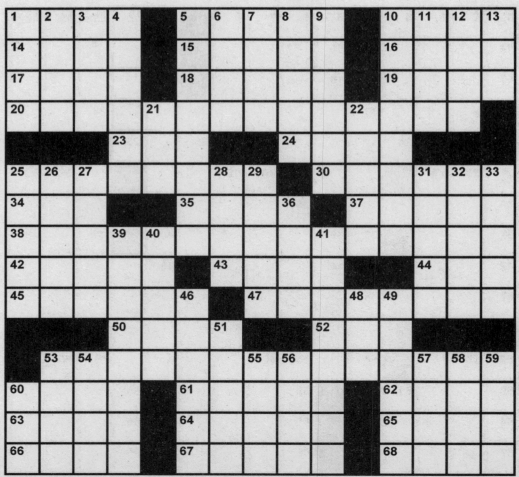

ACROSS

1 Substitute for the unnamed, briefly
5 Togo's chief port
9 Boca ____, Fla.
14 Apple, for one
15 Kingly name
16 Playing marble
17 "____ La Douce"
18 Timber dresser
19 Sled dog of a 1995 film
20 Take a decisive step
23 Punch-line reaction
24 Break a commandment
25 ____-jongg
28 Paroles
31 Speedometer letters
34 Prima donna's repertoire
36 Memorable time
37 Flier's feat
38 Decide not to, say
42 Auction site
43 Poem originally intended to be sung
44 Laughing critter
45 Three Gorges project
46 "A Nation of Immigrants" subject
49 Scale notes
50 State touching Can.
51 Earn
53 Live dangerously
61 Nonnational
62 Chat partner
63 "____ each life …"
64 Short-tailed lemur
65 Freight car hopper, perhaps
66 Is unable
67 Shoe forms
68 ____ for business
69 "____ the night before Christmas …"

DOWN

1 "Ben-Hur," e.g.
2 Atmospheric pressure unit
3 Magazine supplies
4 Animal restrainer
5 Hate
6 Passe
7 Puzzle of perplexing paths
8 At some time
9 Leporid
10 From square one
11 Bath powder ingredient
12 "Iron Chancellor" Bismarck
13 Bright light in the big city
21 Taco condiment
22 Frequent drink
25 Defeated at chess
26 Resort west of Curacao
27 King of Tyre
29 Seamstress
30 "… man ____ mouse?"
31 Suburbanite's tool
32 It gets off the ground
33 Georgetown team
35 "Where" or "how" preceder
37 Conversation opener
39 "____ is an island …"
40 Guy before J.F.K.
41 Denim alternative
46 Handsome young man
47 Drink
48 Shipping unit
50 Without energy
52 King's proclamation
53 Court security
54 Skeletal part
55 Purges
56 Audio feedback, of a sort
57 Haberdashery, e.g.
58 Chew like a mouse
59 Eruptive spot
60 Bibbers

by George Meyers
Edited by Timothy E. Parker
Answers in back

ACROSS
1 Place that attracts many visitors
6 Aerobics class prop
10 Jane Austen classic
14 A-test site, perhaps
15 Huge amount
16 "Abbey" or "Tobacco"
17 Nero Wolfe, for one
18 Words with "instant" or "uproar"
19 What one little piggy had
20 One defintion of "can"
23 Gammon, e.g.
24 Turn on a pivot
25 Made the scene

28 Of Man, but not of woman
31 Impart knowledge
35 Homeric H
36 Down in the dumps
37 In a standoffish manner
38 Another definition of "can"
41 Altogether
42 Arrangement of locks
43 Quilters' gathering
44 Took the plunge?
45 Pull up to a bar?
46 First lady after Eleanor
47 Something copped
49 Bear in Barcelona
51 Yet another definition of "can"
58 Hindu royal

59 Ready and willing
60 Po land
61 The gamut
62 Take corrective measures?
63 Sign of life
64 Unit of inheritance
65 Word with "birth" or "interest"
66 The going rate?

DOWN
1 "Monster ____"
2 "Empedocles on ____" (Matthew Arnold poem)
3 Imitates a dove
4 Provide with a wardrobe
5 First letter, to Aristotle
6 ____ and span
7 Tuneful Turner
8 Go by, as time
9 Kind of code or colony

10 2002 British Open champion
11 Not worth debating
12 More than some
13 Fruity quaff ending
21 Actor Estevez
22 Isolated
25 Beany's friend
26 Do penance
27 Horse blanket
29 Baltimore paper
30 Moocher
32 Hopi home
33 Cruciverbalist's need
34 Pumps up
36 Armed engagement
37 Like laundromat washers, for short
39 Blue ribbon, e.g.
40 Louis XIV, e.g.
45 Maple leaf land

46 Start a computer
48 Raring to go
50 Inadvertent mistakes
51 It may be tempted
52 Privy to
53 Radiate
54 Apportion
55 New Haven university
56 Last word of an ultimatum
57 Took a gander at
58 Old piano tune

233 Hubbub

by Kelly Wilmark
Edited by Timothy E. Parker
Answers in back

ACROSS

1 "Midnight Cowboy" prize
6 Edible tubers
11 Do garden work
14 Asian wild dog
15 Skirt shape
16 Ornamental vase
17 Commotion
19 Stewed to the gills
20 Filled Indian pastry
21 Colonizer
23 Military greeting
26 Former Irish nationalist Timothy
27 Be in debt
30 Public speaker's platform
31 "Sink" or "swim"
32 Dot on a monitor
34 Highland hillside
36 Gangsta recitals
39 Ill-defined
41 Squealer
43 Glance over
44 Moist
46 Hag
47 One of the Jackson 5
49 Policeman's route
51 Bard's above
52 Farm implement inventor
54 Indiscriminate
56 Former name of Kazakhstan's capital
58 Moonshot program
62 Churchill gesture
63 Extreme confusion and disorder
66 "Holiday ___" (1942)
67 Church instrument
68 Bing Crosby's record label
69 Feline, to Tweety
70 Group between 12 and 20
71 Dutch painter Jan

DOWN

1 Two-to-one, e.g.
2 Branch of Islam
3 Suffix with "macro" or "micro"
4 Chorus voices lower than sopranos
5 Not designed to be thrown away
6 Pop-top
7 What's put before the carte?
8 Shampoo instruction
9 Fairytale beginning
10 Be boiling mad
11 Loud clamor
12 Bay window
13 Doorway
18 Abnormal breathing sound
22 Hardly a little angel
24 Blackest part of a shadow
25 Feather bed?
27 "Mr. Holland's ___" (1995)
28 Subtle come-on
29 Commotion
31 Nov. 11 marcher
33 City in southern New York
35 Colorado resort town
37 Certain evergreen
38 Fortuneteller
40 Hubbub
42 Eight-armed creatures
45 Wharton degree (Abbr.)
48 What a cozy covers
50 "Bonanza" son
52 Lifeboat support
53 1940s song "Maria ___"
54 Cattle land
55 French impressionist painter, Claude
57 Container weight
59 Canine pests
60 He made Time
61 Land in the Middle East
64 Comic Aykroyd
65 Annapolis grad.

Page 235

234 Bed Adieu

by Mark Gould
Edited by Timothy E. Parker
Answers in back

ACROSS

1 Burn ___ in one's pocket
6 Like a ballerina's body
11 Medicine meas.
14 Speedy
15 "Talk turkey," e.g.
16 Feeling off
17 Bogart film or Chandler book
19 "Only the Good ___ Young"
20 In-born
21 Andean transporter
23 Muscular condition
24 Like many a brat
26 Byzantine or Ottoman
29 Bridges of "Airplane!"
30 Hawaiian tuber
31 Reason for celebration on the job
32 Mauna ___
35 What sleepy bears take
39 Took command of
40 West Wing workers
41 Protected inlet
42 Santa's subordinates
43 Treats vengefully
45 Inspirational phrases
48 Partner of sink
49 Extended and dramatic narratives
50 Certain charming quality
54 Long-winged sea eagle
55 35-Across activity
58 Game for children
59 Lose underpinnings, e.g.
60 Raptor's spur
61 Any boat
62 Hemstitched
63 Notched, as a maple leaf

DOWN

1 Painter's first class, possibly
2 Physicist Otto
3 "___ sesame"
4 Intoxicating beverage
5 Copyreader's superior
6 Sturdy stocking stuff
7 In a laid-back fashion
8 Bind
9 Gardener's tool
10 Boss
11 Word with "basin" or "wave"
12 "Ghostbusters" goo
13 State "not guilty"
18 Biological trait carrier
22 Cap, as on spending
24 Narrow incisions
25 Put forward
26 And others, briefly
27 Possessing a Y chromosome
28 Nudge
29 Where most strikes occur
31 Gets a lift
32 Nautical mile
33 Icicle's locale
34 They go bananas over bananas
36 Winter footwear
37 Marry a woman
38 Turkish saber
42 Writing shortcut
43 Trumpeter, for one
44 Copy illegally
45 Wrestling contests
46 "Beloved" Winfrey
47 Slight coloring
48 Evidence unit?
50 Give away
51 Cylindrical storage tower
52 Noises from a milk container?
53 A Windsor
56 That steamed feeling
57 Greet a queen

235 Hold Your Horses

by Fran & Lou Sabin
Edited by Timothy E. Parker
Answers in back

ACROSS

1 Theatrical producer Ziegfeld
4 Buddies
9 Show the way
14 Broadcast
15 Big name in games
16 Punjab noble (Var.)
17 "Hold your horses!"
20 Runs while sitting
21 "Becket" actor Peter
22 Cheep lodgings?
23 Women-only residence
25 Long ending?
28 Host or hostess, often
30 Like brothers and sisters
33 Mine finds
35 They could be good or bad
36 "Hold your horses!"
41 Sing a simple song
42 Hindu discipline
43 Solidify
46 7 or 11, in Vegas
51 Nasty fellow
52 ____ Alaska
54 Blood supplies
55 Notoriety
58 Update equipment
59 "Hold your horses!"
63 Year-round coat
64 Put on the books
65 "Got it?"
66 Encyclopedia volume, perhaps
67 Lalique and Magritte
68 Ogee's shape

DOWN

1 Counterfeiting
2 Schubert art songs
3 Challenging words
4 Retired Giant #24
5 From ____ Z
6 Sorority letter
7 Hot corner goof
8 Wimpled woman
9 Lounge group, perhaps
10 Countess' hubby
11 Pangolin, e.g.
12 Corporate biggie, briefly
13 Rural producer
18 St. ____, Fla.
19 Major purchase
23 Attendee's response
24 Son of Zeus and Hera
26 Identifying factor
27 "____ bodkins!"
29 Rich dessert
31 Dairy designation
32 "What ____, chopped liver!"
34 Pigpen's place?
36 "Hold your horses!"
37 Stairway guide
38 Chang's bosom buddy?
39 Give an edge
40 "Zooks!"
41 300, at the Forum
44 Lean against
45 Shaver's foam
47 Beta tester, e.g.
48 Junk
49 Faces the day
50 Woodworking machinery
53 "The Secret of the Old Clock" author
56 Sicilian lava maker
57 Calif., Ore., and Wash. time zones
58 Large mil. units
59 Agency under F.D.R.
60 Tipper's item
61 Prohibition
62 Driving hazard

by Carl Cranby
Edited by Timothy E. Parker
Answers in back

ACROSS

1 Iron fishhook
5 Latest scoop
9 Main force
14 Biblical homicide victim
15 Slugger Moises
16 Nimbi (Var.)
17 Annual Jacksonville event
19 Bobby of tennis fame
20 Previous to, previously
21 Most strict
23 Extended areas of land
26 Turkish title
27 Something to gaze into
33 Balm target
36 Approach
37 Winter, e.g.
38 Involving the ear
40 Commentator Koppel
42 Baby's word
43 Wimbledon champ Gibson
46 Cafe ___ (black coffee)
49 Soft food
50 Subject of many a tabloid photo
53 Spinning toy
54 Delinquent
57 Deviates
62 Intro to math?
64 Cheerio
65 Office door adornment
68 Renders blind
69 Periodic obligations
70 Buffalo's waterfront
71 Possessed, to King James
72 Crib part
73 "___ in the Clowns"

DOWN

1 Totally smitten
2 Towards the stern of a ship
3 Disagreeable stench
4 Type of arrangement
5 Arrest
6 "Xanadu" group
7 Bedazzles
8 Grand Turk, once
9 Artillery assault
10 Nemesis' goal
11 Goad
12 Pesters
13 Assay
18 Scout's task, for short
22 Souffle need
24 Small digit
25 Game with scwarzes and schneiders
28 "The Faerie Queene" character
29 Terhune's hero
30 Memo letters
31 Word with "cream" or "baking"
32 Word with "decision" or "judgment"
33 Bread machine output
34 "___ be a pleasure!"
35 Feel sorry for
39 Psi's preceder
41 Having a cheerless aspect
44 Give over for protection
45 In a tizzy
47 Party purchase
48 Plot differently
51 Goes through the allowance
52 Straight shooters?
55 Fixate upon
56 Like some appliances or sleeves
57 Hyphen's bigger relative
58 "It seemed like a good ___ at the time!"
59 Joined the competition
60 They're slithery and may be smoked
61 First King of Israel
63 Saxophonist's need
66 ___ culpa
67 It takes things to extremes

237 Time for a Game, Mate?

by Alan Olschwang
Edited by Timothy E. Parker
Answers in back

ACROSS

1 Nudges
6 Social one's "gift"
9 Skoal, e.g.
14 Eleniak of "The Beverly Hillbillies"
15 Lubricate
16 Psychoanalyst Fromm
17 Venomous snake
19 Landed estate
20 U.K. reference book
21 South African prelate
23 Pass by, as time
26 Flight school final
27 True to the cause
30 Business news headline
34 Got ready to face the day
37 Bound
39 Confederate commander
40 Sirs of the lowest rank
44 The Crossed Harpoons, in literature
45 Man Fri.
46 Place for a pickup
47 Assails
50 Did a job at a track meet
52 It is a crime to do this for a criminal
54 Canine coat
58 Financier of last resort
63 Clay, later
64 Word with "zinc" or "nitrous"
65 Vertical tie in a roof truss
68 Jocular
69 Home page address, e.g.
70 Unworldly
71 Guilty and not guilty
72 Begley and Begley Jr.
73 More brut

DOWN

1 Type of tea
2 Built-out window
3 Sorta
4 Heart test, for short
5 Marsupial pocket
6 Mongolian desert
7 Exposes to the public
8 Ennui (with "the")
9 Head part
10 Superlative speaker
11 Hokkaido native
12 Glasgow guy
13 By way of, briefly
18 Do as asked
22 Spirited vigor
24 Promote
25 Second-year student, shortly
28 Clerical vestments
29 The bare minimum
31 Zero-star fare
32 Eliel's son
33 What's left over
34 Slaloms
35 Diarist Frank
36 Smoke glass
38 Play part
41 Spud
42 First lady's residence
43 Mythical queen of Sparta
48 Bullock of "Speed"
49 Some monasteries
51 Inconsequential
53 Woman's brimless hat
55 Native from New Zealand
56 Commercial bovine
57 About 1.06 quarts
58 Splendor
59 Skater's maneuver
60 Perform an electrician's job
61 Turkey denizen, perhaps
62 Snigglers' prey
66 "The Simpsons" character
67 Pricing word

by Fran & Lou Sabin
Edited by Timothy E. Parker
Answers in back

ACROSS

1 "To thine own ___ be true"
5 Mature
9 Docetism and Sikhism, e.g.
14 Wild animal's place, perhaps
15 Debtor's loss
16 Bar Mitzvah reading
17 Thessalian mount
18 "Hansel and Gretel" prop
19 Battery terminal
20 Accountant, colorfully
23 Hunk of gum
24 Port in a storm
25 Requiring overtime
27 Marbles, so to speak
30 Connectors for elbows and wrists
34 Took to one's feet
35 Wilson Pickett's "___-Skirt Minnie"
36 Search for truffles
37 Classic auto company
38 Puffed up
41 Took in
42 Common connectors
44 Part of HRE
45 City on the Ruhr
47 Some headlights
49 Needy neighborhood
50 McClurg of "The Hogan Family"
51 Indira's wrap
52 Barrister's practice
54 Megahit
60 At ___ (confused)
62 A flat, thick piece
63 Opposite of 35-Across
64 Z maker
65 After midnight, say
66 In the same book, briefly
67 Klondike territory
68 Had a responsibility
69 Buttonlike?

DOWN

1 Messy eater, e.g.
2 Relaxation
3 Mona ___
4 Saint from Assisi
5 "Cool!"
6 A series of skits
7 Poker declaration
8 Inclination
9 Overdo a fast
10 Ages and ages
11 Lamb or pork cut
12 "Look, Ma, no hands!"
13 Let flow, as tears
21 Sheep shelters
22 Spooky
26 Cornfield unit
27 "___, Plain and Tall"
28 Bullfight site
29 Problem-solving, slangily
30 Occupies completely
31 "___ Two Can Play" (Peter Sellers comedy)
32 Sunday service music
33 Testimony taker
35 Henry Hudson's ship, "Half ___"
39 One of Merv's shows, informally
40 India's first prime minister
43 Turf
46 Like earthquakes
48 Court great Althea
49 Swapped stories
51 Ape Hans Brinker
52 Word with "bones" or "Susan"
53 Felipe, Matty, or Jesus of baseball
55 Capital on a fjord
56 Bear's scratcher
57 Banned, in Bonn
58 Get off the road
59 "Free ___" (Edgar Winter hit)
61 "Full," on Broadway, briefly

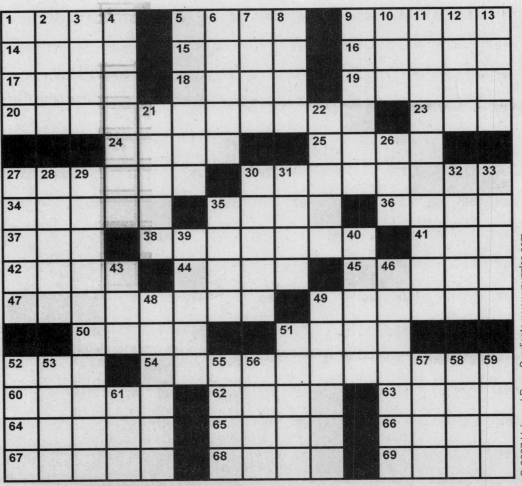

239 Farm Life

by George Meyers
Edited by Timothy E. Parker
Answers in back

ACROSS
1 Certain Egyptian
5 "On Golden ___"
9 Hiker or biker's spot
14 Ox of puzzle fame
15 Midvoyage
16 Recurring-theme composition
17 "Gimme a 'C,'" e.g.
18 Swerves off course
19 Deep chasm
20 Performing a farm chore
23 Bother, in a title of The Bard
24 Society page word
25 Word in a Gibson film title
28 Water nymph, in mythology
30 They are long stories
33 Airport guesstimate, briefly
34 Tease
36 Toddler's ritual
37 Boat front
38 Performing a farm chore
42 Greek porch
43 A Beatle's spouse
44 Word with "black" or "private"
45 Trusted one
46 Capital of Japan
48 Put two and two together
52 Kind of energy
54 Was in charge of
56 Poem of praise
57 Performing a farm chore
61 You may get fooled when it arrives
63 Face up to, as a challenge
64 "The Morning Watch" author
65 Scottish baron
66 Supplies with people
67 Day's "will be"
68 Acted wordlessly
69 Very Soho
70 Start for "while"

DOWN
1 Grand-Island link
2 Certain Iroquoian language
3 "Hoi" follower
4 Lecture
5 Late golfer Stewart
6 Native Americans of Missouri
7 Salamander family member
8 Smidgen of salt
9 Small indefinite quantities
10 Android
11 Not at a specific place
12 Some are fake
13 ___ Lobos ("La Bamba" group)
21 New Delhi is its capital
22 Pass, as time
26 Upon
27 Order precursor
29 Type of code
31 Pester
32 Obstacle to free speech?
35 Decorative pin
37 Hammer part
38 "Immediately, nurse!"
39 Three-dimensional image
40 Printer's need
41 Making haste
42 Health farm
46 Like books and motion pictures
47 Turn in the right direction
49 Insecticide device
50 Landscaping tools
51 Move to another table
53 Northeast state
55 Nervous
58 Thompson or Lazarus
59 Where the caboose is
60 Repose
61 It's filled with bills
62 21st Greek letter

by Mose Lucie
Edited by Timothy E. Parker
Answers in back

ACROSS

1 Put in prison
6 Break one's silence
11 Where musicians expose themselves?
14 "... ___ evil ..."
15 Tabriz citizen
16 Discovery utterance
17 Golfs?
19 It can hold its wine
20 Rain hard
21 It may be tingling
23 They're only temporarily puzzled
27 Brought out of dreamland
29 Place that's really buzzing?
30 Christening activity
31 Some denim garments
32 Poisonous substance
33 "Thrilla in Manila" combatant
36 Roberts' Brockovich
37 Used crosshairs
38 "Just ___ off the top"
39 "Marathon ___" (1976)
40 Word with "renewal" or "sprawl"
41 Nerve conductors
42 Removed seeds from cotton
44 Ersatz
45 Illegal hunter or fisherman
47 It moves tape through a machine
48 Omega's opposite
49 Fjordlike sea arm
50 Assenting vote
51 Do hospital security?
58 Neither's partner
59 Word with "donna" or "ballerina"
60 Hardly the gregarious type
61 Superlative suffix
62 Good news from loan officers
63 Warming drink

DOWN

1 Clairvoyant's forte
2 Danny's frequent co-star
3 "Billy, Don't ___ Hero"
4 No matter which
5 Managers' lists
6 Begets
7 Big high-school event
8 ___ Claire, Wisconsin
9 Massachusetts cape
10 Soft leather
11 Relocating a fight?
12 Ranking above a freeman
13 Cast your ballot
18 Lofty nest (Var.)
22 Sword's superior, proverbially
23 Witch-hunt town
24 "Die Walkure," e.g.
25 Taking one's role to heart?
26 Self-absorbed
27 Like a candle
28 In the center of
30 One sans permanent address
32 Rome's river
34 Evans or Ellerbee
35 "___ the house" (free)
37 "Rule, Britannia!" composer
38 Paul Bunyan's equipment
40 Blue
41 Driveway material
43 "___ bin ein Berliner"
44 Wear a hole in the rug
45 Golfing great Stewart
46 Some dairy sticks
47 Drug-yielding plants
49 Lemon's green cousin
52 Quarry product
53 Fleur-de-___
54 Make amorous advances
55 &
56 Ledger color
57 On the wagon

241 Movies to See with Caution

by Michael Colbert
Edited by Timothy E. Parker
Answers in back

ACROSS

1 Honest-to-goodness
5 Starsky's partner
10 The Amish, e.g.
14 "No" voter
15 Make accustomed (Var.)
16 Seraph's circle
17 Desktop trash can, e.g.
18 Rose perfume
19 Pressing need?
20 Pfeiffer film
23 Police accompaniment
24 Clutch producer
25 Toupee
27 "A Raisin in the Sun" star Ruby
28 Stir up, without a spoon
31 Surgeon's stitch
33 Loughlin of "Full House"
35 Shakespearean loverboy
36 Cruise film
41 Wound up costing
42 Dentist's instruction
43 Make certain
45 Koppel and Turner
47 Took down for the count, for short
50 Hr. deleter
51 Victorian or Big Band
53 '64 event for the Beatles
55 Environmental concern
59 Stereo precursor
60 "It's ____-see!" (rave review)
61 Mrs. Dithers
62 With a bow, musically
63 Stun gun
64 Egg cell
65 Newsy bit
66 Fidgety
67 Electronics giant

DOWN

1 Made a sudden attack on
2 Crate eggs, e.g.
3 On the double
4 Specialized vocabulary
5 With gusto
6 Biblical preposition
7 Ballerina's attire
8 PC problem
9 Greek Mercury
10 Brat's kick target
11 They're found in canals
12 Shutdowns
13 32,000 ounces
21 Commit a blunder
22 Bury
26 Name on Prizms and Metros, once
29 Timber wolf
30 Emulate Vesuvius
32 Ballerina's perch
34 Fortuneteller's opening
36 Didn't have enough
37 Occurrence
38 R-V connection
39 "M*A*S*H" setting
40 Automotive, music or tourism, e.g.
41 Type of meat or pepper
44 Book boo-boos
46 NY-to-Atlanta dir.
47 Balkan province
48 Beat, as in a race
49 Like a teen idol
52 Fellow who sells space
54 Mexican munchies
56 Camera feature
57 Boot out
58 Applications
59 ____ tai (rum drink)

242 Take a Trip

ACROSS

1 "Just the facts, ___"
5 Take a chance
9 "... say and not ___"
14 "Legally Blonde" girl
15 A ___ apple
16 Susan Dey series
17 Atlantic City machine
18 Jazz trumpeter Jones
19 Sheepish
20 Michael Landon series
23 Shape of the world
24 Andrews or Langley (Abbr.)
25 Kevin Costner film role
26 Opposite of whoa
30 Rent alternative
32 Suffix that turns a fib into a bone?
33 Smelting refuse
36 Watering holes in the desert
40 Timbuktu, so to speak
44 Arctic explorer Robert
45 Get ready for the wedding
46 Afternoon party
47 Vote of approval
49 Yuletide toast
52 Penn. Ave. resident
55 Phone button trio on number 3
58 Brady bill opponent, briefly
59 Tom Hanks film
65 Big name in daytime TV
66 Butter substitute
67 Icelandic tale
68 Politico Abzug
69 Symbol in music
70 First place
71 Big Bertha's birthplace
72 Radius, to diameter
73 "A Doll's House" heroine

DOWN

1 Fit together, as gears
2 "___ Have to Do Is Dream"
3 As easy as falling off ___
4 Way of doing things
5 Information bank
6 White as a ghost
7 Lasso
8 "___ Days" (Schwarzenegger film)
9 Shaving cream ingredient
10 Georgia's oldest city
11 "As ___ and breathe"
12 Copenhagen residents
13 American athlete Jesse
21 Seinfeldesque
22 Cable channel
26 Forrest of film and books
27 Tennis bad boy Nastase
28 Modern art movement of the early 20th century
29 Alka-Seltzer-landing-in-water sound
31 "Amazing!"
34 CIO partner
35 Chew, as a beaver
37 Words before "precedent" or "good example"
38 Part of a famous palindrome featuring Elba
39 Circus performer
41 Legendary Dodger pitcher Don
42 Potassium hydroxide, e.g.
43 Intermittently
48 "Much ___ About Nothing"
50 ___ Lanka
51 Certain cloth that has a sheen
52 Delve into
53 Performs in a rodeo
54 They rank above viscounts
56 Years and years
57 Loesser's "Most Happy" one
60 "Easier said ___ done"
61 Rod's partner
62 "___ Anything" ("Oliver!" song)
63 River in Central Europe
64 Wendy's dog

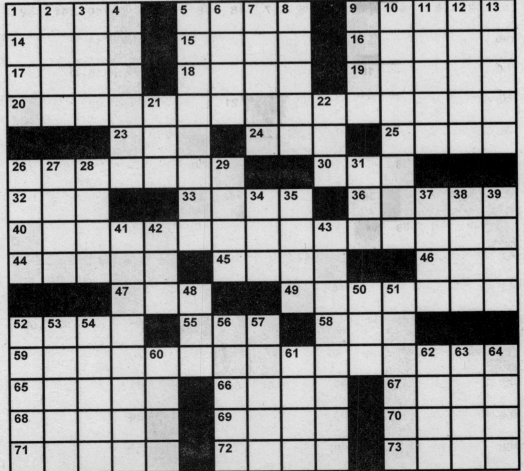

243 Loons

by Missy Lucas
Edited by Timothy E. Parker
Answers in back

ACROSS

1 Bath water residue
5 Fury
10 End of a Cuban countdown
13 A language of Pakistan
14 Bona fide
16 Part of wpm
17 Frenzied rush
19 Globe-trotting journalist Nellie
20 Breakfast chef's creation
21 Happened upon
22 T. follower
23 Small spar
24 Org. for Rehnquist
26 "___ Loves You" (the Beatles hit)
28 Nitty-gritty
33 Trendy
36 Amphilochus, for one
37 Fan's second look
38 Declare
40 Endangered giant
42 Net
43 Edit
45 Floorboard suppliers
47 Pocketlike structure, botanically
48 Bulgur
51 Snowboard cousin
52 Kay chaser
53 Place for non-recyclables
57 WWII figure
59 Basketball hoop
61 Navy builder
62 Eco-friendly feds
63 Landed
66 Creative endeavor
67 Flashing light
68 "I Dream of Jeannie" star Barbara
69 Food coloring, e.g.
70 Fabled storyteller
71 Word sung twice after "que"

DOWN

1 Really fat Japanese guys
2 Charley horse, e.g.
3 Cow's mammary gland
4 Pillowcase material, sometimes
5 Toad-handling consequence, in folklore
6 Former VCR maker
7 Source of ready money
8 Underground railroad leader
9 Vigorous
10 Beach sights
11 Christie's "Death on the ___"
12 Certain jewelry stone
15 Refrains from bothering
18 Neighbor of Pisces
24 Like the Owl and the Pussycat
25 Farm's rat-catcher
27 Great expectations
29 Cheyenne shelter
30 Male mallard
31 Setting for the 1939 Best Picture
32 Lip-___ (mouth the words)
33 Arthur the aardvark's creator Brown
34 Kaput
35 Lay waste
39 Nelson or Mears
41 "James and the Giant Peach" author
44 Avoids, as an issue
46 Stuffed
49 Shyly modest
50 Wall Street activities
54 Residence
55 Underground channel
56 Redhead's secret, perhaps
57 Cabbage unit
58 Agile
60 Teeny bit
61 Ooze
64 Trig ratio
65 Premium cable channel

244 Cutting Words

ACROSS

1 Backdrop for D.H. Lawrence's "Women in Love"
5 Love, Italian-style
10 Bridgelike game
14 Not all
15 Mighty bright stars
16 In the past
17 Sharp-leaved plant
19 Fin or sawbuck, e.g.
20 Hangs on
21 Full of malice
23 "Bet ya can't!" e.g.
24 Bygone time
25 Honesty and fairness, e.g.
28 Advertising award
30 Lifebuoy form?
33 Tram filler
34 Ceiling support
35 "... sail ____ Ship of State"
36 Unflattering word for a ship
37 Artistes may wear them
39 Tiny picnic crasher
40 Put to work
41 One-armed bandit's arm
42 Certain chamber group
43 Links goal, at least
44 Place to worship from
45 Farm machine
47 Weigh station concern
49 Tender to the touch
50 Family business, often
53 Moves speedily
57 Kind of service
58 Fine-edged
60 Pot starter
61 The best of the best
62 Turkish ruler, once
63 Words of contempt
64 Taken in
65 Say "Not so!"

DOWN

1 Altar end of a church
2 Suburban spread
3 Cattle encourager
4 Austrian pastry
5 Brings to the boiling point?
6 Telegraph developer Samuel
7 Macrogametes
8 Precipitate
9 Charles Lamb, notably
10 Clearheaded
11 Chopping surface
12 Legal org. co-founded by Jane Addams
13 Kiss partner
18 "Curses!"
22 Hits the horn
25 Emulate a brat
26 He enjoyed march madness
27 Once-fearsome extinct cat
28 It may be run for
29 Prevaricator
31 Gun-totin' Oakley
32 Whirlybird's prop
34 Joe in a diner
37 Irish county
38 Directed elsewhere
42 Gummed a rubber ring
45 Went bad, in a way
46 Blunders
48 High points
49 Young pig (Var.)
50 Seize suddenly
51 Author Jaffe
52 Yellow Sea feeder
54 Like some excuses
55 "____ Brockovich"
56 Dextrous
59 Kind of code

by Anthony J. Salvia
Edited by Timothy E. Parker
Answers in back

ACROSS
1 Clog, for example
5 Org. that delivers
9 Cookbook phrase
14 Hot torrent
15 Alexandre Dumas, ____
16 Your twin brother's wife's daughter, to you
17 Open a crack
18 Russian royalty
19 Royal horse-race venue
20 Inheritance?
23 Wow
24 Norris Trophy winner for eight consecutive seasons
25 Partition at 704 Hauser Street?
34 Dunderhead
35 Grad
36 Reine's counterpart
37 Another dunderhead
38 Justicialist South American leader
40 Former filly
41 Traditional Japanese sash
42 "Oh, dear!"
43 Biblical tower
44 Something one may do with a football uniform?
48 Supermodel Carol
49 Extinct New Zealand bird
50 Makes entries in travel diary?
59 It originates from the left ventricle
60 Feature of some skirts
61 Prehistoric carnivore, familiarly
62 Some celebrities, to their fans
63 Traditional knowledge
64 Wile E. Coyote's preferred brand
65 CIA director for two presidents
66 Type of architectural arch
67 One of Antarctica's seas

DOWN
1 Side dish, briefly
2 Islamic pilgrim (Var.)
3 Shape runners are attracted to
4 Viscount's superior
5 Chicago entertainment district
6 Six-line stanza
7 Fall preceder
8 Bone-dry
9 Canoe, in relation to ocean
10 Win over by persuasion
11 Prefix with "bel" or "liter"
12 Picture on a desktop
13 Meadowlands team
21 Canter, for one
22 Party-pooperish
25 Lehar's "The Merry ____"
26 Sun-dried clay of the Southwest
27 1993 hurricane
28 Bathroom, in Bath
29 Like an Alaskan winter
30 British rock group of the '70s and '80s, for short
31 Hurler Hideki
32 Oscar-winning actress of "Two Women"
33 Triangular sign
38 They may have many twists
39 Devour
40 Long March king?
42 Minimally
43 Many were burned in the '60s
45 Shake-and roll link
46 Vast enterprise, as in publishing
47 Vandyke's relative
50 Serve entrees, for example
51 Traveled on horseback
52 Wood complement
53 Capital once called Christiania
54 Horsewhip
55 Rating unit
56 Shell alternative
57 Prized possessions
58 Alimony recipients, informally

246 Reboot

by Bruce Venzke
Edited by Timothy E. Parker
Answers in back

ACROSS

1 Dial on the dash
5 Bank lobby call
9 Grimm group
14 Buck tail?
15 Pete's follower?
16 "Ulysses" author
17 Change careers, e.g.
20 Vote in
21 "The ____ Erwin Show"
22 Cross to bear
23 Opera set in ancient Egypt
26 Singer's fallback syllables
28 Place some go to begin anew
36 "... butterfly, sting like ____"
37 Give the cold shoulder to
38 Salsa-topped treats
39 Carrier to Copenhagen
40 Drags down in value
42 Summer camp bunk, often
43 Child's playground retort
45 Chain founded in Sweden
46 Salad slice, briefly
47 Change direction
50 Pershing's WWI command
51 Leveling wedge
52 Kind of D.A.
55 Flow partner
58 "The Addams Family" butler
62 What one may decide to do with a sigh
66 "____ man for himself!"
67 Honeybun
68 Aware of
69 A little on the slow side
70 Means' justifier
71 Get snippy with

DOWN

1 Not risque at all
2 Landlocked ____ Sea
3 Blast furnace fuel
4 Corn pone, by another name
5 Bad check lettering
6 Organ with a drum in it
7 Some Jaguars
8 Type of pilot
9 Breakfast drinks, for short
10 Take a cruise
11 Meg of "Sleepless in Seattle"
12 Hose hue
13 Back lot sights
18 Go ____ (fight)
19 Oahu dance
24 Reality unit?
25 Cinder holder
27 They're often liberal
28 Kind of Army training
29 Make ill at ease
30 Jai alai basket
31 Earth tremor
32 Tears out basting, e.g.
33 Take place
34 Cranny relatives
35 First name in skin care
40 Pamper (with "on")
41 A head
44 Lincoln and Webster, e.g.
46 Dense, puffy cloud
48 Not very many
49 Unctuous
52 Like some wines and cheeses
53 Masters winner Ballesteros
54 Uzi relative
56 ____ one's time (wait)
57 First column bingo call
59 Gifford's replacement
60 Corp. money men
61 Feathered females
63 "Science Guy" Bill
64 "We've been ____!"
65 Part of a name change

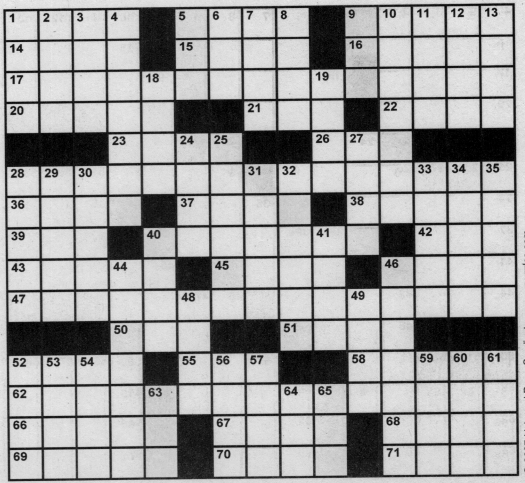

ACROSS

1 Drug agent
5 Prepares a lunchbox
10 Drains
14 Director Kazan
15 Heart chambers
16 Catch in a sting
17 Bunker, for one
18 Nighttime visitor
20 It might wind up on a boat
21 Cell messenger
22 Back talk
23 Like a court witness
26 Spills the beans
30 Yawn-provoking
31 Weapons stash
33 Melting pot island
36 Old hand
37 Cover-up of a sort
38 Carouse
43 Squirt from an octopus
44 Mo. for back-to-school sales
45 Pays attention to
46 Well-known Palace
49 Diesel fuel pollutant
51 Opposing positions
52 John Travolta film
57 Copacabana city, informally
59 Old Ford
60 Infrequent
61 Word to the wise
65 One on a pedestal
66 Enduring symbol
67 Remodeler's concern
68 Bivouac
69 Red Rose, once
70 Checks
71 Stretches of time

DOWN

1 Indian independence leader
2 Earth invader
3 Irritated
4 Got on a radio talk show
5 Walk a beat
6 Unkeyed, as some compositions
7 Zagreb native
8 Do-it-yourselfer's aid
9 Comedian Mort
10 Sugar or flour, e.g.
11 "Exodus" hero
12 Conclusion of a drive, perhaps
13 Person with intelligence?
19 Stretches the truth
24 Sign of a clunker
25 "Entertainment Tonight" anchor
27 Giant of wrestling
28 Howled
29 Snowmobile precursors
32 Tigger's pal
33 Long chronicles
34 Veranda
35 Fancied
36 Game board jumper
39 Nicotine partner
40 "Quiet!"
41 Title word of an Abbott and Costello routine
42 Bottom-line cost
47 Placid
48 Marco Polo destination
49 TV standard
50 Directives
53 Shock rocker Cooper
54 Doppler device
55 Scent
56 Barks excitedly
58 Lottery likelihood
61 Drink slowly
62 Straight start, maybe
63 Nabbed
64 WWII fighter, now

ACROSS

1 Lot measure
5 When doubled, it means quickly
9 Popular storage dump
14 Dogs, in slang
15 O'Neill, Charlie's wife
16 Put a hex on
17 Surfer's stop?
19 Paper source
20 Bar supply
21 Milk curdler
22 Raised the hackles
25 "M*A*S*H" extra
26 Remove the slack
27 It may be mixed
30 Perfume ingredient
31 Uses one of the senses
32 Navy noncom
33 The Concordes, when they flew
34 Kind of tissue
35 Langston Hughes, for one
36 Menlo Park monogram
37 Robert and Elizabeth of politics
38 Migratory goose
39 Land measurer
41 Either side of a doorjamb
42 Jib and spanker
43 Affixes, in a way
44 Set afire
46 Out of bed
47 "Lemon Tree" singer Lopez
48 Desperate, as an effort
52 Plains abode
53 Spheric opening?
54 Beats by a nose
55 Chapter 11 filers
56 Drudge
57 Pesky biter

DOWN

1 Back, on a ship
2 Accelerate, briefly
3 Common Market (Abbr.)
4 Bowl figures
5 Swindlers
6 Sharpened
7 Column to the left of the decimal point
8 Chum
9 Substituted for
10 Rutabaga, for one
11 Attire for private eyes, maybe
12 Words of understanding
13 "____ la vie!"
18 Broadcaster
21 Give it another shot
22 White Sands activity in the '40s
23 Bahamas capital
24 Street urchin
25 Butcher's wares
27 Just over a yard
28 Willing to try
29 Bad to the core
31 Signs of angels
34 Kitty, played by Ginger
35 Getting ready for the prom, perhaps
37 Zeus and Jupiter
38 Dyed indigo
40 Self-centered and then some
41 Longtime Dodgers manager Walter ____
43 Thingamajig (Var.)
44 "Tell ____ the judge"
45 Got taller
46 Designate PG-13
48 Locale for a small computer
49 10th anniversary material
50 Busy one in Apr.
51 Ike's predecessor

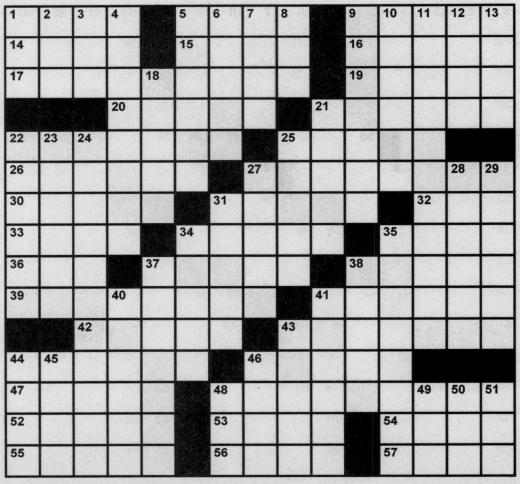

by Missy Lucas
Edited by Timothy E. Parker
Answers in back

ACROSS

1 Kazan resident
6 Poor-box contents
10 Crazy way to run
14 "Don't make ___!" ("Freeze!")
15 Latex application
16 Mongolian desert
17 Type of deck with allegorical cards
18 Gaius' garment
19 Soon, to a poet
20 Make a surprise visit
23 Torn or Taylor
24 Hullabaloo
25 Purify
29 Sticky strip
31 Grand Banks catch
34 Think out loud
35 Globe-trotter's need
36 One of three bears
37 Retire in a hurry
40 Sonic boomerang
41 "That's clear to me"
42 Be a pack rat
43 "___ will be done …"
44 Fox or Rabbit honorific
45 Sportscast feature
46 It may be passed or cocked
47 Kind of "hole" or "holder"
48 Cause of a call to an insurance company
57 Run without rushing
58 ___-de-camp
59 Plains resident
60 Mythical meanie
61 Brainstorming result
62 Napped leather
63 Enthusiasm
64 Take five
65 Of few words

DOWN

1 Makes lace, in a way
2 "The Joy Luck Club" nanny
3 Actor Benicio Del ___
4 Admit frankly
5 Word with "punt" or "kick"
6 Misbehave
7 Exemplar of craziness
8 Gift-giving trio
9 Hold one's ground
10 From square one
11 Helena is its cap.
12 A double reed
13 Benevolent
21 It's easy
22 Lock horns
25 Famous synonymist
26 Geologist's division
27 Suspicious
28 Fascinated by
29 Go-getter
30 1975 Wimbledon champ
31 Plotters, collectively
32 "The Magic Flute," e.g.
33 Old man, to some
35 Workbench gripper
36 Type of deck
38 Like some missiles
39 Checker innovation
44 Emeril's word
45 Name in a 1973 decision
46 Monopoly buy
47 Skirt feature
48 Whole nine yards
49 More than suggest
50 When tripled, a 1970 movie
51 Wait awhile
52 Midmonth day
53 Lecherous guy
54 Wide-mouthed jug
55 No-goodniks
56 Cap site

by Michael Raye
Edited by Timothy E. Parker
Answers in back

ACROSS
1 Stops wavering
5 Ready for a fight
9 Aired "I Love Lucy"
14 Droner, often
15 Oceanic threat
16 Opposite of pencil in
17 "Ben-Hur," e.g.
18 Word with "Lambeau" or "quantum"
19 Useless
20 Horse racing
23 Aspirin, to an ache
24 Gave false hopes
25 Word with "down," "up" or "back"
28 Actress Garr
30 Bloodsucking fly
32 It's fit for a pig
35 The City Without Clocks

38 "Good-bye, old chap!"
39 Wendy Wasserstein play (with "The")
43 Certain field workers
44 Raconteur's inventory
45 Trevino of the links
46 "Finally!"
49 Some bioelectric swimmers
51 Hallucination cause
52 Carved pole emblem
55 Major blood vessel
59 Routinely
61 Dromedary
64 Hospital division
65 Rorschach mark
66 "Toodle-oo"

67 1940s slugger Johnny
68 It hangs around the roof
69 Hardware purchases
70 Quilting events
71 One whose work is constantly changing?

DOWN
1 Big, in bariatrics
2 Term for dad
3 Many lounge combos
4 Type of admirer
5 Fledgling flier's goal
6 Before takeoff
7 Pat-___
8 Quick
9 Rules
10 Some sea birds
11 "Diff'rent Strokes" actress Charlotte

12 Krait kin
13 Cyberhead's place
21 Italian fountain
22 Part of a famous soliloquy
25 Stable part
26 Lauder, of cosmetics
27 Taunt
29 Button on a camcorder
31 And so on, for short
32 Place to run aground
33 College student's armload
34 Ramp sign
36 Parseghian of coaching
37 Observe with dignity
40 Gene's ID
41 Word in the society pages

42 It has five pillars
47 Seismograph part
48 Day-care visitor
50 Turned on the tears
53 A small Tom
54 Start of a counting rhyme
56 Baton-passing race
57 Treasure ___
58 Late-blooming flower
59 Swiss chard, e.g.
60 Some Shoshonean people
61 Truck's passenger area
62 Without further ___
63 1/1000 inch

251 Auto Shop

by Alice Walker
Edited by Timothy E. Parker
Answers in back

ACROSS

1 Elevator, in England
5 Ring engagement?
9 Puccini work
14 An Olympic ring
15 "The Piano" actress Paquin
16 Classic cookies
17 "A Bullet for Joey" star
18 Farmer's bonanza
20 Set of computer files
22 Air currents
23 Chucklehead
24 Voice quality
26 Show pain
29 Sporty shirt
34 It comes before Wednesday once a year
36 Discovery's view
38 Laconic
39 Theater follower
41 Snoops
43 Christmas
44 Portents
46 Eliot's "cruellest month"
48 "… ___ iron bars a cage"
49 Slide used in lighting
51 Manual transmission
53 Loosen
55 Flow regulator
58 Lose stature
62 More merry
65 Certain government site
67 ___ Domini
68 Kitchen scale marking
69 Take in
70 Ongoing quarrel
71 Goodyear pattern
72 "You Are My Destiny" singer
73 Being

DOWN

1 Adds fat for cooking
2 "Don't Let Go" singer Hayes
3 Unnecessary person, on a double date
4 Honshu house mat
5 Rum cake
6 Responsibility
7 Like some needs
8 Faucet
9 Deluge
10 SeaWorld performer
11 Feudal laborer
12 Ducklike bird
13 Hooded snakes
19 Novelist Ferber
21 It often gets picked
25 Different ones
27 The end of night?
28 Chore-related outing
30 Low island
31 Phone connections
32 City on a fjord
33 Parliamentarian
34 Entranced
35 Word with "what" or "where"
37 Iceberg feature, figuratively
40 Protein-producing substance
42 Command to a guest
45 Like bonsai
47 Shown as it happens
50 Like cuttlefish defenses
52 Wine server
54 Place to dive in
56 Serena's rival
57 Disintegrate
58 Robert Burns, for one
59 Kind of hand
60 Ancient alphabetic symbol
61 Quechua speaker
63 Listen!
64 European erupter
66 Where to find good schools?

252 Pick a Card

by Anna Huxley
Edited by Timothy E. Parker
Answers in back

ACROSS

1 Someone with a lot on his shoulders
6 One wearing the apron strings
10 Cry from on high
13 "Twelfth Night" heroine
14 Synonym collector
16 Reward for a sacrifice, sometimes
17 Handy pointer
19 Bradley and Sullivan
20 Spot remover?
21 Meal opener?
22 Left in the lurch
24 Deep violet blue
26 Fancy duds
27 Sufficiently
30 Partner
32 Shared funds
33 "Shallow ___" (2001 film)
34 Quieted a crying baby
37 Two of none?
38 Unauthorized strike
40 Quarry product
41 Wickerwork cane
43 A sucker holds it
44 Waves breaking on the shore
45 Nighttime visitor
47 To begin with
48 Wide scarf
50 Like some decals
52 Barbary Coast pirate
54 Hammer and anvil site
55 No. cruncher
58 ___ chi
59 Parlor
62 Leading Dada painter
63 Drawn-out tales
64 Sharp-eyed hunter
65 Concorde, e.g.
66 Coming up
67 Holyfield rival

DOWN

1 Gung-ho
2 Miniscule
3 Source of riches
4 Draft option
5 German state and one-time kingdom
6 Disparaging
7 Sweetie
8 Incites
9 They'll keep you on your toes
10 Unit of college work
11 Pop singer Paula
12 Thin streaks of smoke
15 Bring forth for inspection
18 Craze
23 Regatta requirement, sometimes
24 Out of sorts
25 Fort Knox stash
27 Mimic
28 Lisa of the Louvre
29 Afterthought
31 Carpet style
33 Female red deer
35 Muffs it
36 Dexterous
38 Classified information?
39 Paddling advocate
42 Artsy town near Santa Fe
44 Confession in a confessional
46 Desert phenomenon
47 Lose one's train
48 Impersonate
49 Takes wing
51 One of the Bobbsey clan
53 Persian Gulf state
55 Machinist's teeth
56 Equestrian contest
57 Sunday sound
60 Ski coating
61 Sci-fi writer Bradbury

by Jule Mason
Edited by Timothy E. Parker
Answers in back

ACROSS

1 Apportion, with "out"
5 Long-tailed parrot
10 Unicorn feature
14 College endower, often
15 Invisible appetizer
16 Song sung solo
17 Elemental duplicate?
19 "Shade" starter
20 One may be terrible
21 Rim coating, sometimes
23 Quenches
27 Showed disapproval
30 Type of moth
33 Elemental choo-choo?
35 Odd, spelled oddly
36 Surround sound's inferior
37 What chit-chat may break
38 Animated owner of a 40-Across
39 Small, moist amount
40 Cheers, e.g.
41 Limit
42 Little fiend
43 Schwarzenegger film
45 Cod or Fear
46 Elemental luminosity?
48 More wan
49 Blown-up area
50 Word with "metric" or "honor"
52 Mmes. of Mexico City
54 Emulated LL Cool J
58 Chicken chaser
60 Elemental serpent?
64 Irish tongue
65 Parting word
66 Bourbon Street veggie
67 Faithful follower?
68 Food and shelter, e.g.
69 Depend

DOWN

1 Anti-attacker spray
2 Assured vigor
3 Filet mignon, when served with lobster
4 Ambassador's office
5 Type of ray
6 ___ de Triomphe
7 Lovey-dovey sound
8 Fuse unit
9 Methods
10 Hounds hunt holler
11 Like a powerful speech
12 Part of a crater
13 Snooze
18 "For Your Eyes ___"
22 Regard with extreme aversion
24 Soldier's knapsacks
25 Prior, to Poe
26 Frozen desserts
28 Houdini specialty
29 More complex
30 Sign of the zodiac
31 Petty officers, at sea
32 Favorably prejudice
34 Close
36 Hindu wrapper?
39 Land at a river's mouth
44 Reserved
45 Insect-repelling compound
47 The jitters
48 Fruit tree
51 Lock with no key?
53 Peruse
55 Toy dog, briefly
56 Countess' spouse
57 Invasion date
58 Burns of documentaries
59 Wrath
61 Poem of praise
62 Type of chart
63 Group of seals

by Judy Denon
Edited by Timothy E. Parker
Answers in back

ACROSS

1 When pinned, it's a lock
5 Lunatic, often
10 "CSI Miami" carrier
13 Arm part
14 Style of dress
15 NL stadium
16 Fear indicator
18 Rhythmic tune
19 Follow a pattern?
20 Put below
21 Cold stick
23 Mulligan, e.g.
24 Gave under pressure
25 Choice word
28 Evening bash
29 More on target
30 Water down
31 Social climber
34 Swabbie
35 Oft-quoted words
38 Slender figure?
39 Symbol of life
41 Dos y uno
42 Peaceful period
44 Spring time?
46 Rug-cleaning device
47 Bottomless pits
49 Hawk's home (Var.)
50 "Citizen Kane" actor
51 May or Man
52 Copycat
55 Tortoise's race rival
56 Like Donald and Daffy
59 High collar
60 Kuwaiti biggie (Var.)
61 Citizen's privilege
62 Out-of-service plane
63 Pop
64 "I agree!"

DOWN

1 OOO, in love letters
2 Very useful plant
3 "Corridors of Power" author
4 Step in ballet
5 High beam?
6 Concede
7 Opinion
8 Ninny uses three
9 Sign of economic upswing
10 Show a yellow stripe
11 Ball girl?
12 Needing no more
15 Canned peaches, often
17 Organic compounds
22 One for the road?
23 Ship's designation
24 Invents a new word
25 James of jazz
26 It abuts Armenia
27 Ragtime one-step
28 More reluctant
30 British wheels
32 Yesteryear
33 Tankard filler
36 Sat in on
37 Three-dimensional photograph
40 Get a move on
43 Shaft of light
45 From Utica to NYC
46 Bats' hangout?
47 Causes for complaints
48 Gravy holders
49 Showed curiosity
51 Kind of tea or coffee
52 Certain smasher input
53 Fountain of music
54 Starting place?
57 Thurman of film fame
58 Gametes

255 Wasting Away

by Michael Raye
Edited by Timothy E. Parker
Answers in back

ACROSS

1 "___, Dolly!" (play starring Carol Channing)
6 Pillages
11 Little white lie
14 "Crime does not pay," e.g.
15 Insurance matter
16 Beatles collection
17 It could be full of worms
19 OAS member
20 Thing done
21 "... ___ iron bars a cage"
22 Bright at night
24 Operate a rummage sale
26 Moore of "Bobby"
28 Says with a scratchy voice
29 One of the cattle in a cattle drive
31 Catnap
33 Sudden impulse
34 Relief
36 Bankruptcy cause
38 "___ on Indolence" (Keats)
39 Small pain in the neck
42 Tigger's bouncing buddy
44 Small duck
45 Scatter
46 Work for an orchestra?
48 Ivan or Peter
50 Political name in Chicago
54 Camel's undoing
56 ___ yet (so far)
58 It has its ups and downs
59 Polishing off slowly
61 Itch
63 Hall-of-Famer Williams
64 Old bronze coin
65 Ordinary folks
68 Dictionary section
69 High-speed transmission
70 Bubbling
71 Animal in several of Aesop's fables
72 Catches one's breath
73 Varieties

DOWN

1 Tease
2 French naval missile
3 Like Red Riding Hood
4 "Parking" or "odd" follower
5 Doomsayer's sign
6 In a panic
7 Jungfrau, e.g.
8 Overturned
9 "Braveheart" garb
10 Defame
11 Result of a court violation
12 Dull
13 "How should I know?"
18 Show sleepiness
23 Blustery
25 Bound
27 1920s Duesenbergs, e.g.
30 Go on a rampage
32 Diminishes
35 Health concern
37 Trampled
39 Grump
40 Cheesy meals
41 On vacation
42 Home to many a penguin
43 Certain Wall Street trades
47 Swindler's prey
49 Palace set
51 Skin moistener
52 Liner location
53 Sings at a high level?
55 Electrician, at times
57 Swamp
60 Sobriquet
62 Neighbor of Mont.
66 Set of parts
67 U.S. crime fighter

256 Make Time

by Missy Lucas
Edited by Timothy E. Parker
Answers in back

ACROSS

1 Aim improver
6 Drained river area
11 What to see in your Chevrolet
14 Bent, in a way
15 Wash away, as soil
16 Prefix with "realism"
17 Later
19 A Bobbsey twin
20 67.5 degrees, in terms of direction
21 Some counting units
22 Glittered
24 Emeritus, for short
25 One of the Cyclades
26 Entire range
28 Delaying excuse
32 Plane's parking place
35 Diner sign
36 OSS follower
37 Orderly
38 Daisylike flower
40 Boxing boundary
41 Mai ____
42 "K-i-s-s-i-n-g" place
43 Accolades
44 Procrastinator's claim
48 Capital of Morocco
49 Word on the society page
50 TV police
53 Capacious
55 Variety of pea or bean
56 Melodic tune
57 Female gametes
58 "Hold on"
62 Blazed the trail
63 "Business as ____"
64 Near-perfect ratings
65 Pulver's rank (Abbr.)
66 Decent chaps
67 ____ jaw (pug's liability)

DOWN

1 Less cracked?
2 Beldame
3 Two quartets?
4 ____ capita
5 Issue
6 Urgent request
7 They may be fine or graphic
8 "Native ____"
9 Bachelor's last words
10 Cronkite and Brokaw, e.g.
11 Not spotted
12 Actor Penn
13 Absolutely first-rate
18 "I'm listening"
23 Syllable for marching
26 Drop one's jaw
27 State with confidence
28 Telegraphic signal
29 Novel by Hailey
30 "Venus de ____"
31 "... 'Cause I ____ me spinach"
32 "Matter" or "hero" prefix
33 Bells' sound
34 Sante Fe and Amtrak
38 Operatic 1987 movie
39 Scottish tartan pattern
40 Prickly seed vessel (Var.)
42 Drinking mug in the shape of a man
43 Hanging on to
45 Three Gorges project
46 Chronology of events
47 Squad
50 Flora's companion
51 Makes reference to
52 Leafy green vegetable
53 Balboa, to Stallone
54 Chamber to bake in
55 Rebounds, e.g.
59 "Oh, what's the ____?"
60 Earth's source of heat and light
61 Lacking value

257 On Lock Down

by Alice Walker
Edited by Timothy E. Parker
Answers in back

ACROSS

1 Narrative of heroic exploits
5 Lamb serving
9 Operetta composer Franz
14 Woeful interjection
15 Reverberation
16 A May birthstone
17 Falls behind
18 Suggestive sneer
19 Restroom door sign
20 Circus attraction
23 Famous West
24 Davy Jones' locker
25 Ditto
27 Sheer delight
31 North Sea tributary
32 Paris pronoun
33 Arctic explorer
36 Operatic legend
39 ___ Blanc
41 Kind of trap
43 Piece on all four corners in 7-Down
44 Like some pond growths
46 Get the ball rolling
48 Dernier ___ (latest fashion)
49 Debtor's burden
51 Sinatra's hometown in New Jersey
53 Inches, as to feet
57 G.R.F.'s choice for VP
58 Exclamations of surprise
59 Discharge of lightning
64 Torah authority
66 "The Long and Winding ___"
67 Wading bird
68 Frighten
69 Dorothy's pet
70 One-third of a war film title
71 Gumbo ingredients
72 Reach across
73 Seal in the juices

DOWN

1 Shaker contents
2 Apple spray of yore
3 Totally smitten
4 Have a finger in the pie
5 Lets loose
6 Breezed through, as an exam
7 Kind of board
8 "M*A*S*H" setting
9 Xena portrayer Lucy
10 Swellhead's problem
11 Wrestling hold
12 "There's ___ In My Beer" (Hank Williams song)
13 Zellweger of Hollywood
21 Lowest tide
22 Jimmy and Rosalynn's daughter
26 Will figure
27 Mrs. Peel on "The Avengers"
28 Like Fonzie
29 Meeting place for the unattached
30 Talks nonstop
34 Soak flax
35 Part of a Beatles refrain
37 Traditional knowledge
38 Birthday suit
40 Pin the ___ on the donkey
42 Gave a long, boring speech
45 Southpaws
47 Lift up a mountain
50 Unspecified ordinal
52 Planetary paths
53 Upper body
54 Hit hard
55 Causes distress
56 Private detective
60 "Star Trek" android
61 Woodwind instrument
62 Old currency in Milan
63 Romanov ruler
65 Bikini top

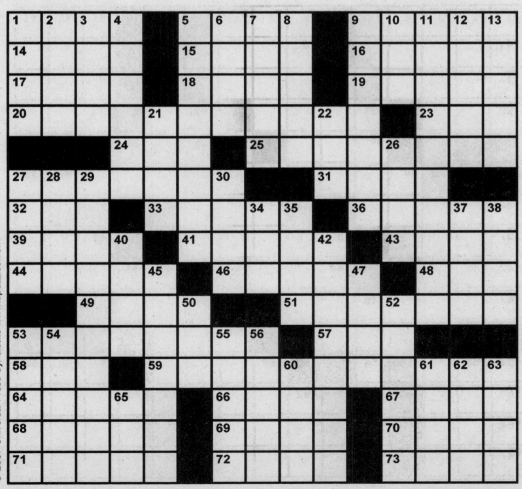

258 Washed Up

by Fran & Lou Sabin
Edited by Timothy E. Parker
Answers in back

ACROSS

1 Daddies' soft drinks?
5 Memorable act
9 Senior moments?
14 Lena of the movies
15 BBs, say
16 Typeface
17 "Symphonie espagnole" composer
18 Money-minded fed
19 State money-maker
20 Washed up
23 Give the ax
24 Bustle along
25 "I did it with ___"
27 Buy back
30 Bolsheviks' foes
34 Chip away
35 Salutatorian's platform
36 Gull-like predator
37 Toothed music-maker
38 Emotionally troubled
41 "___ be back!"
42 Lower classman of yore
44 Pony up
45 Martin Crane's pooch
47 Brighton breaks
49 Embraces tightly
50 Appellation
51 Madeline of "Blazing Saddles"
52 Fish or fish dish
54 Washed up
60 "___ Came Jones" (Ray Stevens song)
62 Paul Desmond's sax
63 Like seances (Var.)
64 Many grads do it!
65 Sampras the tennis star
66 Compulsion
67 Is overfond
68 "___ who?"
69 Quarter acre of land

DOWN

1 Horse-riders' sport
2 Norwegian king, 1957-1991
3 Accumulation
4 Expressed contempt
5 Understand
6 Ant, once
7 Maharaja's maid
8 Grammy winner Braxton
9 Support shaft
10 Outback bounder, briefly
11 Washed up
12 Wee thing
13 Flat-bottomed craft
21 Copse composition
22 Rental agreement
26 Palindromic relative
27 Respond to a buzzing alarm
28 Make disappear
29 Washed up
30 Queen of Hearts' snacks
31 King's address
32 Cup-shaped flower
33 Income source in the retail business
35 Polonius or Claudius, e.g.
39 Yellowish brown
40 Site of India's Jama Masjid
43 Socrates' H
46 Ballet Russes member
48 Self-portraits, e.g.
49 Camp craft
51 Recipient of 44-Across
52 Seek proof of age
53 I Can't Believe It's Not Butter
55 Oval circuits
56 Small circus performer
57 It may be a foot long and edible
58 "Cogito ___ sum"
59 Turned blue, maybe?
61 Map dir.

259 Physical Fitness

by Inez Adams
Edited by Timothy E. Parker
Answers in back

ACROSS

1 "I just won't ___ of it"
5 Lose solidity
9 Room in a maison
14 King of the Huns, in Germanic legend
15 Poet Khayyam
16 Whitney Houston's "All the Man That ___"
17 Displayed one's anger, in a way
20 Wilderness photographer Adams
21 Peter Fonda title role
22 "Soul Food" actress Long
23 Cut, as school
27 Carry out a biblical rite
30 Jacob's twin
31 It causes one's head to swell
32 "A Doll's House" heroine
34 Priest and minister's cohort, in jokes
38 Converse
40 Hoodwinks
43 "The Angry Hills" author
44 Coolly detached
46 "First Lady of Song" Fitzgerald
48 Business with staying power?
49 "Coffee, Tea ___?"
52 Least likely to work
54 Committed a track violation
58 Large Japanese crater
59 Venetian farewell
60 Navigators' Islands, today
64 Short distance
68 Has ___ for (adapts to naturally)
69 Cleveland's lake
70 "Buyer beware" phrase
71 Mean-spirited
72 "Auld Lang ___"
73 Apportion (with "out")

DOWN

1 "Funny ___ or funny peculiar?"
2 007's alma mater
3 Setting for "The Sound of Music"
4 Most likely to fall from a tree
5 "The ___ Squad"
6 Grounded bird
7 Drink like a dog
8 "Rose of ___" (Roger Whittaker tune)
9 Cocktail with lemon juice and brandy
10 "___ away we go!"
11 Hotelier Helmsley
12 Olympian Carl
13 Best and O'Brien
18 "The Magic Kingdom" novelist Stanley
19 Buntline and Beatty
24 Alligator shirtmaker, once
25 A neighbor of Chile
26 Feast on the beach
27 Loser to VHS
28 "(I've Got ___ in) Kalamazoo"
29 Ball-and-mallet game
33 Mighty Joe Young, for one
35 Kind of cheese
36 Trash collectors?
37 "___ It Romantic?"
39 One-time surgeon general C. Everett
41 "Legally Blonde" girl
42 Bessemer leftover
45 Like Howdy Doody's face
47 City near L.A.
50 1502, on monuments
51 Some bivouacs
53 Up the creek, so to speak
54 Shah ___ (Taj Mahal builder)
55 Canada's neighbor, colloquially
56 Broods
57 White-haired with age
61 Clio, Erato or Urania, e.g.
62 Fail to include
63 Polygonal recess
65 "Game, ___ and match"
66 Writer Anais
67 Just-passing grade

260 Later, Dude

by Fran & Lou Sabin
Edited by Timothy E. Parker
Answers in back

ACROSS

1 Dutch dairy export
5 One with a wide-open mouth
10 "Ave!"
14 Kangaroo's gait
15 Top-drawer
16 Radius' neighbor
17 Bend
18 Appearances
19 Picks, picks, picks
20 Military ploys
23 Duel memento
24 Marriage-minded fellow
25 Hitchcock classic, 1936
30 Flexible
34 Keats creation
35 Baby powder base
37 Hair-raising
38 George Washington composition, 1796

42 "The Lady, or the Tiger?" setting
43 "Aye aye, capitan"
44 End of an exchange?
45 In a foul mood
47 Abbreviates
50 "Zip-____ Doo-Dah" from "Song of the South"
52 Needlefish
53 Neil Simon film comedy, 1977
60 First name among sitarists
61 Cantaloupe, e.g.
62 Cancellation stamp
64 Yemen port
65 Love, in Livorno
66 Wee bit
67 Sign of remorse, maybe
68 Local theaters
69 "My sentiments exactly!"

DOWN

1 Santa's helper
2 The Pineapple King
3 Crowning point
4 Yucatan setting
5 Idaho's nickname
6 Reached Dulles
7 Waterfront site
8 Liquid-heating devices
9 Prepare for a big day, in a way
10 More needy
11 Jai ____
12 "Bus Stop" author
13 Colleen
21 Disapproving word
22 Went sniggling
25 Parlor pieces
26 "I don't give ___!"
27 City near Cleveland

28 Western women
29 New York Bay's ____ Island
31 Glacial ridge
32 Month before Iyar
33 Lab projects
36 Ones, twos and fives, e.g.
39 Driving up a wall
40 "Where's ____?" (kids' book)
41 Noted seeker with a lamp
46 Petty officer
48 Poor publication
49 Nonessential facts
51 Plant swelling
53 Pitfall
54 "If I ____ Hammer"
55 Like 10, 20 and 30
56 Shapeless thing
57 Knight time?

58 "Bed" or "bath" follower
59 Beer parlor choice
63 "Hey Nineteen" rockers Steely ____

Page 262

© 2007 Universal Press Syndicate www.upuzzles.com

by Loma Lapley
Edited by Timothy E. Parker
Answers in back

ACROSS

1 "___ dog!"
4 Plant opening
9 "True ___" (John Wayne film)
13 Battle-minded deity
15 Debate focus
16 Dirty Cajun dish
17 "Arrivederci"
18 "___ we all?"
19 Light bulb, in the comics
20 Some consumer come-ons
23 Helping hand
24 Turf partner, in menu headings
25 Thick fogs
30 Worked a 12-hour shift, e.g.
34 Mensa criteria, for short
35 Marquee boasts, briefly
37 Macy's, for one
38 Haberdasher's special
42 Jeweler's measure
43 Hop, ___ and a jump
44 Stephen of "V for Vendetta"
45 Went from 60 to 40, e.g.
47 Like a boutonniere
50 Short lives?
52 Vote against
53 Students' bargains
61 Firth of Lorn port
62 Meir of Israel
63 Tabasco tot
64 Great Bear or Victoria
65 "___ Joe's"
66 "Citizen Kane" prop
67 Became a brunette, perhaps
68 Feed, as a fire
69 "___, team!"

DOWN

1 Earliest of the Three B's
2 La Scala offering
3 "Agreed!"
4 Hoagy Carmichael classic
5 Actress Spelling
6 Petroleum-regulating gp.
7 Gold holders
8 Misbehave
9 Melanie of "Working Girl"
10 Hitcher's hope
11 Bakery specialist
12 Ceylon and green, for two
14 Stuffed seats
21 Devout, to da Vinci
22 Cold-morning ground coating
25 Goes for
26 Perfectly balanced
27 "The Jetsons" pooch
28 Veep's superior
29 Argyles, among many
31 France's longest river
32 Bald eagles' kin
33 Ballet-focused artist
36 Straight, thin cut
39 Gaunt
40 Cooked at home
41 Break in the schedule
46 Evades, as questions
48 Fairy queen
49 Rhone's capital city
51 Offspring in a sty
53 Lawn sign, sometimes
54 Online bargain site
55 Birthday staple
56 Voice below soprano
57 Bismarck's home (Abbr.)
58 Smeared with grease
59 Patella's place
60 Burger go-with

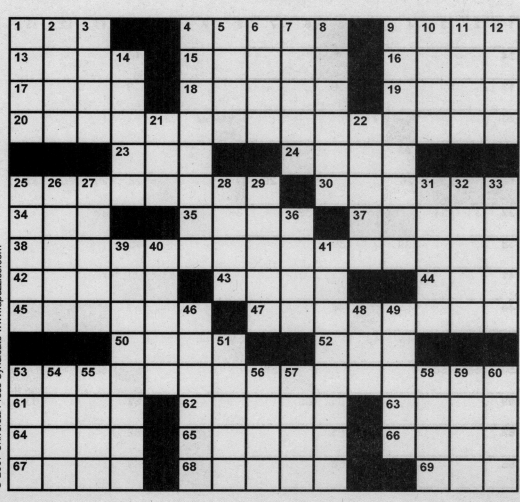

262 Go for It!

by Macy Luck
Edited by Timothy E. Parker
Answers in back

ACROSS
1 Agenda item
6 Pain in the neck
10 Disaster follower?
14 Eocene, for one
15 Third book of the New Testament
16 Cusack or Rivers
17 Go for it!
20 Before, in the beginning
21 "So long!"
22 Alphabet soup letter
23 X's, in bowling
25 Like a Tussaud figure
26 Rooney's network
27 Jolt, as one's memory
28 End of a dash
32 Twisted person or Moore documentary
35 Some stadium covers

37 By means of
38 Go for it!
41 Thurman of "Kill Bill"
42 Comic Robert
43 Rich wall hanging
44 Ensemble
46 Put in practice
47 Sleeve card
48 Bracket shapes
50 Klutzy
54 Colorful flowering bush
57 Court pro Steffi
58 Sigma preceder
59 Go for it!
62 Rummage for truffles, e.g.
63 Southernmost Great Lake
64 Atmospheric layer
65 Green Gables girl
66 Claim-staker's claim
67 Sups

DOWN
1 Does sub work
2 Eyeball-bending drawings
3 Game in "The Sting"
4 "Fire and ___" by Robert Frost
5 It needs balancing
6 Earnest requests
7 Continental currency
8 Wild blue yonder
9 Certain adolescent
10 Four-time Indy 500 winner
11 Crucifix
12 Former Chief Justice Warren
13 Chip in a chip
18 Seeks the same prize
19 "The Simpsons" network

24 Distasteful
25 Word in a Helen Reddy song title
27 Foster of "Panic Room"
29 Allege as fact
30 Tuscany city
31 Diner sign
32 Hit, as one's toe
33 Cookbook author Rombauer
34 Greenish blue
35 Treat a wound
36 Chips, pretzels, etc.
39 Howled at the moon
40 Doodled, e.g.
45 Wipe out electronically
47 At arm's length
49 Aloha garland
50 Van Gogh's village
51 Fluorescent tube gas

52 French river
53 Showers with love
54 Pearl Mosque city
55 Ancient Jerusalem temple site
56 "___ calling!"
57 Smooth-talking
60 J.F.K.'s stepfather
61 Israeli-designed weapon

263 Dress Warmly

by Han Brickel
Edited by Timothy E. Parker
Answers in back

ACROSS

1 Real-life "Best in Show" org.
4 Elude a tag, in a way
9 "Hey, mister!"
13 J.F.K. and R.F.K.
15 Flower's protective leaves
16 Sooners' st.
17 Hardcover's covering
19 Thailand, formerly
20 Put into motion
21 Come into existence
23 Lousy pick?
24 Prevail
26 It stops a run
29 Backed
32 Freudian topic
33 Needed to say "oops"
35 WWII battle site
36 Chicken-king connection
37 Brit. military decoration
38 Tokyo's former name
41 Aurora's counterpart
42 College mil. group
44 Proverbial battlers
46 Do an impression
47 Emulates an eagle on the attack
50 Disguised, in a way
52 Fuddy-duddies
53 "How horrid!"
54 "Hogan's Heroes" setting
56 Spinning-wheel attachment
60 Loser in a fictional upset
61 Game for ringers
64 Beggar's request
65 Kind of offer
66 Ooze
67 Map section
68 Song and dance
69 Some people reach for it

DOWN

1 "Fernando" band
2 McDonald's mogul
3 Aquatic bird
4 Spreads around
5 "Chantilly ___"
6 Variety
7 Easter egg application
8 Reach
9 Pretenders
10 Chophouse offering
11 Coal mine waste
12 Unlikely to bite
14 Pepe Le Pew, for one
18 Incarcerated
22 Field call
24 "___ Geordie"
25 Word with "card" or "finger"
26 Goes like the dickens
27 Subtly illuminated
28 Bearer of heraldic devices
30 Marry in haste
31 Delivered a drug
34 Perez or O'Donnell
39 In a coy manner
40 Plains Indians
43 The Fonz, compared to the rest
45 Printing measures
48 Org. for The Shark and Tiger
49 Tourist magnets
51 Bygone rulers
54 "Pygmalion" writer
55 Fictional piece
56 Royal Russian ruler
57 Anonymous John and Jane
58 Onionlike plant
59 Catch sight of
62 Doggie-bag morsel
63 "Blame It on ___"

by Judith Hunter
Edited by Timothy E. Parker
Answers in back

ACROSS

1 Flows back, as a tide
5 Ocean catches
10 "Survivor" network
13 Cabbage
14 Tara family name
15 Shaq specialty
16 Mob's payment, sometimes
18 Great place for a dip
19 10th-century Holy Roman emperor
20 Hairdo crushers
21 Coarse
22 Solomon's asset
24 Waited and wanted
26 Hindu creator
29 What a library does
32 Plagiarize
35 Pep rally cry
36 Psycho
37 Wallach in "Night and the City"
38 Sleep inducer
40 Wizards' gp.
41 Prods
43 Swell
44 Pain in the neck
45 Wise people
46 Hamper
48 Long
50 First name of a very famous clown
54 Consumer pitfall
56 Planetary path shape
59 More damp and chilly
60 Bryce Canyon site
61 Nostalgic destination
63 Marathoner's concern
64 One of the deadly sins
65 Calc preceder, perhaps
66 White-rumped westerner
67 Fiery horse
68 Hankerings

DOWN

1 Type of macaroni
2 Food fish of the Nile
3 Winter footwear
4 Defended
5 Thumb, for one
6 Bad thing to hear at a checkup
7 Neverland outsider
8 Queen of Soul Franklin
9 Authority
10 Euphoric state
11 Cigar collectible
12 Neverland bad guy
15 "Sun" or "smoke" follower
17 Maker of the fragrance Poison
23 Yucatan civilization member
25 Schedule
27 Cooped-up female
28 Start of a famous palindrome
30 Dollops
31 Sing nonsense syllables
32 Elementary grades
33 Gymnast Korbut
34 One way to ride
36 Supreme Being
38 He smacked 66 in '98
39 Cleaning implement
42 Do a slow burn
44 Form of punishment
46 Turn upside down
47 Small fishing boat
49 Cavorts
51 Apprised
52 Bolshevik hero
53 Bottom-of-the-barrel stuff
54 Chump
55 Relative of etc.
57 Fontainebleau girlfriend
58 Metallic deposit
62 Checkers side

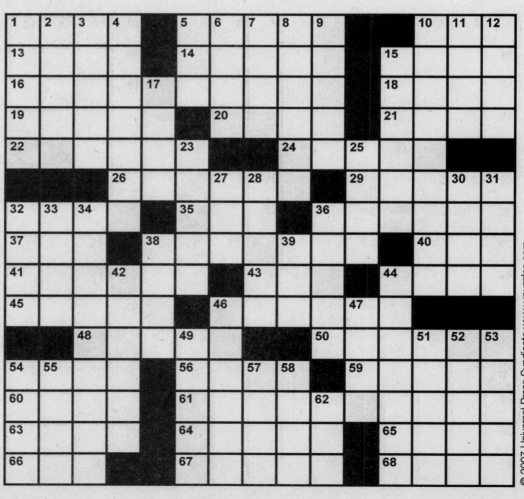

265 Playing with Fire

by Alice Walker
Edited by Timothy E. Parker
Answers in back

ACROSS
1 "Goodbye, Mr. ___"
6 Cup o' joe
10 Some gridiron players
14 Certain cloth
15 Shoshoneans
16 "___ seems"
17 Cause of a wake-up
18 Meddlesome
19 WWII weapon
20 Arouses curiosity
23 "The ___ and the Pendulum"
24 "Xanadu" rock gp.
25 Some choir members
27 Percolate slowly
29 Celestial bear
32 Certain grape sodas
33 "A Midsummer Night's Dream" disguise
35 View from Sandusky, Ohio
37 World Series mo.
38 Test one's intellectual mettle against
42 Relative's nickname
43 Bailiff's bellow
44 Name a price
45 Prestigious award
47 Half of a '50s sitcom couple
49 Neutral hue
53 Coniferous tree
55 Pencil parking place
57 Turned chicken
58 Weightless
62 Forbidden perfume?
63 Condo, e.g.
64 Tightly packed
65 Experts
66 Bit of reality?
67 April 1 baby, e.g.
68 Avian home
69 Sommer of films
70 Friars' fete

DOWN
1 Brooches
2 Beads and headband wearer
3 Like some senses
4 Marquess or viscount, e.g.
5 "Anaconda" menace
6 Former sophomore
7 "This weighs ___!"
8 Sleeveless garment
9 So far
10 Ancient ascetic
11 Mediocre
12 "The Blue Angel" star
13 RR depot
21 Like melting snow
22 Regenerates
26 Jet set jet
28 Way to stand
30 Take by force
31 Creative result
34 Burn
36 Book before Jeremiah
38 Lose
39 Imputes
40 Become altared?
41 '50s nickname
42 Distress call
46 Summer month
48 Parlor piece
50 Head cases?
51 Poker ploys
52 Widespread turmoil
54 Common composition for Liszt
56 Classic TV's O'Reilly
59 Carbon compound
60 Board game of world conquest
61 Peter on the ivories
62 Work on hides

by John Underwood
Edited by Timothy E. Parker
Answers in back

ACROSS

1 Entertainer Will, born in 18-Across
7 CD players?
10 Man of the hour
14 Keyless, in music
15 Louis XIV, e.g.
16 Yoked yaks
17 Word between "Ars" and "artis"
18 State admitted to the union Nov. 16, 1907
20 Enjoyment from cruelty
21 Paris ride
22 Astronaut L. Gordon, born in 18-Across
24 Gap
28 Rabbit ears
31 Olympian Jim, born in 18-Across
32 Some have black eyes
33 Razz
36 Inlet
37 ___ Lingus
38 Those born in 18-Across
40 Short life?
41 Dixie initials
42 Dime's ten
43 Waterfront walk
44 Filmmaker Ron, born in 18-Across
46 Burial urn
49 As a friend, to the French
50 TV personality born in 18-Across
52 Suffuse with color
54 Ball girls
58 Two-time "Sexiest Man Alive" born in 18-Across
61 Famed family of Italy
62 Charged particles
63 Big name in ATMs
64 Prayer
65 Start up, as a computer
66 Reticent
67 Yankee Mickey, born in 18-Across

DOWN

1 Riches alternative
2 Orozco's other one
3 Provoke
4 Leads on
5 Word before "d'etre"
6 Apply quickly, as brakes
7 Hippo tail?
8 Funny guy
9 River sediment
10 Sounds from Santa
11 Prefix meaning "outside"
12 Dream sleep
13 "… ___ slow boat to China"
19 Symbol of McDonald's
23 South African author Alan
25 World's largest peninsula
26 More nimble
27 Recall
28 Parisian ruffian
29 "Batman Begins" actor Liam
30 1943 Pacific battle site
31 Program that stays in RAM
34 Fictional tree creature
35 Greek fabulist
38 Pinch pennies
39 Brit. lexicon
43 Earns
45 Mixed in with
47 1954 hit by The Chords
48 Nature club
50 Word with "uncle" or "oven"
51 Take another shot at
53 Storage boxes
55 Lean sideways
56 Chemical compound
57 Trig ratio
58 Baby wear
59 Joey's nickname
60 12 meses

267 Four Seeable Future

by Jarmuz and Gentry
Edited by Timothy E. Parker
Answers in back

ACROSS

1 North-central Utah city
5 Have a good cry
9 Put in ___ way
14 Round number?
15 Diamond Head's island
16 Posture-perfect
17 SI
20 Grab a chair
21 Rant
22 "I suppose"
26 It means nothing
27 AAA recommendation
30 SEA
33 MS-DOS pt.
34 Neither here ___ there
35 Some South Africans
36 Shout while pointing
40 Blue Grotto isle
43 Fifth-century Chinese dynasty
44 Matched pieces
47 SEE
52 Tax shelter
53 Stomach acid, symbolically
54 Alexander's rule, e.g.
55 Hindu garments (Var.)
58 Poe's "Annabel ___"
59 C
65 ___ resemblance (be similar to)
66 Words after "The doctor"
67 Start of a decision-making process
68 Syrian president Bashar al-___
69 Deadline for Marshal Kane
70 Sportscast tidbit

DOWN

1 Lbs. parts
2 Sales pro
3 After-school workers?
4 One-principle-for-everything theory
5 Diddley and Derek
6 "Open wide" word
7 "Huh?"
8 Ida of "The Sea Wolf"
9 1989 Tom Selleck movie
10 Youngest player to join the 500 HR club
11 Daydream
12 Longtime Elton John label
13 Albert Pujols' team, on scoreboards
18 Words before "boy" or "girl"
19 Proper partner
22 Ford alternatives
23 180-degree turn, slangily
24 Trigonometry ratio
25 Secret target?
28 High craggy hill
29 Ems' followers
31 School in Madison, N.J., for short
32 Rejection after rejection
36 "Pod" starter
37 The moral route
38 Suffix with "hair"
39 Monterrey uncles
40 Dernier ___
41 Ireland's ___ Lingus
42 Some modern TVs
44 Auxiliary wager
45 Author Umberto
46 Pro ___ (for now)
48 Westernmost nation in Eur.
49 Type of hydrocarbon
50 F.D.R.'s dog
51 Parisian brothers
56 Part of a magician's phrase
57 Okay but not great
59 Org. that makes loans to small companies
60 "You betcha!"
61 ___ de Janeiro
62 Larry King's TV network
63 "Step ___ crack …"
64 Big Apple newspaper, initially

268 Term of Endearment

by Carol Lachance
Edited by Timothy E. Parker
Answers in back

ACROSS
1 "See ___ Run"
5 Goes here, there and everywhere
10 Truth in Lending Act stats
14 Fit as a fiddle
15 "Believe it ___!"
16 It holds the line
17 Not fer
18 Like a pomegranate
19 Smurf elder
20 Thurston's honey on "Gilligan's Island"
23 Tube top
24 Keats' "___ a Nightingale"
25 People to follow
27 Make imperfect
28 Depth charge target
32 Eagerly approach
33 "I'm hungry as ___!"
34 Personal appearance
35 Gabriel's dessert?
40 Poetic black
41 Think tank products
42 Daisylike bloom
44 Organic milk dispenser
45 "___ Believer" (Monkees hit)
48 Chef's sprinkle, perhaps
50 "Quo ___"
52 Atlanta-based station
53 Snack for Dustin in a 1982 film?
57 Latin list ender
59 Sap sucker
60 "Tell ___ the Marines!"
61 Make angry
62 "Cheers" role
63 Lake bird
64 Kind of vaccine
65 Satisfies fully
66 Spiritual or ballad, e.g.

DOWN
1 Hebrew salutation
2 Temple of the Far East
3 A Twist of Dickens
4 Article of faith
5 ___ Hashana
6 Two-tone treat
7 Again
8 Vintage Ford
9 Thing to be in
10 "Mustache Hat" artist
11 '60s war protester
12 Witty exchange
13 Applies carelessly
21 "Could ___ more specific?"
22 Roman household god
26 "The Count of Monte Cristo" author
29 "Air" or "canto" opener
30 Big galoot
31 Skunk cabbage or calla lily
33 "___ of God" (play and movie)
35 Something to vote in
36 Favorable response to "Do you mind?"
37 Like Simon's "Couple"
38 Jay preceder
39 Do the honors at Thanksgiving
40 Certain spring holidays
43 Bean-spiller
44 More work?
45 "Ditto"
46 Berle of TV fame
47 Having the same reach
49 Prepares for target practice
51 Nutmeg covers
54 "Follow ___ car!"
55 Trig ratio
56 Roman calendar date
58 Albanian currency

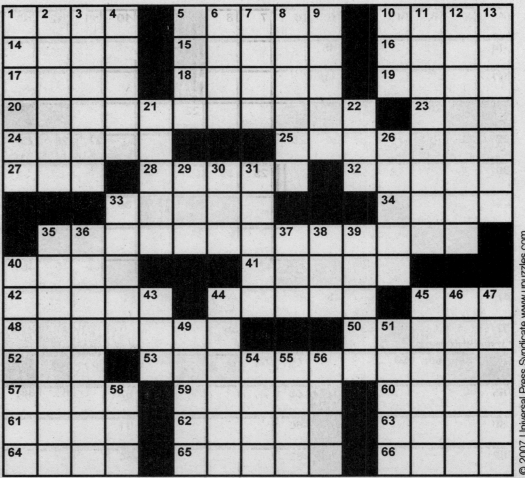

269 Time for a Change

by Mick Mabe
Edited by Timothy E. Parker
Answers in back

ACROSS

1 Angel's overhead?
5 Chinese dog
9 Weeps
14 Hospital ward
15 Spanish greeting
16 What a banker does
17 Type of skirt or computer
18 "Battle Cry" author
19 More mature
20 See another doctor for this
23 Hawaiian instrument, shortened
24 "Room" or "hall" preceder
25 Capsizes
29 Stated
31 "Iron" or "Stone" follower
34 Beg
35 Commits an offense
36 Wound mark
37 Hero or heroine
40 Roof edge
41 Certain cultivated grains
42 King-size
43 Delivery person's ter.
44 Refreshes a stamp pad
45 Endorsed
46 Anger
47 Military address
48 Stylish
55 Clear
56 Verve
57 Out of the ordinary
59 Seed to flavor liqueur
60 Revolt
61 Invalid
62 Caesar or Waldorf, e.g.
63 Talk back
64 Flower stalk

DOWN

1 Buzz
2 Black cuckoos
3 String
4 Of the ear
5 Thick masses
6 Crowd
7 Hodgepodge
8 Hornet
9 Copied
10 Souvenir
11 Beginning of China
12 "East of ___"
13 One-time communist land, briefly
21 Excel
22 Native to Dublin
25 Higher in place
26 Fold
27 Do duty as a soldier
28 Comfort
29 Weeds out
30 Social insects
31 Type of squash
32 Standard
33 Made a mistake
35 Drench
36 Carpet with thick pile
38 Group of nine performers
39 1988 Nobel Prize sharer
44 Pressed
45 Book backs
46 "___ far, far better thing …"
47 Gather
48 Arm bone
49 Bucket
50 His and ___
51 Director Kazan
52 Vessels
53 Strained
54 Novelist Gardner
55 Dance step
58 Ornamental shade tree

Page 271

by Cory Ross
Edited by Timothy E. Parker
Answers in back

ACROSS

1 ___ I Am (Dr. Seuss character)
4 Traps by stealth
10 Forest unit
14 April number cruncher
15 Hide out indefinitely
16 "On Golden Pond" bird
17 One way to be left
19 Comfy cozy
20 1920 Preakness and Belmont winner
21 Computer programmer, e.g.
22 ___ even keel
23 Truman's state
27 Place to find meat over a flame, briefly
31 Past potentates
34 Back on the boat
35 Moses' river
36 "Independence Day" assailants, for short
37 Certain doctrine or theory
40 As well
42 Bossy's chew
43 Campus marchers' org.
45 Abet partner
47 A round at the tavern, often
49 What some win by
53 Not one of the gang
54 You must reed this?
58 Midshipman's counterpart
60 Parts of a service
62 Way off base?
63 Standard newspaper page
66 Unvaried
67 Good books in hotels?
68 Bronx cheer
69 Peeping Tom, e.g.
70 Tracy to Hepburn, often
71 Unusual gift of sight

DOWN

1 Bonehead
2 Concerning bees
3 ___ Carta
4 "Begin the Beguine" bandleader Artie
5 Generic
6 Astronaut with Armstrong and Collins
7 Color of Mao's little book
8 Continental abbr.
9 Austin Powers, for one
10 Nonwinner
11 Presidential advisor, informally
12 Bounder
13 Bldg. contractor's hire
18 Employee of the Month, e.g.
21 Kind of scout
24 Treadmill site, perhaps
25 Refine, as flour
26 Preminger of film
28 Letters on a radial
29 Hazy appearance
30 Proof letters
31 Bird over the waves
32 Long Greek promenade
33 First domed ballpark
38 Wise words
39 Actress Rogers
41 Kimono tie
44 More like Simon Legree
46 Parent, back and forth
48 Methuselah's father
50 Giant legend Mel
51 Add more seasoning
52 Egg quality
55 Pioneer bathyspherist William
56 Popular cookies
57 Legally block
58 Check out, as a joint
59 Vacationing, e.g.
61 Gorby's former domain
63 Brit. broadcaster
64 Spanish river
65 They make hosp. deliveries

271 Sounds Good

by Oscar Fremantle
Edited by Timothy E. Parker
Answers in back

ACROSS

1 Woman in a "Paint Your Wagon" song
6 Path behind a mower
11 Semi section
14 Delicate discrimination
15 Intense obsession
16 Pay stub?
17 Awe-inspired shriek
19 To the ___ degree
20 Set at an angle
21 Iron and Bronze
22 Turn on a dime
24 Defensive effort
26 Gala get-together
27 Engage in unrealistic fantasizing
33 Word with "brief" or "tender"
36 Like most colleges today
37 Mrs. Eddie Cantor
38 Auction site
39 Legendary miniseries
40 Cookbook instruction
41 Its cap. is Buenos Aires
42 Westernmost Aleutian Island
43 Decks
44 React to a broken bone, perhaps
48 He played Venus Flytrap
49 Mubarak's predecessor
52 Czech-born composer Rudolf
54 Spanish surrealist
57 Popular salad
59 Word with "parking" or "odd"
60 "Hosanna," for one
63 Street address abbr.
64 "Pale Rider," e.g.
65 Prepare mushrooms
66 Part of MPG
67 Physicist Bohr
68 Church areas

DOWN

1 List-ending abbrs.
2 Carefree or spirited adventures
3 "The best ___ to come!"
4 Illegal passenger
5 Pershing's WWI grp.
6 Metro-area haze
7 Grow dim
8 "No ifs, ___ or buts!"
9 No-win situation?
10 Talked nonstop on one subject
11 Outwardly curved surface
12 Vocal range
13 Thai bread
18 Dry wash in Africa
23 "... Lord, is ___?" (Matthew 26:22)
25 Orr's org.
26 Ness and co.
28 "Rob Roy" author
29 Saw feature
30 Pause
31 Prefix meaning "peculiar"
32 They may be ringing
33 Rachel's sister
34 River through Aragon
35 Comic's employee
39 Fridge invasion?
40 Golfer's bugaboo
43 Hyundai rival
45 Moon buggy
46 WWI president
47 "Like, no way!"
50 How roast may be served
51 U.S. legal tender
52 What flags do in the wind
53 Emulate nomads
54 Be fond of
55 "The Clan of the Cave Bear" novelist Jean M.
56 PO Box contents
58 Tar's affirmatives
61 "Bali ___"
62 Explorer Johnson

by Michael McKray
Edited by Timothy E. Parker
Answers in back

ACROSS

1 Weather-beaten
5 Certain pack animals
10 Best-of-the-best
14 Weapon in the game Clue
15 Big bang cause, briefly
16 Da capo ___
17 Bird worshipped in ancient Egypt
18 "... but to no ___"
19 "Good for what ___ ya"
20 Writer who was once a jockey
23 Cousin of "hmmm!"
24 SPCA pt.
25 "Christ of St. John of the Cross" artist
27 Leave a blot on
30 Make oneself heard
34 Albany-to-Buffalo waterway
37 Guitar, to a guitarist (Var.)
38 A wink or a nod, perhaps
40 "The Forsyte ___" (Galsworthy)
41 "The Andromeda Strain" writer
44 Yawn producer
45 Jennifer Lopez title role
46 "... tell them I'll be there ___ long"
47 Black cats and others
49 "Jurassic Park" mosquito preserver
50 "___ Kapital"
51 Not returnable
53 "Got milk?" answer?
55 Barrier breaker, for short
57 "It" writer
64 Debused, e.g.
66 Barkin or Corby
67 Bleachers sound
68 Any day now
69 On the qui vive
70 Trollope's "Lady ___"
71 Faxed
72 Does dock work
73 Auto with an acronymic name

DOWN

1 Far from wet
2 A desert in central Asia
3 "Beowulf," for one
4 Study stations
5 Political upheavals
6 Hindu deity
7 ___ the Man Musial
8 "Layla" singer's first name
9 Based on good judgment
10 Car club
11 Created
12 Cairo's river
13 Facilitate
21 Bone cavity
22 Animal pouch
26 Cowboy La Rue
27 Caribbean dance
28 Universally accepted truth
29 Refreshment of mind or body
31 Distant admirer?
32 Word of surrender
33 Biblical weeds
35 Greek marketplace
36 Country roads
39 Unctuous balms
42 Biddies
43 Church law
48 Boom preceder
52 Quite a bargain
54 Gumbos
55 Lip service
56 Plumlike fruit
58 Scat master Fitzgerald
59 Supplicated
60 Where the gang is
61 Inner Hebrides island
62 Grandma, in child-speak
63 Snatch
65 Explosive inits.

ACROSS

1 M, in personal ads
5 Hire again, as an act
11 Panama, for one
14 Eclipse, to the ancients
15 "The Glass Menagerie" character
16 Hail from the past
17 Like some memories
19 Means of enlightenment
20 ____ Dawn Chong
21 Sources of unglamorous hands, perhaps
23 Type of maid
26 Part of DOS
27 Word on some tags
28 Weapons stockpile
30 Last part of the last name of a "Dallas" actress
31 Familia member
32 More rangy
35 Not the best type of affection
40 Made the roads slick, in a way
41 Be decisive
43 Coryza or yaws, e.g.
46 It may be penciled in
49 Bolivian buddy
50 ____ canto singing
52 As a result of
53 Acted as arbiter
55 Verb used in recipes
56 Deli order
57 Much better than "not bad"
62 Shepard drama "A ____ of the Mind"
63 Ready for a cold takeoff
64 "Or ____!" (veiled threat)
65 Acoustic organ
66 Sandinista leader
67 First name in classic TV husbands

DOWN

1 Angry crowd
2 Jack Horner's last words
3 Allow
4 Beef Wellington, for one
5 One in a million
6 Bad ____, Germany
7 Humorously coarse
8 "____ the loneliest number ..."
9 Keats favorites
10 "Serial Mom" Turner
11 Golf course obstacle, e.g.
12 Vindicate
13 Past and present, for two
18 Acquire through merit
22 Man with a mission?
23 Wrestling site
24 "Journey Into Fear" author Ambler
25 Fyodor I, II or III
26 Satisfy, as thirst
29 Way with strays?
30 Light-headed
33 Annual hoops event, familiarly
34 Prepare to be knighted
36 Grammarian's concern
37 John Wayne film or Cadillac model
38 Tender
39 Dalmatian's marking
42 Word with "faced" or "fisted"
43 Taj Mahal material
44 Aviator Earhart
45 Spotter's opposite
47 Canoer's worry
48 Moved slightly
50 Suit the occasion
51 Bring out
54 Fancy vase
55 Burghoff's co-star
58 Part of a stool
59 "____ Buttermilk Sky"
60 Covert org., once
61 "Agnus ____"

by Judith Hunter
Edited by Timothy E. Parker
Answers in back

274 The Horrors

ACROSS
1 "Discontinue this" computer key
4 Automobile need
9 Haunted house sounds
13 "But of course!"
14 Greta Garbo's role in "The Temptress"
15 Rich cake
16 Bird of the Paridae family
17 Diabolical concoction
19 Brand, in a way
21 "Take Good Care of My Baby" singer Bobby
22 Capture
23 Cumin, mace et al.
25 Spread
29 Aristotle, to Alexander the Great
30 Cry of discovery
31 Stadium roof, perhaps
32 Moonscape traverser
33 Walk like Frankenstein
35 "The Flight of the Innocents" author Yutang
36 Crazy condition
40 Swiss canton
41 Gave a darn
42 Aries, e.g.
43 Kodak's eye
45 Automaton drama
46 Regular order (with "the")
48 Cloaked caterpillar
50 "Tristram Shandy" author
51 Simpson's judge
52 Like some jack-o'-lanterns
53 Partly open
55 Sorensen, to Kennedy
60 Ice or Iron
61 Cantina chip
62 In reserve
63 Windy City athlete
64 Feel for
65 Less well
66 New Zealand parrot

DOWN
1 Greasy spoon sign
2 Least extroverted
3 Hurling, as with a sling
4 Kitten's cry
5 "___ Twist"
6 Heads, in Le Havre
7 "___ upon a midnight dreary …"
8 "Go team!"
9 Snatched apples
10 Hockey great
11 Coy animal ending?
12 Keep in stitches?
15 Winter Palace resident
18 Bury
20 Knightings, e.g.
24 "Broom-Hilda," for example
25 Booted
26 Big name in old rock 'n' roll radio
27 Muslim leader
28 Opposite of admit
30 "How the ___ Half Lives"
33 Make music, in a way
34 As such
36 Cartoonist's idea?
37 Precinct
38 Straight's partner
39 Dern in "Jurassic Park"
44 Like a rustling skirt, perhaps
46 Articulates
47 Confederation
49 Conductor Klemperer
50 Stringed solo instrument
52 Fat-removal procedure, for short
54 Singer McEntire
55 U.S. econ. indicator, once
56 Japanese affirmative
57 Mo. for goblins
58 Kind of terror
59 Numbered hwy.

by Fran & Lou Sabin
Edited by Timothy E. Parker
Answers in back

ACROSS

1 An established custom
5 Enjoys a bath
10 Scottish resort
14 Virginia willow
15 Discombobulated
16 Infatuated
17 2005 Edward Norton film
20 Certain geologic epoch
21 Contest group, perhaps
22 Engulfs in amusement
23 Battle site
25 Wine listing
28 Okla., once
29 Contemptuous exhalation
30 Adventurous
31 Mover's challenge
33 Hired hand
34 1989 Kevin Costner film
38 Watercourse
39 In a maudlin mood
40 It's between John and Romans
41 Over the length of
43 "The Lord of the Rings" beast
46 Mighty small
47 Home of the Pyramid of Djoser
48 It's in the same animal order as a rhino
50 Talking bird of poetry
52 Acute shortage
53 Classic Frank Sinatra song
57 Construction piece
58 "Death, Be Not Proud" poet
59 Hike kickoff
60 Trumpet-shaped flower
61 A lump on a battery?
62 Lamarr in "Algiers"

DOWN

1 Most outspread
2 Filmdom's Peter
3 Type of smell
4 Dred Scott decision chief justice
5 Rational
6 Hubbell's teammate
7 Burier of Pompeii
8 Zoo employee
9 Erudite one
10 Lust after, in a way
11 Place for a cotillion
12 Form query
13 Slangy refusal
18 Good tennis serves
19 "Santa" trailer
23 Herod's year
24 Basking locale, for some
26 Conduit angles
27 H.S.T. successor
29 Blue
30 Sound like an ass
31 Pod objects
32 Nauseated
33 Apiece
34 Come to grips with
35 Temporary cessation
36 Insurance covers it
37 Newspaper, derogatorily
38 Aviary sound
41 Work list
42 Lady Bird's man
43 Duller of the senses
44 Encircled
45 Unsettling
47 Stowe's Little ____
48 Salt
49 Some Mennonites
51 Ethereal
52 Unfettered
53 Word describing Abner
54 Ben ____-Wan Kenobi
55 Alphabet trio
56 Common tie

by Robert H. Wolfe
Edited by Timothy E. Parker
Answers in back

ACROSS

1 Big name in Norway
5 Animation art pieces
9 French clerics
14 Wee hole
15 Useful plant
16 Shoreline
17 Highway tax
18 Nose cone covering
19 Bistro offering
20 Ranch owner?
23 Born
24 They're a laugh a minute
25 Disarranged
27 Corner of a diamond
30 Silvery fish
31 Org. for McBeal
32 Kind of drum
35 Mind-boggling time spans
38 Survive, just
40 Reproduction needs
41 Computer part
42 Start to date
43 Piece of cloth
45 Sra. relative
46 Give away
48 Tenant
50 Like some fruits
52 Burning
54 Varnish ingredient, perhaps
55 Instrument for determining the distance of an object
60 Major potato producer
62 Tobacco dryer
63 Hatcher of TV
64 "Dallas" Miss
65 Late Slav leader
66 Genuine
67 One with a net income
68 "I knew ____ instant"
69 Comic Johnson

DOWN

1 Makes up one's mind
2 Robber's haul
3 Singing son
4 Zipper alternative
5 Terminal of a cell
6 "Cats" inspirer
7 Reclines lazily
8 It's planted
9 Grow, as capital
10 It can constrict
11 Stunt flies, as at a fair
12 Cosmetician Lauder
13 Ranch animal
21 Tightly curled
22 One-named model
26 Winter transport
27 Adventure story
28 "____ Holden" (Bacheller)
29 Open audition
30 Bed support
33 Chicago, in a song
34 F.D.R. creation
36 Alaskan town
37 Hook's aide
39 Partner of birds
41 Oteri of "SNL"
43 Protein source
44 Davis of "Amen"
47 Uncomfortable spasms
49 Nissan model
50 "Lord of the ____"
51 Big server
52 "Come ____?"
53 Roman holiday
56 Reply to the Little Red Hen
57 Venison source
58 QED part
59 Annoy
61 Hurry

by Bruce Venzke
Edited by Timothy E. Parker
Answers in back

ACROSS

1 Sprees
5 Use FedEx, say
9 Black playing card
14 Leap for Lipinski
15 Like some tales
16 Evenings, promotionally
17 A certain thumbs down
18 Bailiwick
19 Others, south of the border
20 A warm quip (Part 1)
23 Castaway's refuge, perhaps
24 Take a siesta
25 Timid
26 Like jalapeno peppers
28 Reindeer kin
31 Like the gray mare
33 Queens stadium name
35 Fare fit for Fido
37 Reacted with awe
41 Quip (Part 2)
44 Mrs. Cruise
45 Pisan pronoun
46 States aloud
47 Certain woman in a personal ad, briefly
49 Cuts up a bit outdoors?
51 "Well, lah-di-____!"
52 Oft-misspelled possessive
55 Biblical word before "verily"
57 Get snippy with
59 Quip (Part 3)
65 Orderly spread
66 Short car?
67 Contrite person
68 "The Twist" was one
69 Cliff feature
70 Volcano on Sicily
71 Plied a needle
72 Have a restless night
73 Cartoon impact word

DOWN

1 Mud of a sort?
2 Cans
3 "Wise up, dude!"
4 Blackthorn fruits
5 Legal drinking age, e.g.
6 Famed racer who snoozes and loses
7 Robert of "The Sopranos"
8 Not fancy
9 Winter storm need
10 Kind of helmet
11 Some razors
12 One of Franklin's two certainties
13 Op-Ed article
21 Cakes partner
22 Paulo or Tome
26 Triter writer?
27 Workplace protection org.
29 Swiss artist Paul
30 Involuntary twitch
32 Homer's exclamations
34 Some Ivy Leaguers
36 Estimator's words
38 Make like wild geese in the fall
39 "A Day Without Rain" singer
40 Amount of salt in some recipes
42 Youthful and naive
43 Sleeps noisily
48 Not "agin"
50 KLM rival
52 Colorful Apples
53 Yankee skipper for 12 seasons
54 Boater material
56 "Is that ____?"
58 Carpentry fastener
60 Skyline obscurer
61 Coin released 1/1/02
62 Airport postings, for short
63 Chanteuse Horne
64 Apothecary's weight

by Carol Lachance
Edited by Timothy E. Parker
Answers in back

278 A New Leaf

ACROSS

1 Graham Greene's "___ of Life"
6 Spaceship Earth is its icon
11 It may have a certain ring to it
14 1980s-'90s TV drama
15 "There's ___ in my bucket …"
16 Go astray
17 Any Platters platter
18 Tender spots
19 Time of one's life
20 Rec room game, perhaps
22 Nave bench
23 Harem chambers
24 City near Danang
25 Zip, to Zapata
27 Extremely chubby
30 European language
33 Freight weight
34 Rarely
37 Frick collection
40 Earth's canopy
42 Center X or O
43 "Permission granted"
44 Soft-furred monkey
47 Shelter act,briefly
49 Creative spark
50 Seven Wonders of the World, e.g.
55 Slight advantage
58 "The Three Faces of ___"
59 Shuffle along
60 Short name for a bunny man
62 Peace-loving hippie
65 "Catch-22" pilot
66 The "Clown Prince" of basketball
67 Medieval stringed instruments
68 "O sole ___"
69 Deflect
70 "___ my case!"
71 Chang's other half
72 Shepherds sheep
73 Boito's Mefistofele, e.g.

DOWN

1 "That's-hooey!" link
2 Tetley competitor
3 Antique Louisville Slugger or derogatory name for grandma
4 Vehemently denounces
5 Dainty, in Devon
6 Become less intense
7 One way to make a PBS pledge
8 Husky subject?
9 Vegetable oil component, often
10 "The Gondoliers" girl
11 Historical Boston event
12 The munchies, e.g.
13 Cold one
21 "I owe you one"
26 Telephonic trio on 3
28 Just okay
29 Caught on
31 Take a gander
32 USN rank
35 Leather worker
36 Diez minus dos
37 "What Kind of Fool ___?"
38 X-ray dose unit
39 Noisy amphibian
41 "You betcha!"
45 "Spy vs. Spy" magazine
46 What "mum" is
48 Ancient storage jar
51 The Olympics are full of them
52 Privileged classes
53 At a minimum
54 Combines with
56 F-sharp equivalent
57 French student
60 Where the heart is
61 Land o' Blarney
63 Black cat, for one
64 Plagiarize

279 Brain Stems

by Alice Walker
Edited by Timothy E. Parker
Answers in back

ACROSS

1 Canadian strait
6 Boot attachment, perhaps
9 Fierce Indian of the Amazon
14 A Middle Easterner
15 Component of bronze
16 Battery terminal
17 Flippant remark
19 Butler off-screen
20 Eligibility factor
21 Wapiti
22 Accepted doctrine
23 Infamous Panamanian
26 Wore
27 Broadway trademark
31 Friends in battle
34 Concluding shout
35 Black gold
36 Peggy and Spike
37 Class for some U.S. citizens-to-be
38 Boater's haven
39 Word that sandwiches "oh"
40 Hasidism, e.g.
42 Tail
44 Deadeye
47 First name in "The Cocoanuts" cast
48 Some proofs-of-purchase
52 Visit unannounced
54 Pounded dish
55 Brazil's tourist lure
56 Unnatural
57 It can give you a sinking feeling
60 Stage deliveries
61 Hikes, as prices
62 Busybody
63 Unresponsive
64 Morsel for a meal?
65 "The Morning Bath" painter

DOWN

1 "The Comic" actor Jerome
2 Pancho, to Cisco
3 More meanspirited
4 It has no letters on a phone
5 Facial twitch
6 German WWII camp
7 Try for three points
8 Printer's supply
9 Confined
10 Like some watches
11 Legendary outlaw
12 Not up to much
13 Gripe
18 Partner for Kelly
22 Barn storage unit
24 Wading bird
25 Before, for poets
26 WWW letters
28 Must
29 VCR replacement, for some
30 Did away with
31 Church donation, often
32 Rachel's rival
33 "Stormy Weather" singer
37 Sound on the rebound
38 Shopper's convenience
40 Least clumsy
41 X Games network
42 Impassive
43 Spell
45 Double-edged sword
46 Woodwind player
49 Borneo tree-dweller
50 Atlantic crosser of old
51 Thirst quenchers
52 Where some cut the mustard?
53 Buggy driver's control
54 Cocoon resident
57 Status completer?
58 Elizabethan dramatist Thomas
59 Visualize

by Ted Milspaugh
Edited by Timothy E. Parker
Answers in back

ACROSS
1 Ship's deck
5 Corporal O'Reilly
10 "A Girl Like I" author
14 Exclamation of acclaim
15 Piano piece
16 New Rochelle college
17 Hollywood legend
19 "Excuse me"
20 "Chi" lead-in
21 Cut off
23 Las Vegas establishments
27 Art and literature genre
31 French one
32 Markey who played Jane
34 Tours of duty
35 Mat victory
36 "Peek-___!"
38 Downspout sites
39 Hollywood legend
43 Far from famished
44 Norman of sitcom fame
45 CD forerunners
47 Typing pool members
49 Word in a Descartes conclusion
51 AKC physician
52 Gets comfy, in a way
54 Disheartens
56 "___ Is Born"
58 Orchestra-funding org.
59 Impressively great
62 Film starring our Hollywood legends
67 Off one's rocker
68 Actor's study
69 Hollywood's Ken or Lena
70 Word with "forward" or "up"
71 "At the Movies" name
72 Patron saint of sailors

DOWN
1 Plastic pipe material
2 Van Gogh's "Irises," e.g.
3 Macrogametes
4 Novel beginning?
5 Like some telecasts
6 "Now ___ theater near you!"
7 Makes tracks?
8 Psychiatrist Alfred
9 "Speed" star
10 Jim Carrey film
11 Sound of delight
12 Something for the road
13 Wal-Mart guy
18 Welles portrayal
22 Digested
23 Soup order, perhaps
24 Bring to life
25 Governing bodies
26 Prophetess
28 Engage
29 Increase, as an incline
30 What eds. edit
33 Gift receiver
37 Actors Sharif and Epps
40 Burt Reynolds-Liza Minnelli film
41 Sacred cows
42 Church musician
43 Certain ID
46 Blvd. cousins
48 Resolve, as a dispute
50 Pindaric poetry
53 Indian title of respect
55 "Platoon" star
57 Russo of "Ransom"
59 Golfer Ernie
60 "Crack" or "jack" follower
61 Swelling soother
63 Debussy's "La ___"
64 Start of a promise, perhaps
65 Tiny one of literature
66 Start with "Cone" or "Cat"

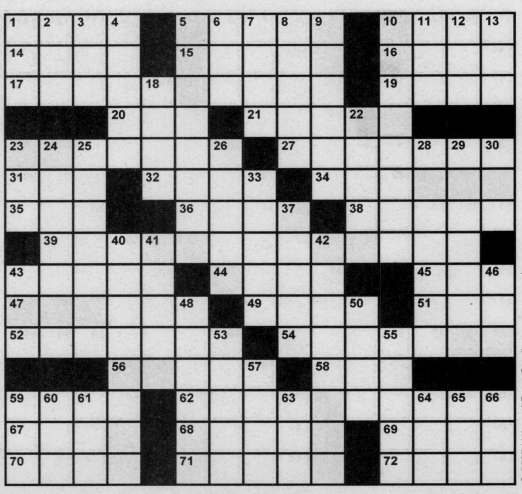

by Carl Cranby
Edited by Timothy E. Parker
Answers in back

ACROSS

1 Balfe's "Joan of ___"
4 Breathing device
9 Role for Redford, ___ Pepper
14 Hawaii's Mauna ___
15 Beat, as the heart
16 Troy story
17 Object of Rimsky-Korsakov's flight
19 Pt. of TNT
20 "Let Us Now Praise Famous Men" author
21 Pumbaa, for one
23 Abbreviate
25 Sunflower, for one
29 Pt. of ETA
30 Physical starter
32 Master Sgt., for one
33 "Paper Roses" singer Bryant
36 Bishop's hat
37 "... provoked with raging ___" (Shakespeare)
38 Part of a pasha's palace
39 Article in Acapulco
40 "The Dresser" director
42 Words with a ring to them?
43 "Doonesbury" segment
45 Treat a wound
46 Vermouth complement
47 Wheeling's river
48 Big holiday mo.
49 Give a hard time to
51 Drive mad
55 Teenager's terror
58 Shootout time
59 Trans-Alai peak
62 Birthplace of F. Sinatra
64 She doesn't live here anymore
65 Not chronic, medically
66 Superior suit?
67 Bath flooring
68 Armature of a motor or generator
69 Suffix for "hatch"

DOWN

1 Troubadours' serenades
2 Fairway boundary
3 Grandmother's keepsake, perhaps
4 Gateway City's airport code
5 Masticating one
6 "___ Cowboy"
7 Transvaal settler
8 Look the other way, e.g.
9 "The Crucible" actress
10 Adjust, as wheels
11 Inflamed
12 ___ es Salaam
13 "Deep Space Nine" role
18 Lambaste
22 "I ___ war" (Roosevelt)
24 People tumble on these
26 Couple
27 TV's "Green ___"
28 Loamy deposit
30 "Tonka" star Sal
31 Wrap-up abbr.
33 "___ Wind in Jamaica" (1965)
34 Olympian Comaneci
35 Items in the fire
36 "We Are Not Alone" star
41 Known by few
44 Cousin of "psst!"
48 "You Bet Your Life" sponsor
50 Paprika, e.g.
51 Coming out
52 Present
53 His goose is cooked
54 "Have a good time!"
56 "___ Lap" (1983 racehorse film)
57 Batty or bonkers
59 Back muscle, for short
60 "Boola Boola" collegian
61 Zilch
63 "Plunk" preceder

by Henry Quarters
Edited by Timothy E. Parker
Answers in back

ACROSS

1 Course guidelines?
5 Inquires
9 "Love conquers all," e.g.
14 Dance bit
15 "___ to My Lou"
16 Old World finch
17 Poole Pulitzer-winner
19 City on the Nile
20 2 oz., e.g.
21 Word in a Carly Simon title
22 Chest hardware?
23 Horse opera
25 Opportunities for repentance
26 Sinclair Pulitzer-winner
31 Burdened one
34 Go head to head
35 "Hard ___!" (helmsman's cry)
36 Auditory apparatus
37 Status of some baseball players
41 Observe
42 "Henry V" opener
44 Pianist Cliburn
45 Turn over
47 Buck Pulitzer-winner
51 Greek victory goddess
52 Dependent
56 Urge with sweet talk
59 Big soiree
60 What Mr. Brown can do, in a Dr. Seuss title
61 Small African antelope
62 McPherson Pulitzer-winner
64 French film director
65 Fountain order
66 Actress Sommer
67 More skillful
68 Was outstanding?
69 Admit (with "up")

DOWN

1 "Don't give me that!"
2 "___ to Kill" (Grisham novel)
3 "The defense ___!"
4 Sunblock-bottle initials
5 Capital of Eritrea
6 Going downhill?
7 Potter's oven
8 "And Moses sent them to ___ out the land of Canaan"
9 Upward movement
10 Lowest lake
11 Sutherland solo
12 Funny one of film
13 Abel's nephew
18 Turns aside
22 Skinflint
24 QB's quests
25 Scissor
27 Sheep-ish?
28 Choice word?
29 Arcade patron
30 Listen
31 Kerouac's generation
32 Per
33 Comic Johnson
38 Call forth
39 Manufactured
40 Jesse James, e.g.
43 Common
46 Greek letter
48 Greasier
49 Tillable
50 Replenish ammo
53 Mexican agave
54 Alcoves
55 Bibliophile's units
56 Robin Cook novel
57 Riyadh denizen
58 Tumbler of rhyme
59 Radiate
62 "Foucault's Pendulum" author
63 Court figure?

by Maurice Rice
Edited by Timothy E. Parker
Answers in back

ACROSS

1 Luxurious resorts
5 "Cut bait" alternative
9 River to the Missouri
14 Stumblebum
15 1952 Olympics host
16 "Exodus" actor
17 Korbut of gymnastic fame
18 Place for cowards?
19 Whimsical poet Nash
20 Team strategy meeting
23 Serious biker's machine
24 One of the broody bunch?
25 Klutzes
29 Great Giant of old
31 Nonstick surface
33 Make a bundle
37 Where decisions for the branch are made, probably
40 Skilled
42 ____-mo replay
43 Of a musical key
44 Creative idea
47 Title role for Jodie Foster
48 Possessive words before "oneself"
49 Chicken piece
51 Retort to "Are not!"
52 Plow into
55 Product rollout
60 Take care of business
63 Room at the top
66 Lose on purpose
67 Kit item
68 Confiscate
69 Keep the car warm
70 Certain chemical compound
71 Struck with the patella
72 Grabs some shut-eye
73 Las Vegas alternative

DOWN

1 Flounder in water
2 "Beer Barrel ____"
3 Predict from omens
4 Avoid the inevitable
5 "The Day of the Jackal" author
6 Shrink's reply
7 Cut prices to the bone
8 Neigh-sayer
9 Melville tale of the South Pacific
10 OK in writing
11 What's more
12 "Fancy that!"
13 One billion years, in astronomy
21 Kate's "Titanic" co-star
22 Division preposition
26 Dress with a flare
27 Centrally located, as a point
28 Fishline attachment
30 New Age pianist John
32 New newt
33 Coffee cake flavored with rum
34 Relevant, in legalese
35 Performs a Lutz
36 Typify
38 Cosell's longtime foil
39 Cutie pie
41 Blaster's need
45 Tall crop
46 Does away with, electronically
50 Welcome road sign, often
53 Introduce to the mix
54 Famous Asia Minor peak, briefly
56 Say
57 Peter of Herman's Hermits
58 Perform like Alfalfa
59 Word on many nametags
61 Like most cupcakes
62 Assist
63 Be inquisitive
64 Like many fifth graders
65 No-win situation

284 Glee Club

by Judith Hunter
Edited by Timothy E. Parker
Answers in back

ACROSS
1 Updo or ponytail, e.g.
5 Where "Falstaff" premiered in 1893
10 Orchestral instrument
14 Ponte Vecchio's river
15 Avoid
16 Cattle encourager
17 Character in a Lehar work
19 Mozart's "___ kleine Nachtmusik"
20 Word in a Tom Hanks film title
21 Liver, for one
22 Wilbur Post's horse
23 Bryce and Zion locale
24 Repeated exactly
27 Its capital is Bamako
29 First X
32 Certain skirt material
33 Jackson and Winslet
34 Reconstruction, for one
35 Engrossed
36 Dugout vessel
37 Some whiskeys
38 Second sight, for short
39 Sturdy fabric
40 Vista or Park
41 "...where is ___ sting?"
42 Subject of study
43 Gets cheeky with
44 Unnerve
46 Truck stop entree
47 Martin or Lawrence
49 Honduras neighbor
54 Fizzy drink
55 Flag for Blackbeard
56 "Good for what ___ you"
57 Like some circles
58 Clean a pipe
59 Sheep sound
60 Bad news beasts?
61 Descry

DOWN
1 Some rotating parts
2 Baseball great Hershiser
3 Concerning, to a lawyer
4 First in order
5 Whimpered
6 Like Princeton walls
7 Ones wearing knickers
8 Bustling commotions
9 Never used
10 It may be light or grand
11 1934 Shirley Temple film
12 O'Neill, Charlie's wife
13 First place
18 WWI battleground
21 Elevator man
23 Peter Fonda title role
24 White-plumed heron
25 Word with "dive" or "land"
26 Stage musical, with "The Most"
27 Craze
28 Basic building block
30 "Goodnight" lady
31 Spanish houses
33 Welles character
36 Part of a bird's beak
37 Presidential mount
39 Stupor
40 More despicable
43 Dionysian attendants
45 "Halt!" to a salt
46 In better health
47 Strike-breaker
48 ___ and trouble
49 Decamped
50 A human arm bone
51 Quite a spell
52 Word with "quantum"
53 A type of armed service
55 Triangular sail

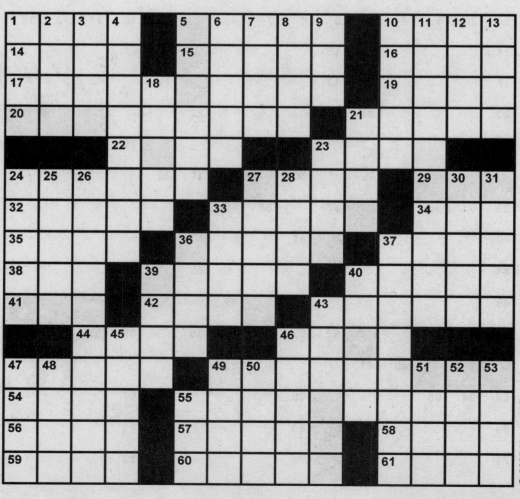

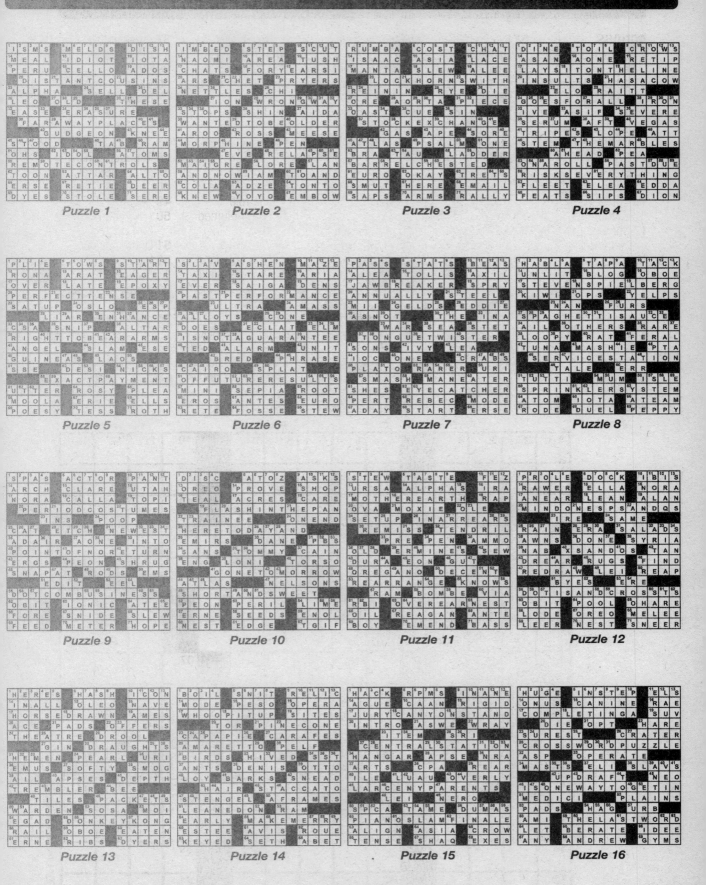

Puzzle 1

Puzzle 2

Puzzle 3

Puzzle 4

Puzzle 5

Puzzle 6

Puzzle 7

Puzzle 8

Puzzle 9

Puzzle 10

Puzzle 11

Puzzle 12

Puzzle 13

Puzzle 14

Puzzle 15

Puzzle 16

Answers

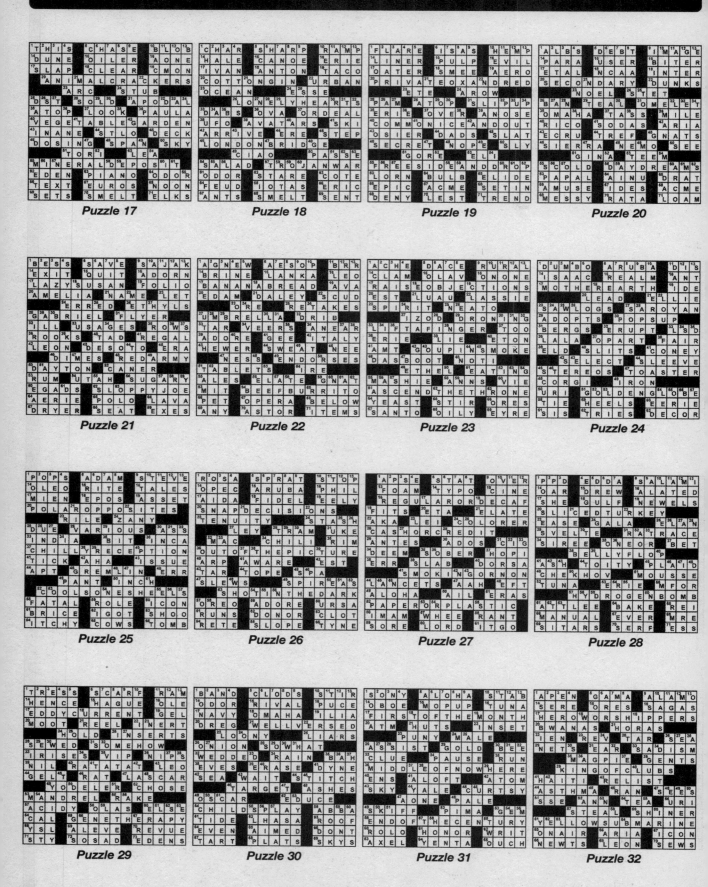

Puzzle 17

Puzzle 18

Puzzle 19

Puzzle 20

Puzzle 21

Puzzle 22

Puzzle 23

Puzzle 24

Puzzle 25

Puzzle 26

Puzzle 27

Puzzle 28

Puzzle 29

Puzzle 30

Puzzle 31

Puzzle 32

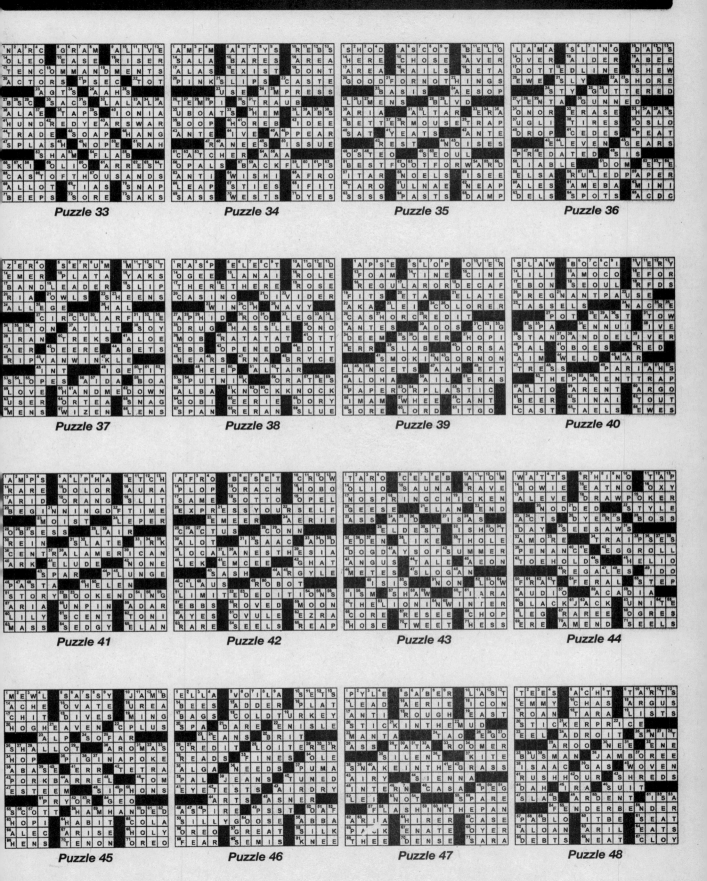

Puzzle 33

Puzzle 34

Puzzle 35

Puzzle 36

Puzzle 37

Puzzle 38

Puzzle 39

Puzzle 40

Puzzle 41

Puzzle 42

Puzzle 43

Puzzle 44

Puzzle 45

Puzzle 46

Puzzle 47

Puzzle 48

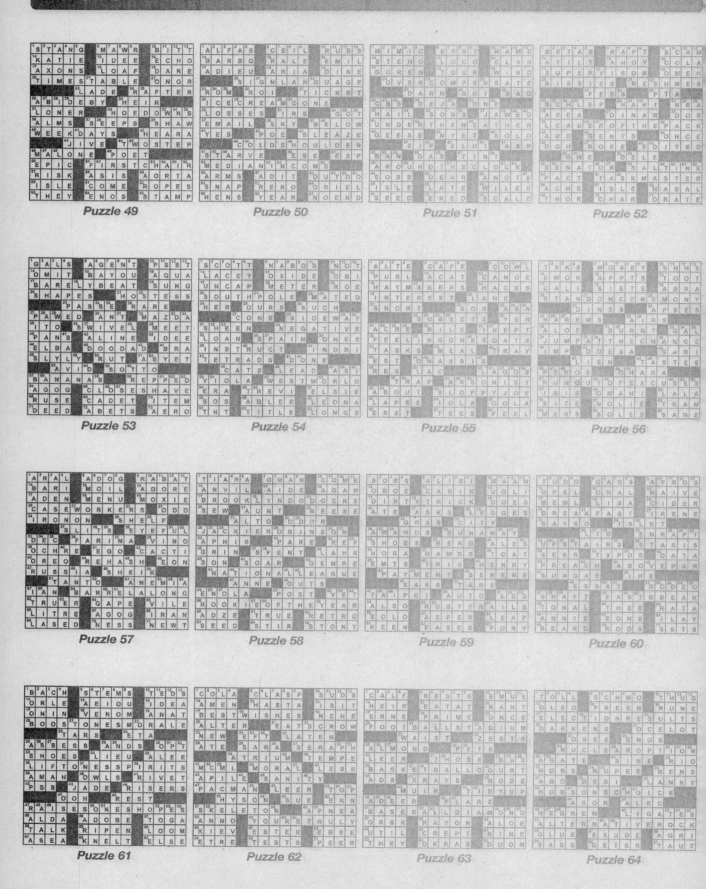

Puzzle 49

Puzzle 50

Puzzle 51

Puzzle 52

Puzzle 53

Puzzle 54

Puzzle 55

Puzzle 56

Puzzle 57

Puzzle 58

Puzzle 59

Puzzle 60

Puzzle 61

Puzzle 62

Puzzle 63

Puzzle 64

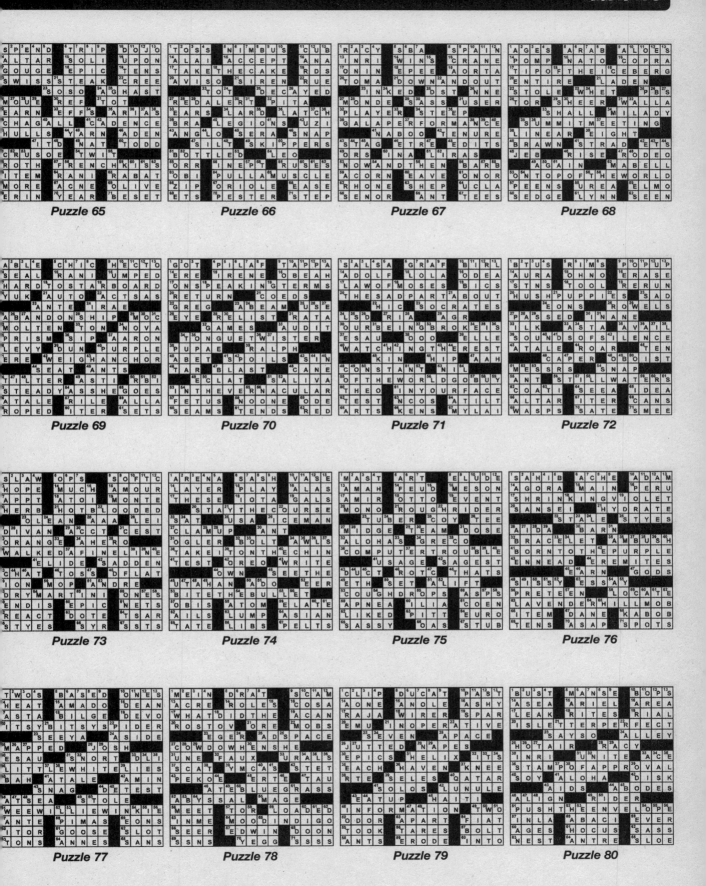

Puzzle 65

Puzzle 66

Puzzle 67

Puzzle 68

Puzzle 69

Puzzle 70

Puzzle 71

Puzzle 72

Puzzle 73

Puzzle 74

Puzzle 75

Puzzle 76

Puzzle 77

Puzzle 78

Puzzle 79

Puzzle 80

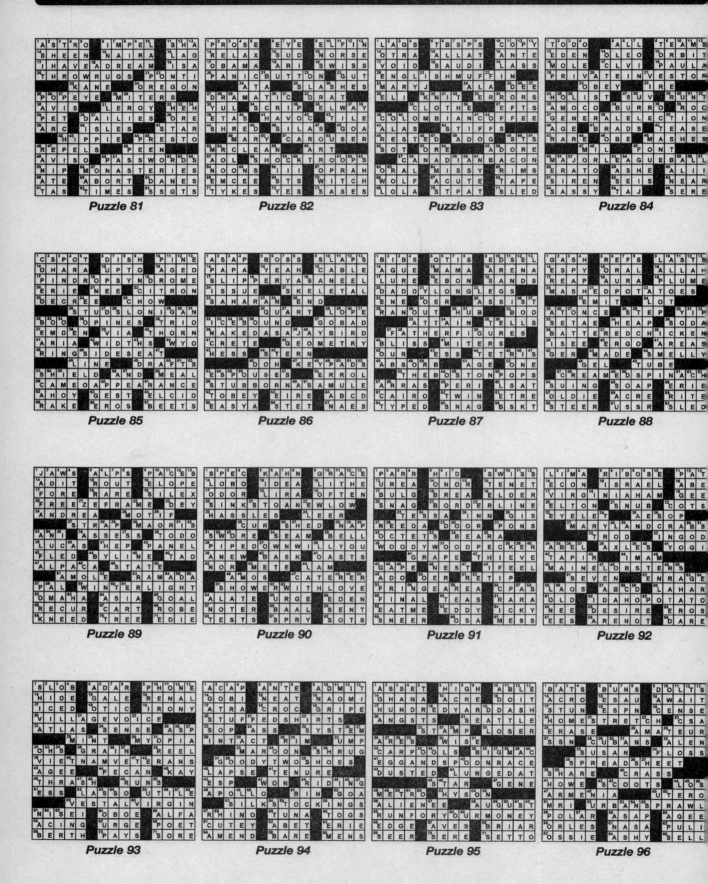

Puzzle 81

Puzzle 82

Puzzle 83

Puzzle 84

Puzzle 85

Puzzle 86

Puzzle 87

Puzzle 88

Puzzle 89

Puzzle 90

Puzzle 91

Puzzle 92

Puzzle 93

Puzzle 94

Puzzle 95

Puzzle 96

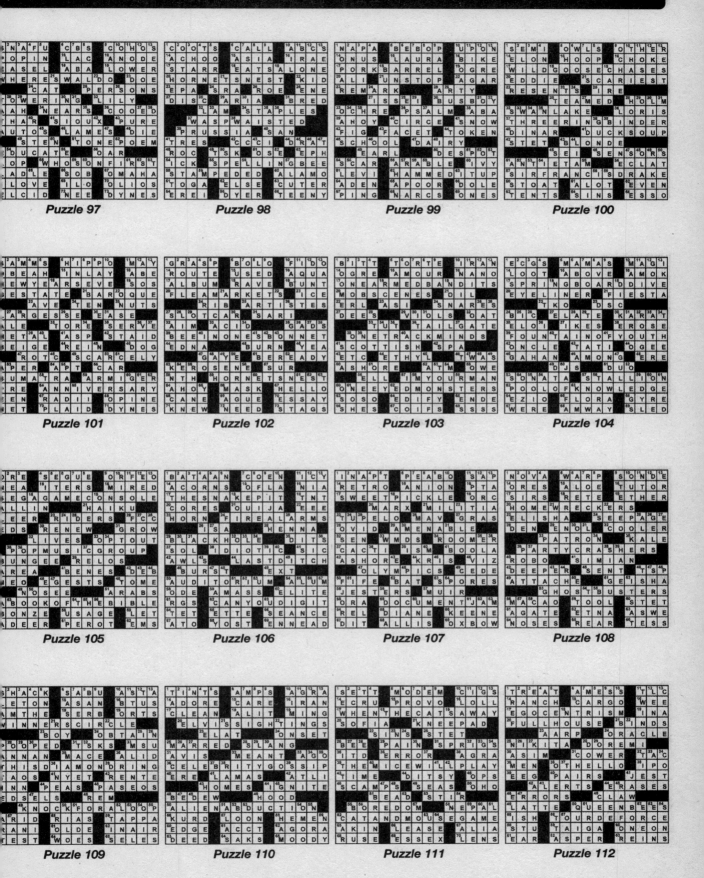

Puzzle 97

Puzzle 98

Puzzle 99

Puzzle 100

Puzzle 101

Puzzle 102

Puzzle 103

Puzzle 104

Puzzle 105

Puzzle 106

Puzzle 107

Puzzle 108

Puzzle 109

Puzzle 110

Puzzle 111

Puzzle 112

Answers

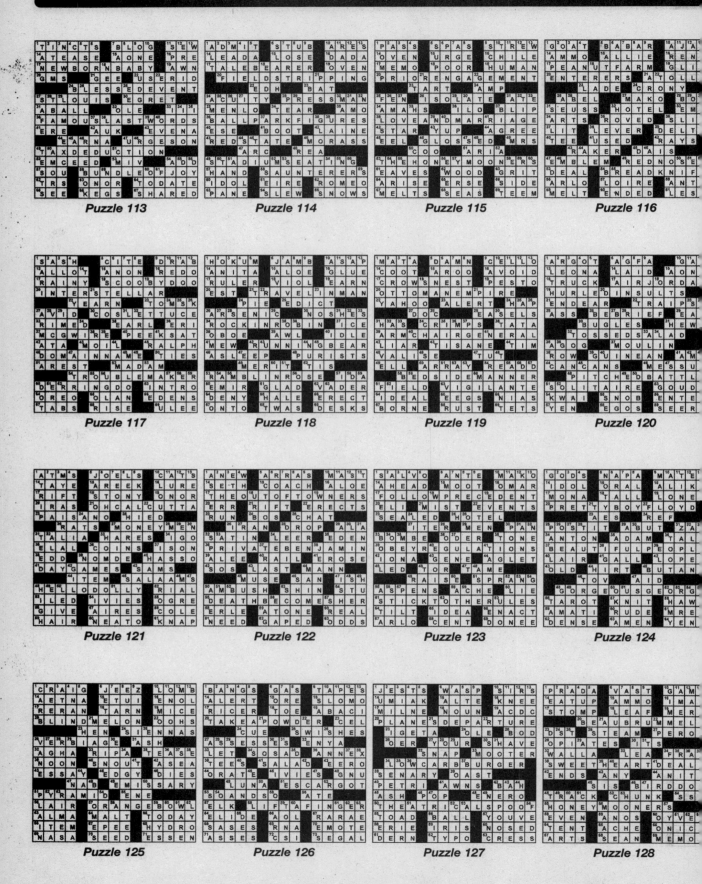

Puzzle 113

Puzzle 114

Puzzle 115

Puzzle 116

Puzzle 117

Puzzle 118

Puzzle 119

Puzzle 120

Puzzle 121

Puzzle 122

Puzzle 123

Puzzle 124

Puzzle 125

Puzzle 126

Puzzle 127

Puzzle 128

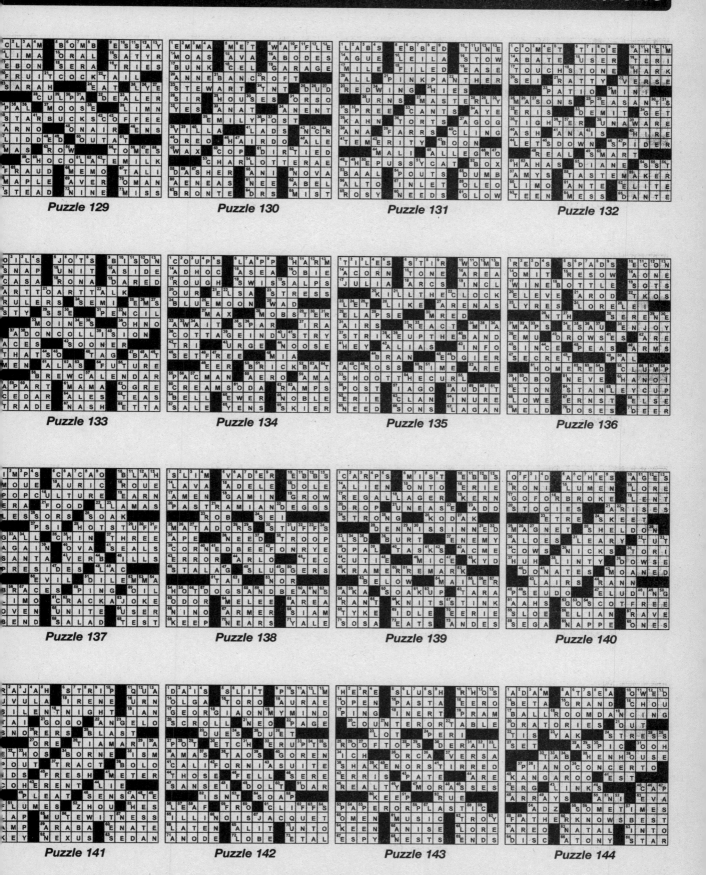

Puzzle 129

Puzzle 130

Puzzle 131

Puzzle 132

Puzzle 133

Puzzle 134

Puzzle 135

Puzzle 136

Puzzle 137

Puzzle 138

Puzzle 139

Puzzle 140

Puzzle 141

Puzzle 142

Puzzle 143

Puzzle 144

Answers

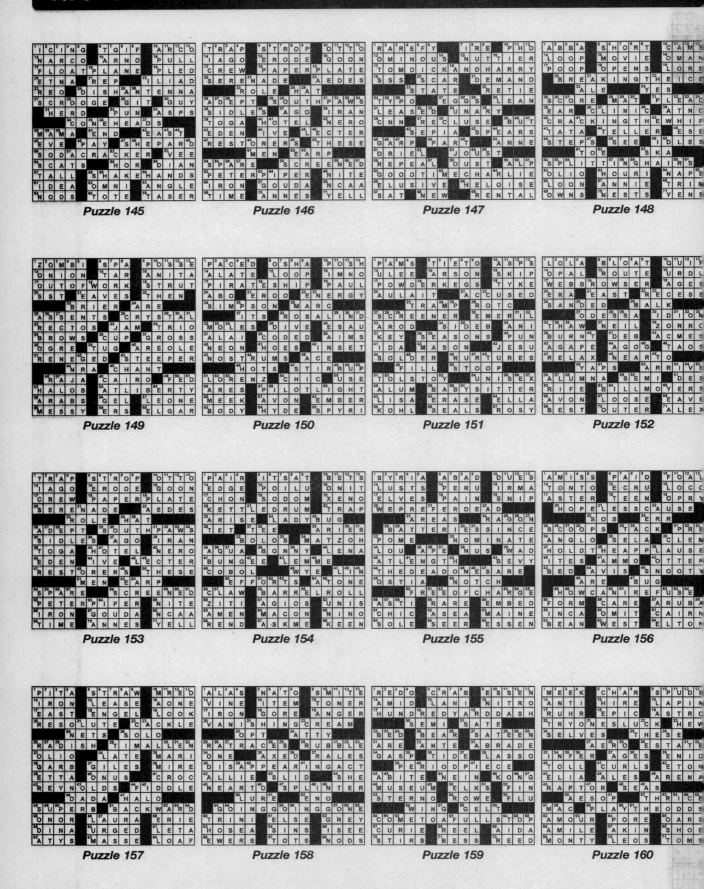

Puzzle 145   Puzzle 146   Puzzle 147   Puzzle 148

Puzzle 149   Puzzle 150   Puzzle 151   Puzzle 152

Puzzle 153   Puzzle 154   Puzzle 155   Puzzle 156

Puzzle 157   Puzzle 158   Puzzle 159   Puzzle 160

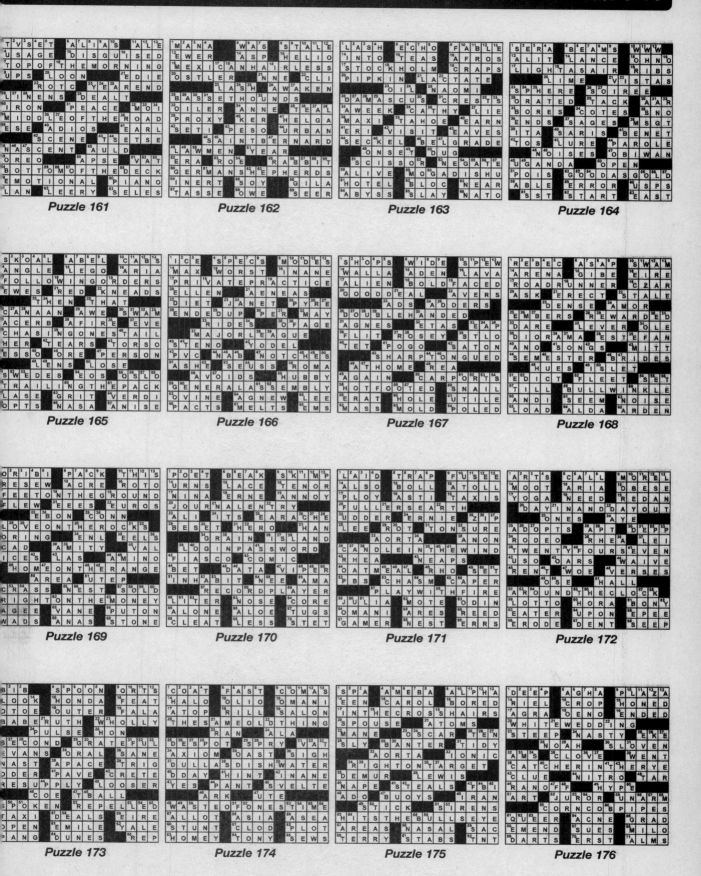

Puzzle 161

Puzzle 162

Puzzle 163

Puzzle 164

Puzzle 165

Puzzle 166

Puzzle 167

Puzzle 168

Puzzle 169

Puzzle 170

Puzzle 171

Puzzle 172

Puzzle 173

Puzzle 174

Puzzle 175

Puzzle 176

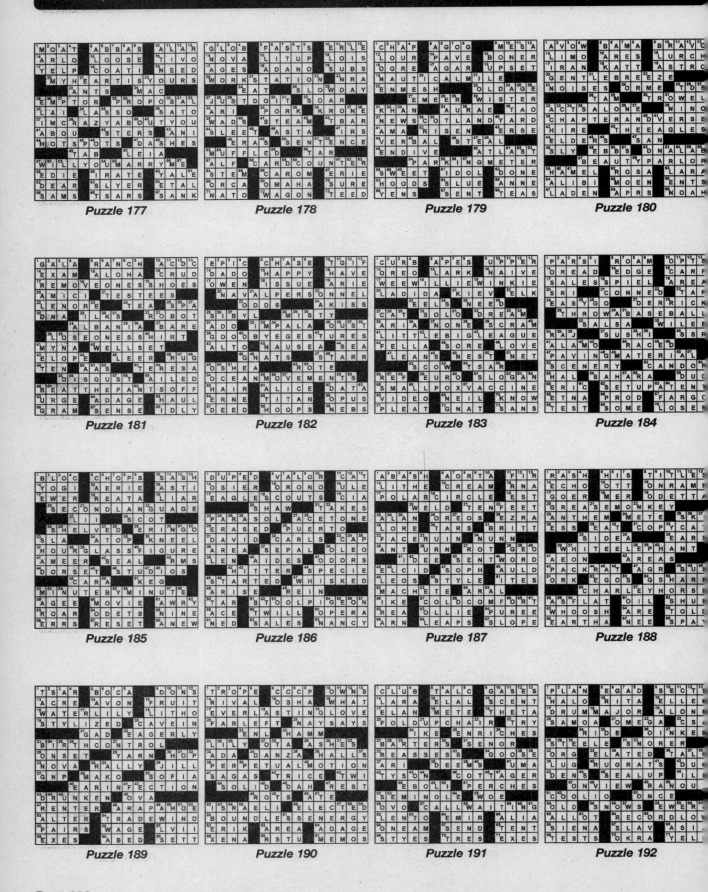

Puzzle 177

Puzzle 178

Puzzle 179

Puzzle 180

Puzzle 181

Puzzle 182

Puzzle 183

Puzzle 184

Puzzle 185

Puzzle 186

Puzzle 187

Puzzle 188

Puzzle 189

Puzzle 190

Puzzle 191

Puzzle 192

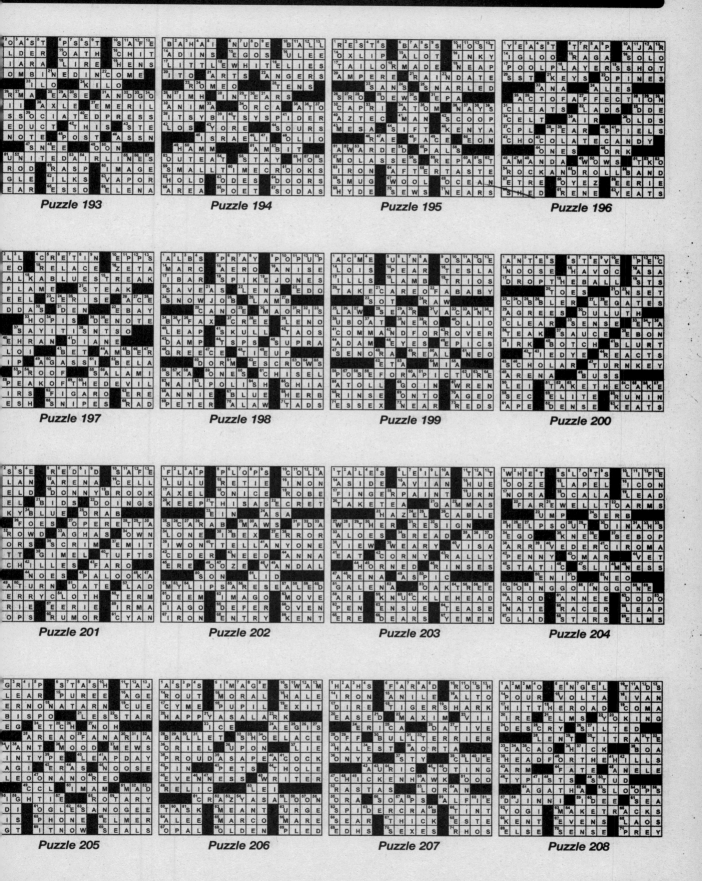

Puzzle 193

Puzzle 194

Puzzle 195

Puzzle 196

Puzzle 197

Puzzle 198

Puzzle 199

Puzzle 200

Puzzle 201

Puzzle 202

Puzzle 203

Puzzle 204

Puzzle 205

Puzzle 206

Puzzle 207

Puzzle 208

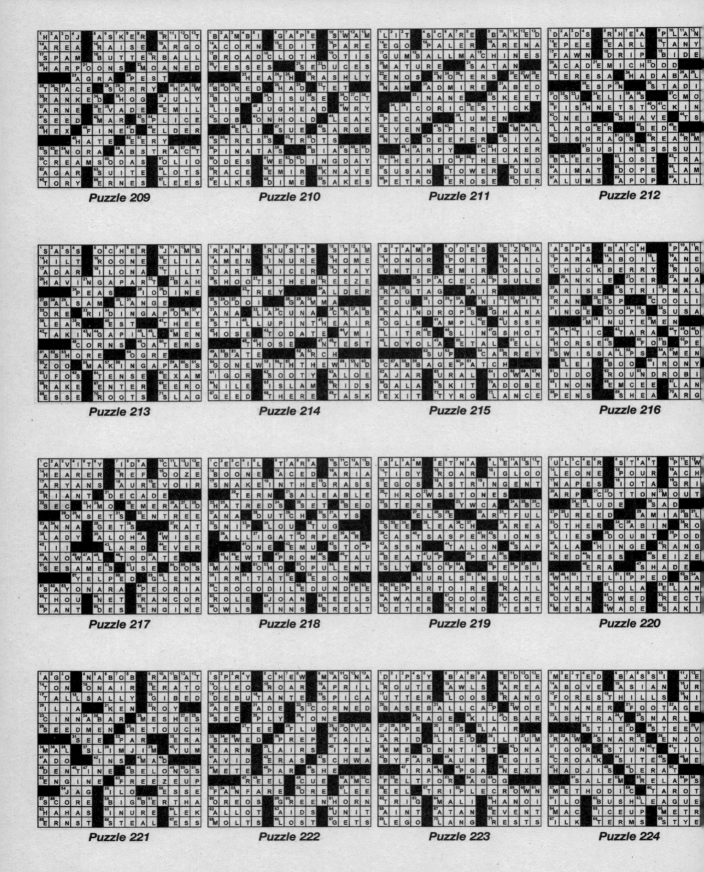

Puzzle 209

Puzzle 210

Puzzle 211

Puzzle 212

Puzzle 213

Puzzle 214

Puzzle 215

Puzzle 216

Puzzle 217

Puzzle 218

Puzzle 219

Puzzle 220

Puzzle 221

Puzzle 222

Puzzle 223

Puzzle 224

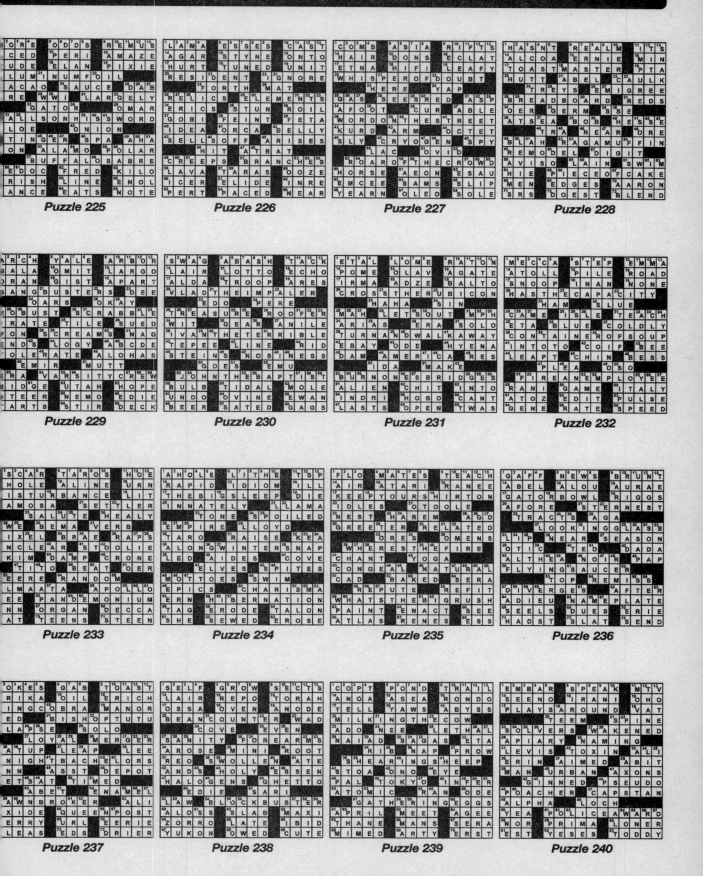

Puzzle 225

Puzzle 226

Puzzle 227

Puzzle 228

Puzzle 229

Puzzle 230

Puzzle 231

Puzzle 232

Puzzle 233

Puzzle 234

Puzzle 235

Puzzle 236

Puzzle 237

Puzzle 238

Puzzle 239

Puzzle 240

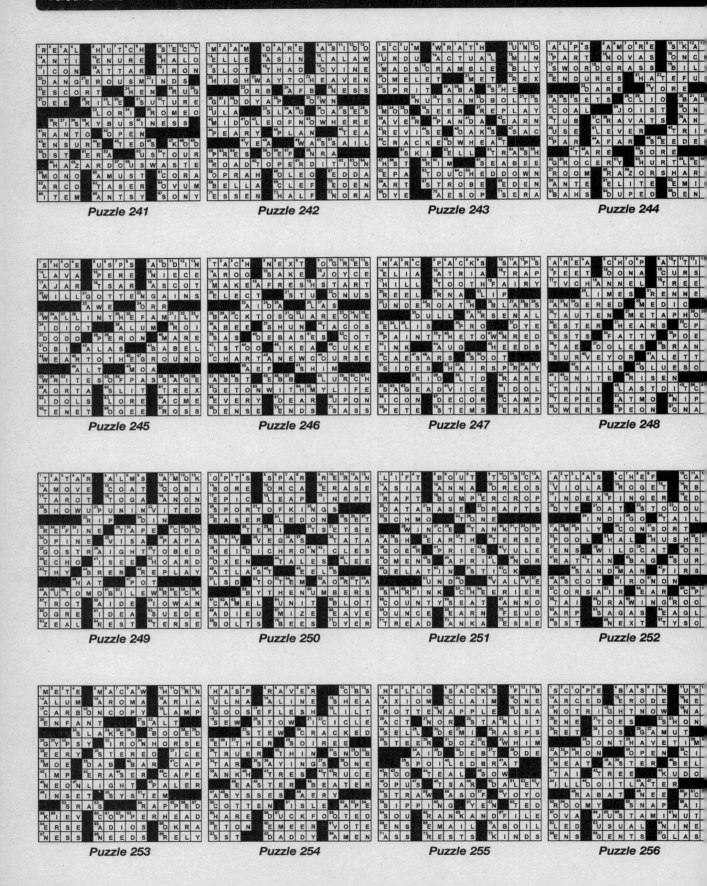

Puzzle 241

Puzzle 242

Puzzle 243

Puzzle 244

Puzzle 245

Puzzle 246

Puzzle 247

Puzzle 248

Puzzle 249

Puzzle 250

Puzzle 251

Puzzle 252

Puzzle 253

Puzzle 254

Puzzle 255

Puzzle 256

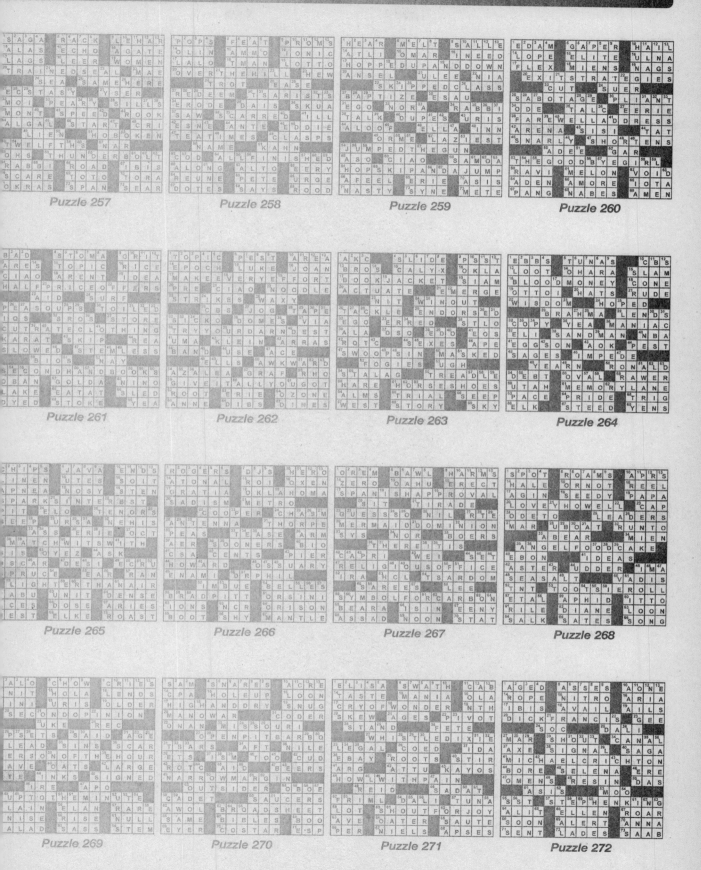

Puzzle 257

Puzzle 258

Puzzle 259

Puzzle 260

Puzzle 261

Puzzle 262

Puzzle 263

Puzzle 264

Puzzle 265

Puzzle 266

Puzzle 267

Puzzle 268

Puzzle 269

Puzzle 270

Puzzle 271

Puzzle 272

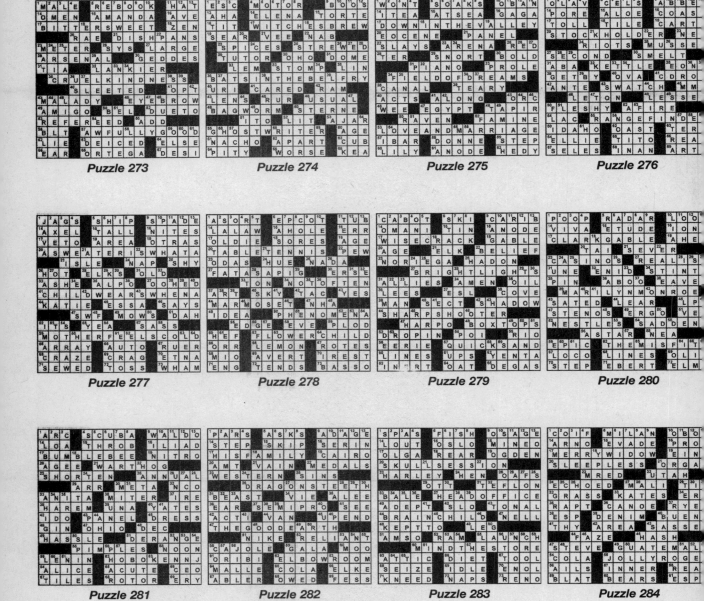

Puzzle 273

Puzzle 274

Puzzle 275

Puzzle 276

Puzzle 277

Puzzle 278

Puzzle 279

Puzzle 280

Puzzle 281

Puzzle 282

Puzzle 283

Puzzle 284